British Teapots
&Tea Drinking

pl.1 Thomas Twining, the founder of the firm. Painted about 1730

ROBIN EMMERSON

British Teapots & Tea Drinking

1700-1850

Illustrated from the

❦ TWINING TEAPOT GALLERY ❦

Norwich Castle Museum

 Norfolk Museums Service   **TWININGS**

London: HMSO

ISBN 0 11 701224 6 (hbk.)
ISBN 0 11 701509 1 (pbk.)

British Library Cataloguing in Publication Data

A CIP catalogue record for this book
is available from the British Library

Design: HMSO Graphic Design, Guy Myles Warren

Norfolk Museums Service is a joint service
provided by the County and District Councils

HMSO publications are available from:

HMSO Publications Centre
(Mail and telephone orders only)
PO Box 276, London, SW8 5DT
Telephone orders 071-873 9090
General enquiries 071-873 0011
(queuing system in operation for both numbers)

HMSO Bookshops
49 High Holborn, London, WC1V 6HB   071-873 0011 (counter service only)
258 Broad Street, Birmingham, B1 2HE   021-643 3740
Southey House, 33 Wine Street, Bristol, BS1 2BQ   0272-264306
9–21 Princess Street, Manchester, M60 8AS   061-834 7201
80 Chichester Street, Belfast, BT1 4JY   0232-238451
71 Lothian Road, Edinburgh, EH3 9AZ   031-228 4181

HMSO's Accredited Agents
(see Yellow Pages)

and through good booksellers

Printed in the United Kingdom for HMSO
(hbk.) Dd 294213   C10   12/91
(pbk.) Dd 294215   C20   12/91

For June

It's love alone
Makes too but One

(on a teapot *c*.1780, see p.103)

Contents

Introduction and Acknowledgements

Since 1989 the Twining Teapot Gallery and Ceramic Study Room at Norwich Castle Museum have housed the greatest collection of British pottery and porcelain teapots in the world. This book draws on the resources of the collection to tell the story of tea-drinking in Britain and of the British teapot during what is probably its most exciting period, the 18th century and the first half of the 19th century. It is especially fitting that Twinings and Norfolk Museums Service are working in partnership because Twinings are the oldest firm of tea blenders in the country – probably in the world – and were founded in 1706. This means that even the earliest of the teapots at Norwich is likely to have started its useful life dispensing Twinings' teas. The modern visitor to their London shop, at 216 the Strand, enters through a doorway made in 1787 and crowned with two seated Chinamen, and is then in premises which the firm has occupied since the early 18th century. Twinings' archives and historical collections are an important source of information on everything related to tea and tea-drinking, and both they and the company's historian, Mr Sam H.G. Twining OBE, have played an invaluable part in the creation of this book.

The Norwich collection includes some 2,600 teapots, and a complete catalogue of them all would therefore require a book many times the size of this one. The first purpose of this volume is to show why so much care and attention was lavished on the design and making of teapots, by explaining the social importance of tea-drinking in the 18th and 19th centuries. The second purpose is to discuss a representative selection of teapots from about 1720 to 1850, incorporating the results of recently published research, and using description and illustrations to show the distinctions between the work of different makers.

There would be no teapot collection at Norwich but for the Bulwers. Colonel and Mrs Edward A.E. Bulwer were married in 1899, but did not begin collecting until the death in 1910 of Bulwer's father, General W.E.G.L. Bulwer of Quebec House, East Dereham, Norfolk. The General had marshalled a collection of over 100 teapots and bequeathed them to his son. Suddenly the Bulwers were infected with a passion for collecting, and from then until his death in 1934, the Colonel and his wife collected nearly 600 more teapots. In 1921 they moved from Lichfield to Norfolk and built a special room for the teapots on to their house at Heydon Grange near Aylsham.

It was a golden age for collectors of 18th-century pottery and porcelain. The Bulwers bought most of their pots for only a few pounds, but for the occasional really special piece they were prepared to lash out and spend ten or even twenty pounds. Twenty pounds was serious money in 1920, but even allowing for inflation, the prices make modern collectors wish they had been born a few generations earlier. The Bulwers bought from Sotheby's or local auctions, from dealers in the West End of London or wherever they went, for example on holidays in Jersey. The dealer with whom they did most business, however, was W. Pease of Nottingham. Like Bulwer, he came from the Dereham area, and the two became friends. Letters in the museum files show Bulwer sending Pease presents of game shot on the estate, and also exchanges in verse. Bulwer replied to some doggerel about the teapot collection by adding:

> And then a party large and choice
> Collected from the rest.
> They had a look of pride, and seemed
> All of the very best!
> In clear and dulcet varying keys
> Arose from these proud pots:–
> 'Oh we all came from Mr Pease
> Who lives in County Notts!!'

How many dealers nowadays could afford to send a favoured client the birthday present which Bulwer received from Pease, a little white salt-glazed stoneware teapot of about 1740 with blue-stained relief decoration? (See the entry for cat. no.10.) Mrs Bulwer's brother C.H.B. Caldwell was another leading ceramics collector, who on the eve of war in 1939 presented his exquisite collection of custard cups to the museum. Caldwell's generosity to his brother-in-law included presents like his 'Easter egg' of 1923, a leaf-moulded Chelsea teapot with the early triangle mark (cat. no.140).

Colonel Bulwer was an early member of the English Ceramic Circle and relished the challenge of identifying 'problem' pots, sharing his expertise and seeking advice from others, sometimes at one of the Circle's 'Miscellany' meetings (see cat. no.146). As Treasurer of the Friends of the Norwich Museums from 1927 until his death, he created the nucleus of the museum's ceramics collection. His will bequeathed the teapots to the museum, with a life interest for Mrs Bulwer. She succeeded him as Treasurer of the Friends, serving until her own death in 1953. In 1946 she relinquished her interest in the teapots, which have graced the museum ever since.

At the period when the Bulwers were collecting, there was little scholarly interest in 19th-century ceramics and even in some types of late 18th-century wares. As the years passed and interest in the later wares grew and prices rose, it seemed increasingly unlikely that the museum would ever be able to acquire a comprehensive collection of these later wares to continue the story of the teapot from where the Bulwers had left off. In 1988, however, Philip Miller offered to sell the museum a collection of 2,000 teapots amassed over the previous two decades. Philip Miller knew the Bulwer collection well, and knew that his own, whose strength lay in the period from about 1780 to 1850, would complement it admirably. The collection was made in the same pioneering spirit of intellectual enquiry as Bulwer's two generations before, as an instrument of ceramic research and with similarly comprehensive aims, but Bulwer would probably not even have heard of some of the factories whose products Mr Miller had so astutely gathered together.

The Miller collection was offered at an advantageous price, and the response to the appeal for funds was magnificent. Grant-in-aid came from the Museums and Galleries Commission, the National Art-Collections Fund, the National Heritage Memorial Fund, the Friends of the Norwich Museums (who made their largest ever purchase grant), The Norwich Town Close Estate Charity, the Sedgwick Group and the Norwich Decorative and Fine Arts Society.

R. Twining and Company Limited, in the person of Mr Sam Twining, the ninth generation of the family since the founder, were already involved in the negotiations for the future of the Miller collection, and made it possible for it to come to Norwich. Twinings have funded not only the Twining Teapot Gallery, together with a study room where students may handle the collection by appointment, but also a national touring exhibition and the promotion and future development of the collection. The generous financial assistance of Twinings towards the production of this book is gratefully acknowledged. Mr Brynley J. Evans (Group Managing Director), Mr Ian W.K. Dewar (Commercial Director, UK) and Mr Sam Twining himself have been wholeheartedly supportive and encouraging throughout the project. This seriously understates Mr Twining's role in the book, because from his unrivalled knowledge of tea and tea-drinking he has provided major assistance with the text as well as the illustrations. The first two chapters would have been immeasurably poorer without his help.

It is often not fully appreciated that a collection is only as valuable as the knowledge applied to it. The Bulwer collection has mirrored the progress of ceramic research over half a century, and has been enriched by the observations and judgement of many visiting researchers. This includes group visits by the English Ceramic Circle and more specialised groups like the Derby Porcelain International Society, the Friends of Blue and the Spode Society. In such a broad field it seems invidious to single out names, but some must receive individual mention: Gilbert Bradley, W.J. Grant Davidson, Professor Alan Smith, Donald Towner, Peter Walton and Dr Bernard Watney.

The author benefits from standing upon the shoulders of many scholars and connoisseurs of much greater stature than himself. During the preparation of this book he has received help from David Barker, Sheila Bidgood, Robert Cumming, Pat Halfpenny, Minnie and Tim Holdaway, Susan McCrary, Rosalind and Martin Pulver, Robin Reilly, Deborah Skinner and Tom Walford. Most importantly, Philip Miller has been unstinting of information, and without his help we should certainly not have been able to identify work by such makers as John Yates or Hicks and Meigh. This book owes much to the work of the author's predecessor, Sheenah Smith, on the Bulwer Collection. Both of us have benefitted immeasurably from the expertise of Dr Michael Signy on 18th-century wares of all kinds. Any errors in this book should be laid at the door of the author alone.

The previous Director of the Norfolk Museums Service, Francis Cheetham, his successor Catherine Wilson, and the Principal Assistant Director Brian McWilliams have provided help and support throughout the project. The museum owes a great and frequently overlooked debt to its dedicated and expert voluntary assistants. In the packing and unpacking, marshalling, recording and study of the Miller pots, and the preparation of this book, the assistance of Rebecca Frances, Marian, Pam and Pennie Ford and Sue James was literally invaluable. All the author's colleagues in the Norfolk Museums Service, but especially Andrew Moore, Norma Watt and Liz Buckton, provided plentiful help and support. The drawings of details of pots were made by Rebecca Frances and June Emmerson, Rebecca being responsible particularly for the drawings of neoclassical decoration in Chapter Six. The pots were photographed by Alan Griffee of GGS Photography, Norwich. Grateful thanks also go to the Trustees of the Wedgwood Museum, Barlaston for permission to quote from documents held in the Wedgwood Archives at the University of Keele. Philip Glover, Stuart McLaren and Guy Myles Warren at HMSO somehow managed to keep a wayward author up to the mark and ensure production to both a high standard and a tight deadline. Finally I wish to thank my wife, June, without whose constant inspiration, support and encouragement the Miller and Bulwer collections would not have been united and this book would not have been written.

ROBIN EMMERSON

Abbreviations

ECC	*English Ceramic Circle Transactions*
EPC	*English Porcelain Circle Transactions*
NCSJ	*Northern Ceramics Society Journal*
NCSN	*Northern Ceramics Society Newsletter*

The Growth of Tea-Drinking

The death of Oliver Cromwell was reported in *The Gazette* newspaper, issue 432 for 2 – 9 September 1658. In its pages is also found the earliest known British advertisement for tea:

> That Excellent, and by all Physitians approved, China Drink,
> called by the Chineans, Tcha, by other Nations Tay, alias Tee, is
> sold at the Sultaness-head, a Cophee-house, in Sweetings Rents by
> the Royal Exchange, London.

Coffee-houses had sprung up in London during the previous six years, selling coffee to take home as well as for consumption on the premises. They were beginning to add tea and chocolate as further strings to their bow. Thomas Garway opened his coffee-house in Exchange Alley in 1657, and claimed in a broadsheet three years later that he had been the first to sell tea 'in leaf and drink, made according to the directions of the most knowing merchants and travellers into eastern countries.' The centre of activities for these merchants was the Cornhill area, and it was there that the first coffee-houses were clustered, catering for their cosmopolitan customers' taste in exotic drinks and no doubt leaving their heads a good deal clearer for business than a visit to the tavern would have done. It was probably one of these shops which supplied Samuel Pepys in 1660 on the occasion he recorded in his diary: 'I did send for a cup of tee (a China drink) of which I never had drank before.' Thomas Twining spent his early years in business with Thomas D'Aeth, an East India merchant, before leaving to start his own business in a coffee-house in 1706.

The East India Company, or more properly 'The Governor and Company of Merchants of London trading into the East Indies', received its royal charter as early as 1600. At first much of the British trade with China was indirect, with Bantam in Java as the main British depot until its capture by the Dutch in 1682. The Portuguese, based at Macao, regarded trade with Canton as their prerogative, so from the middle of the 17th century the English based themselves at Amoy. There the Fukien dialect was spoken, and that is why we still follow Amoy in calling our drink 'tea' instead of following the Cantonese and calling it 'cha'. The East India Company only began to import tea as an article of trade, that is for re-sale, in 1678, when 4,713 pounds weight were unloaded in London. The small but promising scale of the imports is indicated in a letter sent from the directors of the company to their representatives at Fort St George, Madras, in southern India, in 1685:

> In regard Thea has grown to be a commodity here and we have great occasion to make presents therein to our great friends at Court, we would have you send us yearly five or six canisters of the very best and freshest thea which will colour the water in which it is infused, a greenish complexion . . .[1]

Anything imported by the East India Company was likely to be described as 'India', even if it came from China. Most people's geography of the Far East was fairly hazy, but China was in contemporary terms part of 'the East Indies', and many Chinese goods were purchased by the company in India, after shipment from China by others. 'India' was used as an adjective rather as we might say 'oriental'.

The fashion for tea at court appears to have been started by Charles II's queen, Catherine of Braganza. She came from Portugal, and the Portuguese were familiar with tea, having traded with China since the early 16th century. The court poet Edmund Waller wrote an ode in her praise in 1662, and even managed to turn the tea-plant into a classical attribute:

> Venus her Myrtle; Phoebus has his Bays;
> Tea both excels, which she vouchsafes to praise.
> The best of Queens, and best of herbs, we owe
> To that bold nation, which the way did show
> To the fair region where the sun doth rise,
> Whose rich productions we so justly prize.
> The Muse's friend, tea does our fancy aid,
> Repress those vapours which the head invade,
> And keep the palace of the soul serene,
> Fit on her birthday to salute the Queen.

There was no shortage of advocates for the medicinal properties of tea. One day in 1667 Pepys found his wife 'making of Tea . . . a drink which Mr Pelling the potticary tells her is good for her cold and difluxions.' Perhaps the apothecary had been reading Thomas Garway's advertisement which claimed that tea would help cure – among other ailments – headaches, giddiness, heaviness, colds, dropsies, scurvies, agues, surfeits and fevers.

Part of the attraction of tea-drinking lay in the strange and delicate equipment it required. The ships which brought the tea from China brought also strange pots with spouts and cups and saucers of white porcelain or of fine, hard red pottery. Porcelain has been known ever since as china. The Chinese had been making porcelain for a thousand years, but for most British consumers the Chinese wares looked like nothing they had seen before. Their delicacy, and the whiteness and translucency of porcelain, put them in a different class from the relatively coarse British pots. They became a status symbol, and British potters determined to imitate them. Tea-drinking provided an opportunity for people to show off their wealth and taste with glamorous imported porcelain. The only alternative material of higher status was silver, but this was not suitable for the little teabowls – cups without handles – from which tea was drunk. Even those who could afford an entire service of silver preferred not to burn their fingers but to use porcelain teabowls and saucers together with the silver. They were just as likely to use oriental porcelain for the other items too, since it was part and parcel of the exoticism of drinking Chinese tea.

The Private Closet of Elizabeth, Duchess of Lauderdale, at Ham House in Surrey retains the 'Tea table, carved and guilt', recorded there in an inventory of 1683, together with the matching chairs described as 'Japaned backstooles with Cane bottomes'. The table is Javanese lacquer and was evidently treasured; although it is low in the oriental manner, the Duchess had an extra stage added to bring it up to the usual height for Western chairs. The chairs with their black 'japanned' finish imitating oriental lacquer were made in England to go with the tea-table, and are an early example of Western interior decoration attempting to imitate the Orient. The duchess also kept in the room 'One Japan box for sweetmeats & tea', and next-door in the White Closet 'One Indian furnace for tee garnished with silver', which sadly does not survive. The ensemble suggests how tea-drinking created a taste for exotic utensils and decoration.[2]

The Duchess would certainly not have agreed with Henry Saville who wrote in 1678 to his uncle Henry Coventry, Secretary of State, comparing him favourably with other friends '. . . who call for TEA instead of Pipes and Bottles after dinner, a base unworthy Indian practise, and which I must ever admire your most Christian family for not admitting. The truth is, all nations are grown so wicked as to have some of these filthy customs . . .'

Tea was kept by the duchess in a box in her private sanctum because it was an exotic and precious delicacy and extremely costly. Thomas Garway's teas were priced from 16 to 50 shillings a pound, but by the time of Thomas Twining's first surviving ledger, of 1710–29, prices were somewhat lower. There were two main types of tea, black from the fermented and green from the unfermented leaf. Black teas included: flowery pekoe (from the Chinese 'pak-ho', meaning the white hairs on the fine downy tips of the young buds), orange pekoe, pekoe souchong ('siau-chung' meant little plant or sort), souchong, congou ('kong-fu' meant labour, the leaves being hand-rolled for this type of tea) and bohea ('wu-i', from the mountains of Fukien, the centre of black tea country). Green teas included: gunpowder, imperial hyson (from 'yu-tsien', meaning before the rains, or from 'tu-chun', meaning flourishing spring), singlo or twankay (the hyson shrub improved by cultivation, a variety from the Singlo mountain in Kiangnan). Tea was grown for local consumption in all parts of China except the far north, but the provinces that grew tea for export were those in the south-east.

In 1706 Thomas Twining bought his own coffee-house, Tom's, in Devereux Court just off the Strand in London. The competition was intense, for there were already over two thousand coffee-houses, but Twining gave himself two advantages. The first was his location, out of the City and near the newly developed West End, where the aristocracy were building new houses in the aftermath of the Great Fire of London. Different coffee-houses had their own special attractions, and Twining's second advantage was the sale of a wide range of the best quality dry tea. Since no lady would be seen in the male preserve of a coffee-house, they would wait outside in their sedan chairs, sending a footman in to make their purchases. Bohea, the most popular black tea, was available from Twining's at between 16 and 24 shillings a pound retail price, and the dust was sold for 12 to 16 shillings. Hyson, the most popular green tea, cost from 14 to 20 shillings, apart from the finest, which at 36 shillings a pound was the most expensive tea the firm sold. At this time 12 or 14 shillings, the price of a pound of fairly standard tea, was a week's wages for many master craftsmen.

The gradual decrease in the price indicates the growing popularity of the new drink during this period. A sure sign of increased consumption was the Government's invention of a specific tax on tea, which came into force in 1698. Since 1660 tea in liquid form had attracted a tax of eightpence per gallon, which was a general levy on beverages, but this was the first time that dry tea was singled out for special attention. The rate was a shilling per pound weight of tea for imports by the East India Company, or two shillings and sixpence per pound weight for anyone else. The duty was doubled in 1704, and increased again in 1712. The powerful lobby of the brewers encouraged this taxation, fearing that tea might replace ale as Britain's staple breakfast drink, but public demand proved stronger than taxes or private interest.

pl.2   A pot of about 1790 invites one to choose between ordinary green tea, Hyson (a rather special green tea) and Bohea, the most popular black tea

William III's chaplain, the Revd. J. Ovington, in his 'Essay upon the Nature and Qualities of Tea' in 1699 noted: '. . . the Drinking of it has of late obtained here so universally, as to be affected both by the Scholar and the Tradesman, to become both a private Regale at Court, and to be made use of in places of public entertainment . . .'.

Tea-drinking became a mark of gracious living to such an extent that some families chose to be shown drinking tea together in their portraits (col. pl.1). It is the years around 1700 which mark its establishment as a major force in British social life. 20,000 pounds weight of tea a year was being imported by 1700, but in 1721 the figure exceeded a million pounds weight. From about 1700 onwards there is a wealth of surviving silver teaware which can be accurately dated by its hallmarks. In 1713 the growth of these ancillary trades attracted satirical comment from Daniel Defoe:

> It is impossible that Coffee, Tea and Chocolate can be so advanced in their Consumption, without an eminent Encrease of those Trades that attend them; whence we see the most noble Shops in the City taken up with the most valuable Utensils of the Tea-Table.[3]

Alexander Pope's lines about Queen Anne in 'The Rape of the Lock' are often quoted as evidence that tea was pronounced 'tay' in the 18th century:

> Here thou, great Anna, whom three realms obey,
> Dost sometimes counsel take and sometimes tea.

In 1720, however, Matthew Prior's 'Young Gentleman in Love':

> . . . thanked her on his bended knee
> Then drank a quart of milk and tea.

On one occasion, when Alexander Pope required the help of his legal adviser, William Fortescue, he addressed his letter to him at the premises of Thomas Twining, Tom's Coffee-house. Its proximity to the Temple made it a favourite haunt with lawyers, for whom an area was especially set aside. Fortescue already had an account with Twining's when their first surviving ledger opens in 1710. The business flourished and at this time Thomas was acquiring adjoining property. While continuing the coffee-house, by 1717 he had opened the Golden Lion next door. This was the first shop in Britain – quite possibly in the western world – dedicated to the sale of dry tea and coffee. Since it was quite separate from the coffee-house, ladies could walk in from the Strand without any impropriety. Twining's female customers made it a fashionable place of resort.

The Golden Lion is printed on a rare surviving piece of the paper in which Twinings wrapped tea for their customers (pl. 3): the inclusion of Daniel Twining with his father Thomas dates it to 1734 or soon afterwards, for in that year he was taken into partnership. Tea was by now very much the main part of the business, for in the first year of the partnership the firm sold 13,114 pounds weight of tea, 5,137 pounds of coffee, and 2,897 pounds of chocolate. By the time of Thomas Twining's death in 1741, the annual sales of tea had topped 20,000 pounds weight. The wholesale trade was an important part of the business, for the Golden Lion supplied tea to many coffee-houses, apothecaries, mercers, goldsmiths and even milliners for resale. The fact that

Thomas & Daniel Twining,

AT the Golden Lyon in Devereux-Court, near the Temple, fell all Sorts of fine Teas, Coffee, Chocolate, Cocoa-Nuts, Sago, and Snuff: Alſo true German Spaw, Pyrmont, Bath and Briſtol Waters, Arrack, Brandy, &c.

pl.3 The Golden Lion, on a wrapper used for Twining's tea, about 1734

such shops were selling it rather than grocers indicates that it was still regarded as a luxury or a medicinal product rather than as part of a standard range of provisions. Thomas Twining let out Tom's coffee-house, in which he saw no future, and later the premises were used by the company as a warehouse.

At the same time that Thomas Twining was expanding his business, the opening of tea-gardens was encouraging the spread of tea-drinking. These ranged from modest little havens of tranquillity, long since forgotten, to the famous pleasure gardens like Vauxhall and Ranelagh which often included tea in the rather high price of admission. Leopold Mozart, the violinist father of a more famous son, wrote of Ranelagh in 1764: '. . . on entering, everybody pays 2s 6d. For this he may have as much bread and butter as he can eat, and as much coffee or tea as he can drink. Vauxhall is even bigger and grander. Here every person pays only one shilling for the pleasure of seeing many thousands of people, and the most beautiful lily garden, and to hear lovely music.'

Tea and other refreshments were taken in rows of little alcoves open on one side, which provided some shelter from the uncertainties of the weather. The tea-gardens survived until the middle of the 19th century, but gradually came down the social scale and became known more as the haunt of prostitutes than as the resort of polite society. They were replaced by tea-shops, the first of which was opened near London Bridge by the Aerated Bread Company (ABC for short) in 1864. J. Lyons, Fullers, Express Dairies and Kardomah tea-shops are fondly remembered to this day.

By the middle of the 18th century tea was trickling inexorably downwards through the social order. Its pleasures for the poor were enhanced by its associations with polite manners and the leisurely life of the gentry. It would be hard to overestimate the dynamic impact of this desire for 'genteel' behaviour and 'good breeding' (which simply meant good manners) on the whole of 18th-century British society. Duncan Forbes, Lord President of the Court of Session, wrote to Lord Tweedale on New Year's Day 1743 that tea had '. . . now become so common, that the meanest familys, even of labouring people, particularly in the Burroughs, make their morning's Meal of it, and thereby wholly disuse the ale, which heretofore was their accustomed drink; and the same Drug supplies all the labouring women with their afternoons' entertainments . . . at present there are very few Coblers in any of the Burroughs of this Country who do not sit down gravely with their Wives and familys to Tea.'

Domestic servants now expected their terms of employment to include the provision of tea and sugar, or in some instances a money allowance for the purpose. This may have been enlightened self-interest on the part of their employers in order to prevent pilfering. Dean Swift in 1745 published his hilarious *Directions to Servants* modelled on genuine books of instruction but written from the servant's point of view. His 'Advice to the Waiting Maid' mentions the 'execrable Custom got among Ladies . . . the Invention of small Chests and Trunks, with Lock and Key, wherein they keep the Tea and Sugar, without which it is impossible for a Waiting-maid to live. For, by this means you are forced to buy brown Sugar, and pour Water upon the Leaves, when they have lost all their Spirit and Taste.'

No wonder that Georgian ladies carried their keys with them, making a virtue out of necessity by attaching them to a large piece of jewellery known as a 'chateleine' and hung from the waist. As Swift suggests, the maid would then be reduced to re-using her mistress's spent tea-leaves, and would probably be unable to afford white sugar. The sort of chest to which he refers is shown in pl. 4. Covered with shagreen leather and decorated with silver mounts and lockplate, it contains two matching silver tea-jars with tight-fitting covers, and a covered sugar-bowl. It was usual to use one jar for black and one for green tea. The central bowl seems to have been more commonly used for sugar than for mixing teas to achieve the desired blend. The *Cabinet-Maker's London Book of Prices* in 1793 gave estimates for the internal fittings of tea-chests including a 'hole cut to receive the sugar bason', and 'making a case for the sugar bason to lift out'. The tea-jars would not have been referred to in the mid-18th century as 'caddies', although straight-sided examples were likely to be called 'tea-canisters'.

pl.4 Two jars for tea (one for black, one for green) and a dish for sugar, in their lockable chest. The lock was to prevent the servants pilfering the tea and sugar (see p.7). Silver by Samuel Taylor, London, 1752

When the working classes took up the drink, their 'betters' were shocked. Jonas Hanway, in his 'Essay on Tea' of 1757, exclaimed:

> To what a height of folly must a nation be arrived, when the common people are not satisfied with wholesome food at home, but must go to the remotest regions to please a vicious palate! There is a certain lane near Richmond where beggars are often seen, in the summer season, drinking their tea. You may see labourers who are mending the roads drinking their tea; it is even drank in cinder-carts; and what is no less absurd, sold out of cups to Hay-makers.

Even Dr Johnson, a confirmed tea addict, admitted that 'tea is a liquor not proper for the lower classes of the people, as it supplies no strength to labour, or relief to disease, but gratifies the taste without nourishing the body.' The agricultural reformer Arthur Young remarked in 1771: 'As much super-fluous money is wasted on tea and sugar as would maintain four million more subjects on bread.'

It is ironic that the working class change from ale to tea, which was to be advocated so strongly by the Temperance Movement in the 19th century, was widely criticised in the 18th as a sign of physical and moral decline. There were two prongs to the critical attack. As Hanway put it: 'Tea which should by no means be exposed to the air, being brought from China in the packing of porcelain to serve the purposes of saw dust, or sold in the streets out of wheel-barrows, you must imagine will make a most delicious liquor!'

This was echoed by Dame Dorothy Bradshaigh who founded an almshouse called 'the Receptacle' in Lancashire in 1775. Her rules expressly forbade 'any foreign Tea, commonly called by the names of Bohea and Green . . . Those who can afford to indulge themselves in an article so unnecessary, so expensive, so destructive of both time and health (the tea such people drink being poison), I shall not allow to be proper objects of this Charity.'

The problem was the high cost of tea, and the lack of preventive measures against its adulteration by unscrupulous dealers. The cheaper kinds available to the poor were likely to contain mouldy tea-leaves rejuvenated with dried hawthorn leaves or ash tree leaves boiled in copperas or sheep's dung. A law of 1776 made it an offence 'to dye or fabricate any sloe leaves, liquorice leaves, or leaves of tea that has been used.' The penalty was £5 or one year's imprisonment for every pound of tea 'fabricated'. Since there was no system of regular inspection to enforce the law, it was largely ineffective.

The consumption of tea and the tax on it were both increasing. When the duty was drastically increased in 1747, the figure for tea imports fell just as dramatically. This may not reflect the true picture, however, because it covers only legal imports, and the incentives for smuggling tea were now very great. The average annual weight of tea legally imported rose from 3.2 million pounds in the 1750s to 5.8 million in the period 1770–83. By then the average price of a pound of tea was 4s 7¾d before tax, and eight shillings after tax. It has been suggested that almost as much tea may have been imported illegally, which gives some impression of the importance of the smugglers' trade. The memoirs of William Hickey record that when he was travelling home on an East Indiaman in 1770, the captain received a payment of £12,024 for sixty-eight chests of tea sold from aboard ship in the English Channel.[4]

In 1777 the Directors of the East India Company were full of woe, 'Our sales having been lately much affected by the great quantity of tea smuggled, particularly from our own ships, which we are informed has sometimes been to the amount of three or four hundred chests each ship . . .'. By comparison with Hickey's figure, this should represent illicit deals for as much as £60,000 at a time, an immense sum of money in 18th-century terms. Those who were prepared to evade the duty included such pillars of the community as Parson James Woodforde of Weston Longville in Norfolk. His diary for 29 March 1777 records: 'Andrews the Smuggler brought me this night about 11 o'clock a bag of Hyson tea 6 pound weight. He frightened us a little by whistling under the parlour window just as we were going to bed. I gave him some Genever [gin] and paid him for the tea at 10s 6d per pound.'

In the American Colonies the Townshend Act of 1767, which taxed tea and other imports, made tea a focus for growing political discontent with British rule. The attempt to enforce British taxes in 1773 led to direct action against the East India Company's tea and tea ships in American ports. The tipping of tea into the harbour in the famous Boston Tea-Party of 16 December was followed by similar demonstrations at New York, Philadelphia, Annapolis, Greenwich, New Jersey, and Charleston. Supporters of independence renounced the drinking of tea as a political gesture. The following verses enjoyed a wide circulation:

'A Lady's Adieu to Her Tea-Table'

FAREWELL the Tea-board with your gaudy attire,
Ye cups and ye saucers that I did admire;
To my cream pot and tongs I now bid adieu
That pleasure's all fled that I once found in you.
Farewell pretty chest that so lately did shine,
With hyson and congo and best double fine;
Many a sweet moment by you I have sat,
Hearing girls and old maids to tattle and chat;
And the spruce coxcomb laugh at nothing at all,
Only some silly work that might happen to fall.
No more shall my teapot so generous be
In filling the cups with this pernicious tea,
For I'll fill it with water and drink out the same,
Before I'll lose LIBERTY that dearest name,
Because I am taught (and beleive it is fact)
That our ruin is aimed at in the late act,
Of imposing a duty on all foreign Teas,
Which detestable stuff we can quit when we please.
LIBERTY'S The Goddess that I do adore,
And I'll maintain her right until my last hour,
Before she shall part I will die in the cause,
For I'll never be govern'd by tyranny's laws.

The young lady's 'double fine' was her white sugar, and she displays a nicely ambiguous attitude about sacrificing her pleasure.

It is one of history's ironies that in 1784, immediately after the War of Independence, William Pitt's Commutation Act removed most of the hated tea tax. The immediate cause was the bad harvests and high grain prices which were putting ale, traditionally the staple drink of the poor, out of their reach. In an age without adequate public supplies of clean drinking water, the boiling of water for tea or its fermentation into ale were necessary in order to make it reasonably safe. Richard Twining, son of Daniel and grandson of Thomas Twining, the founder of the firm, was then Chairman of the Tea Dealers, and had several meetings with the Prime Minister. Twining advocated that the tax be removed altogether, and that the merchants pay a lump sum to the Treasury to make up the loss of revenue for four years. The Government recognised that 'tea has become an economical substitute to the middle and lower classes of society for malt liquor, the price of which renders it impossible for them to procure the quantity sufficient for them as their only drink.'

The Act replaced the high duties, which often amounted to 100 per cent, by a flat 12½ per cent of the value of tea imported. The Government compensated for its anticipated loss of revenue by an increase in window tax. In his budget speech Pitt pointed out that the additional window tax applied only to houses with seven or more windows. He argued that a household paying 10s 6d a year for ten windows would consume seven pounds of tea a year, and from the decrease in the tea tax would be making a net gain of 15s 4d. The East India Company was allowed to retain the monopoly on the sale of tea which it had held since 1721, but on the very important condition that it must import enough tea to meet demand without raising the price.

The average retail price of tea dropped by almost three shillings a pound. In 1785 Richard Twining was offering Bohea at two shillings a pound, Green tea at between 3s 4d and five shillings, and Hyson from six to ten shillings. The effect was an immediate and sharp rise in consumption. *The Whitehall Evening Post*, no.60, for 26 to 28 January 1786, offers a useful summary:

> First, it is to be observed that the average quantity of tea sold by the Company for ten years prior to the passing of the Commutation Act, was little more than six million of pounds weight per annum; but within the first twelve months after the act took place, the quantity sold exceeded 16,000,000 pounds.
>
> 2dly. The amount of the duty still continued upon tea has, in the first year only, exceeded the estimate by £60,434.
>
> 3dly. The total sum paid by the purchasers for teas sold since the passing of the Act, amounts only to £2,770,799 . . . but had an equal quantity been sold at the former prices, the purchasers must have paid not less than £4,826,261. Consequently the public have been benefited to the amount of £2,055,462 by this regulation.

Within ten years of the Act, tea imports had quadrupled.

Twinings' business boomed, and in 1787 the firm opened a frontage on to the Strand, building the delightful doorway which still welcomes one to their premises, complete with its Chinamen sitting on the pediment. No.5585 of the *Morning Chronicle and London Advertiser* for 7 April that year announced: 'Messrs TWINING respectfully gives notice, that their new Tea Warehouse, No. 216 Strand, the corner of Devereux Court, in the Strand, will be open on Tuesday next, the 10th instant.'

The most important, but most easily overlooked, aspect of the Commutation Act was its official recognition that tea was now a necessity for all classes of British society. It marks the point at which we can see it becoming established as the national drink. Rochefoucauld in 1784 commented: 'The drinking of tea is general throughout England. It is drunk twice a day, and although it is still very expensive, even the humblest peasant will take his tea twice a day, like the proudest: it is a huge consumption. Sugar, even unrefined sugar, which is necessary in large quantities and is very dear, does nothing to prevent this custom from being universal, without any exception.'[5]

By the late 18th century much of southern England was suffering serious deforestation as a result of industrial growth (including shipbuilding). At the same time the enclosure movement was at its height, fencing off common land for private profit so that ordinary people could no longer collect fuel for their fires. In consequence, many cottagers did not have sufficient fuel for cooking, but only enough to boil the occasional kettle, and lived on a monotonous dry diet of bread with perhaps cheese and, if they were lucky, some bacon. The tea with which they washed this down was probably the only warm and comforting item in their diet. No wonder that it was so important to them.

Sir Frederic Eden in his 1797 survey of the state of the poor commented:

> Exclusive of beer, when he can afford it, and spirits, the quantity of water, which with tea forms a beverage which is seldom qualified with milk or sugar, poured down the throats of a labourer's family is astounding. Any person who will give himself the trouble of stepping into the cottages of Middlesex and Surrey at meal times, will find that in poor families tea is not only the usual beverage, in the morning and evening, but is generally drunk in large quantities even at dinner.

A writer in the *Edinburgh Review* commented in 1823: 'When a labourer fancies himself refreshed with a mess of this stuff, sweetened by the coarsest black sugar and with azure blue milk, it is only the warmth of the water that soothes him for the moment.'

The writer could afford to feel superior because those in his social class did not run the risk of being poisoned, like the poor, by drinking cheap green tea dyed with verdigris. In aristocratic households like that of the Stanhopes, tea was by now acquiring its legendary status. The Regency socialite Captain Gronow recorded in his memoirs:

> When our army returned to England in 1814, my young friend, Augustus Stanhope, took me one afternoon to Harrington House, in Stableyard, St James's, where I was introduced to Lord and Lady Harrington, and all the Stanhopes. On entering a long gallery, I found the whole family engaged in their sempiternal occupation of tea-drinking. Neither in Nankin, Pekin, nor Canton was the teapot more assiduously and constantly replenished than in this hospitable mansion . . . General Lincoln Stanhope once told me, that after an absence of several years in India, he made his reappearance at Harrington House, and found the family, as he had left them on his departure, drinking tea in the long gallery. On his presenting himself, his father's only observation and speech of welcome to him was, 'Hallo Linky, my dear boy! delighted to see you. Have a cup of tea?'

In 1833 the East India Company lost its monopoly of the tea trade, prices fell and consumption increased again. In 1830 it stood at 30 million pounds weight, but in 1836 at 49 million. China remained the source of the tea. Major Robert Bruce had discovered in 1823 that the tea-plant was indigenous to Upper Assam, but nothing was done about growing tea in Britain's own colonial domains until 1834 when the Governor General, Lord William Charles Cavendish Bentinck, set up a committee to plan the introduction of tea-growing into India. The Chinese seed imported was not particularly successful, but in 1839 the first tea from Assam was auctioned in London. It was later discovered that cultivating Assam's native tea-plants produced much better results. As late as 1857, only 3 per cent of the tea imported into Britain came from India. It was the years between 1885 and 1890 which saw the rapid rise of Indian tea from 38 per cent to 70 per cent of the British market.

2

The British Tea Ceremony

Four o'clock tea as a social institution really dates from the 19th century. Before then the British tea ceremony was most solemnly performed when the ladies retired after dinner to take tea in the drawing-room. The men remained in the dining-room and drank heavily before going to join them. When books of instruction for servants discuss serving tea, they tend to situate it after dinner, including the satirical 'Advice to the Butler' offered by Swift in 1745:

> When you are to get Water on for Tea after Dinner (which in many Families is Part of your Office) to save Firing, and to make more Haste, pour it into the Tea-Pot, from the Pot where Cabbage or Fish have been boyling, which will make it much wholesomer, by curing the acid and corroding Quality of the Tea.

Since dinner at this period was likely to begin at two o'clock, the diners would probably find themselves drinking tea at about five o'clock. What most impresses about Georgian tea-drinking, however, is its ready availability, its lack of fixed times and occasions. Apart from its use at breakfast and after dinner, it served as a diversion or to oil the wheels of society at any time. The issue of an invitation to dinner required serious consideration by both host and guest, but a casual acquaintance might be asked to take tea without any anxious sense of obligation on either part. When the visitor arrived, they might find just the family or other company as well, and depending upon the establishment and the occasion there might be cards, music or even dancing.

It is easy to take such a free-and-easy social life for granted, and to forget the insistence on differences in rank which still made most social occasions very formal in 1700. It was a major achievement of the 18th century to enable anyone who could call themselves a lady or a gentleman to mix with relative informality and even sit at the same table with an earl or countess. The process is most obvious in the running of Assembly Rooms, such as that of Bath, presided over by Richard Nash. It succeeded because of the increased emphasis on good manners for anyone claiming to be a lady or gentleman. The aristocracy were less worried about losing their dignity by associating with their social inferiors once they were confident that the latter would behave themselves properly.

The process of levelling down could only be achieved by setting off those with genteel, 'well-bred' manners from the rest of society. Well-bred meant simply well-trained, and deportment and etiquette were learned from the age of five at the hands of a dancing master until they became second nature. This behaviour was central in separating polite society, 'the quality', from the rest.

Polite behaviour sought areas in which it could demonstrate its accomplishments, such as the art of managing elaborate clothing[1] or tea utensils. In doing so, it encouraged their development, and they in turn became increasingly bound up with notions of what constituted polite behaviour. The ritual around the tea-table thus celebrated the genteel manners of the participants and reinforced the social bond between them. Defoe's comments (p.5) on the importance of teawares in the shops, and the reaction when the poor took to tea (p.8) suggest that tea-drinking was indeed an important catalyst in creating the polite society of which the century was so proud.

In this respect the former British colonies on the eastern seaboard of the United States mirrored British practice. When supporters of independence gave up tea for the duration of the war, it was no empty gesture but a real sacrifice. Afterwards, Americans returned to their tea. As a French visitor noted in 1781, 'The greatest mark of civility and welcome they can show you, is to invite you to drink it with them.'[2] Moreau de St Mery observed in Philadelphia in 1795 that 'the whole family is united at tea, to which friends, acquaintances and even strangers are invited.'[3] The journal of another Philadelphian, Nancy Shippen, between 1783 and 1786 reports a succession of tea-parties, like the following:

> Mrs Allen and the Miss Chews drank Tea with me and spent the evening.
> There was half a dozen agreable and sensible men that was of the party.
> The conversation was carried on in the most sprightly, agreable manner,
> the Ladies bearing by far the greatest part – till nine when cards was
> proposed, and about ten, refreshments were introduced which concluded
> the Evening.[4]

Tea-parties of this sort offered valuable informal opportunities for young men and women to meet and get to know each other, in a society where such openness was still fairly limited. Match-making thrived at the tea-table as much as gossip of a less salubrious kind. Those of stern moral rectitude might inhibit such wickedness in their drawing-rooms by placing in front of the guests a teapot painted with the Crucifixion (no.59, pl.24) or inscribed 'Let Your Conversation be upon the Gospell of Christ' (no.71, pl.28). They would have disapproved of the pot decorated with 'the Miller's Maid' as an encouragement to salaciousness (no.57, pl.26). Others bought pots decorated with political slogans in support of popular figures like John Wilkes (no.60, pl.27). Some of these were probably specially commissioned for use at electioneering tea-parties where votes were canvassed, and can be connected with particular elections (no.65, col. pl.8).

The teapot was evidently expected to lend its tone to the proceedings around it. Rochefoucauld noted that drinking tea '. . . gives the rich an opportunity to show off their fine possessions: cups, teapots, etc., all made to the most elegant designs, all copies of the Etruscan and the antique.'[5] Fashionable design and good workmanship demonstrated one's taste and worldly substance, just as one's management of the tea ritual showed one's manners.

English silver teapots do not seem to have taken on standard shapes until shortly after 1700, the same period at which the other elements of the 'tea equipage', as it was called, were becoming established. The earliest surviving example, in the Victoria and Albert Museum, is engraved with an inscription recording that 'This silver tea-Pott was presented to the Committee of the East India Cumpany . . .' by George Lord Berkeley, a member of the committee, in 1670. It simply copies the shape of the coffee-pots used in coffee-houses, being a tall, tapering cylinder, and without the inscription one would not know that it was a teapot at all.[6] The first standard form to emerge was the pear or bag shape, followed in about 1720 by the globular or roughly spherical shape. Both these shapes are also found in imported Chinese porcelain, and both were copied by British potters (see pp.58 and 62).

The Duchess of Lauderdale in 1672 bought '18 tea cups' of silver.[7] These may have imitated the form of imported Chinese cups without handles, for such silver examples survive in the Victoria and Albert Museum and at the Holburne of Menstrie Museum, Bath. On the other hand, these must have been unbearable to hold when filled with scalding tea, and silver cups were also made with handles (Ashmolean Museum, Oxford, and Burrell collection, Glasgow).[8] By about 1720, however, Chinese porcelain seems to have won the day, and even those who could afford an entire equipage of silver made an exception for the cups: see col. pl.2. As such portraits illustrate, the cup could be held in several different ways with perfect propriety. The variety of positions shown suggests that this was an opportunity for people to exhibit their dextrously well-bred manners.[9] Edward Young in a poem of the 1720s, 'The Love of Fame, the Universal Passion', suggests that even amorous passions might be aroused:

> Her two red lips affected Zephyrs blow,
> To cool the Bohea, and inflame the Beau;
> While one white Finger and a Thumb conspire
> To lift the Cup and make the World admire.

The rest of the equipage as shown in the portrait comprises a teapot with a lamp beneath to keep it hot, a tea canister, a covered sugar dish and tongs, a slop bowl, a spoon boat with teaspoons, and a covered jug whose wooden handle shows it is for hot liquid, either water or milk. It has often been supposed that milk was not drunk in tea before 1720, but Thomas Garway refers to it in his handbill of about 1660, and Rachel Lady Russell wrote to her daughter in 1698: 'Yesterday I met with a little bottle to pour milk out for tea, they call them milk bottles, I was much delighted with them and so put them up for presents to you.' The East India Company's sales of oriental porcelain included milk pots, with or without covers, in 1706 but not earlier.[10]

Many silver equipages included a tray to put them on, known confusingly as a 'tea table'. George Booth, Earl of Warrington, ordered for Dunham Massey in 1741 '2 Mahogany stands to set the silver tea and coffee tables on',[11] and the wooden table survives there complete with its silver 'tea table', a tray with four feet which fit into specially designed notches in the edges of the wooden top.[12]

The heater under the teapot kept the tea stewing until presumably it had lost its savour. A better idea was to put it under a kettle, which could be used to

pl.5   The earliest English silver tea-kettle, London 1694. Beneath is a spirit lamp to keep it hot

dilute the tea or replenish the teapot as required. The earliest surviving English silver tea-kettle, in Norwich Castle Museum, dates from 1694 (pl.5). The heater under the teapot went out of fashion except in Scotland, where they were still being made in the 1740s. These Scottish pots often look like kettles but were intended to hold tea, and have strainer holes at the base of the spout to prove the point.[13] By about 1720 the tea-kettle might have a special tripod table with a triangular top made to accommodate its three legs.[14] The very wealthy even had them made in solid silver, either topped off with a tray[15] or made in one with the heater so that the kettle could be placed directly on top.[16] At a time when very little English furniture was made of silver, its choice for kettle stands is another indicator of the respect accorded to the tea ritual.

Silver was appropriate for the kettle and tea canisters because they were used not only in the drawing-room but by the family rather than the servants. Once

pl.6 A toy tea and coffee service in silver, by David Clayton, London, about 1720. The legs of the tray are a later addition. The tea-kettle is only some three inches high

the servants had brought in the steaming kettle and the rest of the equipage on its tray, the mistress would unlock the box containing the two canisters of tea and the covered dish of best double-refined sugar (col. pl.3). She might depute the making of the tea to one of her daughters, but it would be under her supervision. Then 'the mistress of the house serves it and passes it round.'[17]

The East India Company's imports of porcelain reflect the rise in tea consumption just as the development of tea silver does. In 1698 a charter was issued to a second company, which was generally referred to as the New Company to distinguish it from the Old. It seems to have been the New Company which began importing porcelain in quantity. The two companies were amalgamated in 1709 as 'the United Company of Merchants of England trading to the East Indies.' One very good reason for buying porcelain was stated by Robert Douglas, the chief 'Supra-Cargo' or officer in charge of trading on the New Company's ship, Macclesfield, at Canton in 1700:

> . . . china ware is but scarce and what is procurable not extraordinary and were it not that we are under a necessity to take some for helping to ballast our ship, I should not have adventured upon much because of the great quantity that I am advised goes from Emoy [Amoy] . . .[18]

pl.7 Tea-drinking on a Worcester porcelain pot of about 1760 (see cat.no.167)

Chests of porcelain continued to be used for 'flooring' the hold immediately above the ballast proper. In 1765 the crew of the ship Earl of Elgin at Canton were '. . . employed clearing Hold and levelling the ballast to receive the china ware.'[19]

The majority of the company's imported porcelain was painted in blue underglaze, that is before glazing. Such porcelain will withstand sea water without damage, as the 'Nanking Cargo' demonstrated when it was recovered recently from the Dutch ship the *Geldermalsen*, which sank in the South China Sea in 1752. The porcelain, which could risk getting wet, was therefore packed below, while the tea, which could not, stayed on top high and dry.

There was a definite preference for bowls, dishes and other shapes which would pack together tightly, saving on expensive space and providing the maximum weight for volume in the bottom of the hold. A typical instruction, written in 1704, is: 'we would have you provide china ware as far as twenty tons in useful sorts, which stow-close.'[20] Teacups without handles, nowadays known as teabowls, continued to be imported throughout the century not just because that was the Chinese form but because handles would have wasted space. The choice of shapes was not left for the Chinese potters to dictate, for in 1710 a certain Joshua Bagshaw was paid the large sum of £23 'for wood patterns for china ware'.[21]

pl.8 A porcelain tea service of about 1795–1800 by Chamberlain's factory at Worcester. Inside the teapot cover is inscribed the name of the factory and 'Warranted', meaning warranted not to break when boiling water was poured in

The 'dish of tea' which a Georgian hostess offered was a teacup or teabowl placed on a saucer. The use of terms for differentiating drinking vessels was still fairly free and imprecise by modern standards. There is, however, a persistent tale that tea was once drunk from the saucer. A mid-19th-century account relates:

> The saucer seems to have perplexed our ancestors at the time of its first introduction; its first use was believed to be merely to cool the tea, and then it was unfashionable to drink from the cup; at a later time the use of the saucer was understood to be confined to saving slops, and thence forward the cup alone was to have the honour of being raised to the lips.[22]

Evidence from the 18th century suggests that the practice was not considered polite. The Swede Peter Kalm noted in America that 'when the English women drank tea, they never poured it out of the cup into the saucer to cool it, but drank it as hot as it came from the teapot.'[23] A portrait of the Auriol and Dashwood families, painted by Zoffany about 1780, appears to show a lady pouring tea from a teabowl into a saucer which is on the table,[24] but this was painted in India where British ladies had good reason to cool their tea. The old maid who drinks from the saucer in a print of 1771 (pl.9) is obviously not on her best behaviour and shares her tea-table with the cat. She only

THE OLD MAID

The Lady here you see display'd,
By some is still an ancient maid,
But if her inward thoughts you'd view,
She thinks herself as young as you,
Oh! Puss forbear to lick the cream,
Your Mistress longs to do the same.

pl.9 Bad manners: an old maid drinking out of the saucer, 1771
(Reproduced by courtesy of the National Library of Congress)

prevents the cat's weight from tipping it over by placing her hand on the table.

The East India Company's records supply useful evidence of the development of the tea service. In 1719 the three ships *Montagu*, *Carnarvon* and *Sarum* were each ordered to purchase for the company 12,000 milk pots, 6,000 teapots and 45,000 cups and saucers.[25] There was no mention yet of sets as such. As late as 1775 the company ordered only 80 teasets but 1,200 teapots, 2,000 covered sugar bowls, 4,000 milk-pots and 48,000 cups and saucers. There was a problem about sets, as the company complained in 1781:

pl.10 Bad manners, 1792: is George III drinking out of the saucer?
(Reproduced by courtesy of the Trustees of the British Museum)

We think it necessary to repeat, we continue to sustain very heavy losses by
the china ware being much false packed, that is to say the goods have come
of a variety of Patterns, where they should all have been alike particularly
in Table and other sets – In some cases there have been so many patterns
and so very different from each other that they could not possibly have
been put up to Sale in Sets but have been obliged to be sold as odd pieces.
We seldom open a parcel of sets especially Table and tea, but we find
several articles different from the pattern.[26]

The cheaper teasets ordered in 1774, referred to as breakfast sets, were to
comprise a teapot, sugar-box with cover and plate, a slop bason, milk pot, and
twelve cups and saucers. The larger teasets comprised two teapots, one
middle sized and one bigger, a slop bason and plate, a sugar-box and cover, a
milk pot and stand, a tea canister, twelve cups and saucers, and twelve coffee
cups with handles.[27] Silver services of the late 18th or early 19th century
sometimes include two teapots but these are usually of the same size, one for
black tea and one for green.[28] The inclusion of coffee cups in the services
ordered from China makes one wonder whether the second teapot in fact
served as a coffee-pot.

The company's employees made their earnings from the 'private trade' which
they were permitted to carry on its ships on their own account. This was very
considerable, and tended to include porcelain of higher quality and more
varied types than the company's own standard bulk imports. The profits
could be great, but so were the risks, as the Court Minutes recorded in 1785:

21

Mr James Wood, chief mate of the late ship Harcourt representing that since the china ware brought home by him on his Private Adventure has been in the Company's warehouse there is a deficiency therein of 5,406 pieces and praying that as the memorialist saw his said china ware packed up in Canton himself and that the packages were whole when delivered out of the ship in the River Thames, an enquiry may be made . . .

In 1791 the company decided to stop importing Chinese porcelain on its own account. Import duties on it were 50 per cent, and there was currently a falling market. The decisive factor, however, was probably the discovery that leading London china dealers had been operating a 'ring' at the company's auction sales to keep prices artificially low. The company refused to release to the dealers, including Miles Mason, the wares they had bought at auction in December 1787, and proceeded to take them to court.[29] Ceasing the imports was their final retaliation. At the same time they limited private trade, resolving 'that the Commanders and officers of the Company's ships be prohibited from shipping any china-ware whatever as Private Trade except the same be packed in half-chests and made use of as flooring for the Company's teas . . .'.

It was apparently not until 1795 that the British china-dealers remonstrated. Perhaps they hoped to wait for the company's anger to cool, or perhaps it was just because existing stocks and orders took several years to work their way through the system. It probably came as no surprise to Miles Mason when in April that year the company turned down his request 'to know on behalf of the dealers in china ware upon what terms of freight the Company will permit their officers in the Company's service . . . to import china ware.'[30] Mason's response was to form a partnership to produce in England porcelain of as nearly as possible the same kind as the Chinese imports (see p.235). The moment was well-chosen, because Britain was just becoming capable of matching Chinese porcelain tewares not only in price but also in the equally important matter of durability (see next chapter).

The early English teawares, like the Chinese imports, seem to have been sold in less fixed groupings than the standard services which emerge in the later 18th century. There was probably not yet so much concern that the cups should match the pattern of the milk-jug or teapot. The Chelsea factory's sales in the 1750s show them selling variously grouped teawares as individual lots, with the teacups and saucers usually in sets of eight.[31] Christie's sale of Worcester porcelain in 1769 shows the elements of the service crystallising:

> 12 teacups and saucers
> 6 coffee cups
> teapot with cover and stand
> sugar dish with cover and stand
> slop bason and stand
> tea canister and cover
> milk-pot and cover
> spoon tray

The forty-three pieces of this teaset became something of a standard number, although the actual elements varied and it was not usual to count the covers separately. When Job Ridgway in Staffordshire worked out his range of prices for china teasets in 1813,[32] the forty-three pieces were:

12 teacups and saucers
12 coffee cans
teapot and stand
sugar-box
slop bason
cream jug
large plate
small plate

The same saucers still served both for the teacups and coffee cups, but the two plates of different sizes were now clearly intended for bread and butter rather than as stands for the sugar dish and slop bason. The tea canister had disappeared because, now that tea was cheaper, more was drunk, and it was kept in larger receptacles, the boxes or compartmented tea-trunks which were by this date sometimes called caddies. The coffee cans and teapot stand were not included in many cheap tea services, like the one John Riley described as a 'Hawker's Tea Set' in his recipe book in the 1820s.[33]

The scarcity of the little oval dishes known as spoon-boats or trays is noticeable, and suggests that they were often not supplied. The covers on early sugar dishes often have a raised ring which would have acted as a foot when the cover was turned the other way up, and it is possible that they were used for this purpose. It is difficult to see what purpose the spoon-boat could have served once the etiquette of the teaspoon was established to show that one did not want a refill. The Prince de Broglie in 1782 reported:

> I partook of most excellent tea and I should be even now still drinking it,
> I believe, if the Ambassador had not charitably notified me at the twelfth
> cup, that I must put my spoon across it when I wished to finish with this
> sort of warm water. He said to me: it is almost as ill-bred to refuse a cup of
> tea when it is offered to you, as it would [be] indiscreet for the mistress of
> the house to propose a fresh one, when the ceremony of the spoon has
> notified her that we no longer wish to partake of it.[34]

Thomas Cosnett in 1823 advised servants when to remove a cup: 'You will easily know when they have done, by their putting the spoon in the tea-cup.'[35] De Broglie may have meant placing the spoon diagonally across the cup in this way rather than trying to balance it across the top, which is surprisingly difficult to do. A cartoon shows an unfortunate Frenchman who has had to keep on drinking because he did not know this etiquette (col. pl.1). This ceremony of the spoon seems to have replaced an earlier custom of placing the cup upside-down on the saucer, which is shown in Hogarth's painting of the Wollaston family.[36]

Teaspoons and sugar nips were a necessity with a tea service. The first nips were U-shaped bow tongs as shown in a portrait of about 1730 (col. pl.2) but by this date they were more often hinged like a pair of scissors. The neoclassical taste of the 1770s preferred the simpler line of the bow tongs, and the scissor form never regained popularity.

A silver equipage of 1735 by Paul de Lamerie at Temple Newsam House, Leeds, comprises two canisters, a sugar-box, a cream jug, twelve teaspoons, a pair of sugar nips, two knives and a spoon with a pierced bowl and long, pointed handle.[37] Spoons of this type are nowadays known as mote spoons, but were described at the time as strainer spoons. They could not have been used for straining by pouring tea through them because their bowls are too narrow, and they were not required for straining sugar, which was added to the tea in lumps with the nips. They were evidently used for removing 'motes' or particles of foreign matter floating in the cup, at a time when tea was less rigorously sifted than it is nowadays. It has been suggested that they were also used to extract tea from the jar or canister, straining out the accompanying tea dust.[38] The pointed handle of the spoon was used for unblocking the strainer holes at the base of the teapot spout. This was done from inside the body of the pot. The strainer holes saved the spout from becoming blocked, and the spouts of most 18th-century pots are in any case too curved to allow the passage of the spoon handle.

The necks of the early jars and canisters, narrow to prevent spillage and preserve the flavour of the precious tea, are wide enough to accommodate a strainer spoon. A portrait of the Walpole family attributed to Hogarth, dating from the 1730s, shows Lady Walpole measuring out the tea in the cover of the canister, but this was not always possible since some canisters after 1720 have their covers attached with a hinge. The wide-bowled 'caddy spoons' beloved of modern collectors were not introduced until at least the 1760s, and would not have passed through the narrow neck of an early canister. They were designed for use with the later, larger forms of container with a more generous opening. Some such spoons had shell-shaped bowls, which are thought to be inspired by the real shells placed in the tops of chests of tea by the Chinese to serve as scoops. Caddy spoons of the 19th century were often made in fanciful shapes such as jockey's caps.

The lowering of tea prices and the rise in consumption is reflected in the scale of the tea equipage. Not only were more people drinking tea, but they were drinking more of it at a sitting. The teapots of the 1740s look small compared to those of the 1770s, and in the years after the Commutation Act of 1784 the increase in size is still more marked. The same development made the small porcelain or silver tea-jars and canisters outmoded, replacing them with larger boxes. These were called caddies, after the Malayan word 'kati', denoting a measure of tea weighing about 1¾ pounds. The change of scale encouraged the treatment of the caddy as a piece of miniature furniture, using exotic woods, papier mâché, or veneers of ivory, tortoise-shell or mother-of-pearl. By the 1830s the caddy was losing its high status as tea became cheaper and was increasingly made in the kitchen by the servants rather than by the mistress in the drawing-room.

By 1760 tea-kettles were growing too large and awkward for the hostess to manage with elegance. To avoid the necessity of lifting them, some were made with a tap fitted low on the body. Once the vessel was static, it no longer needed to be kettle-shaped, and became the rather misleadingly named tea urn, dispensing boiling water rather than tea (col. pl.1). Several different heating systems competed to maintain what Cowper called 'the bubbling and

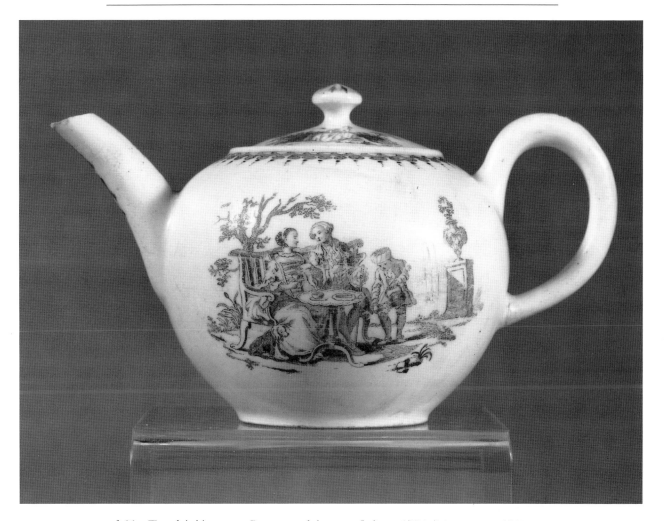

pl.11   Tea-drinking on a Bow porcelain pot of about 1754–7 (see cat.no.151)

loud hissing urn throwing up a steaming column.' The earliest was a perforated brazier for charcoal, from which an inverted funnel served as a flue and carried the heat up through the body. In 1774 John Wadham patented the use of a red-hot cylindrical bar of solid iron, inserted in a copper socket down the centre of the urn. Transferring the heavy bar of red-hot iron from the kitchen fire to the urn must have been a dangerous business. Spirit lamps do not seem to have been much used with tea urns before about 1790.

The ultimate form of urn was the 'Compleat Tea Equipage', developed around this time and made in Sheffield plate. A central hot water urn flanked two smaller urns which held tea and coffee. The larger urn swivelled on its base, enabling the smaller ones to be refilled without being moved. It was perfect for the sideboards of country houses where the family and friends would drift down to breakfast throughout the morning, helping themselves according to the English custom.

Hot water was sometimes provided in a second teapot. Thomas Cosnett in 1823 instructed servants to 'have a teapot on the tray with hot water in it, in case any of the ladies' tea should be too strong.'[39] This may account for the second, smaller teapot supplied with some services at this period (see nos. 471 and 472, col. pl.21), which has usually been explained as for private use in

A TEA GARDEN

pl.12 *A Tea Garden*, an engraving after a painting of about 1790 by George Morland

bedroom or dressing-room. The 'déjeuner' or 'cabaret' services for no more than two people, which included a teapot of small size, were used for that purpose.

For Cosnett the most important occasion for serving tea was still after dinner in the drawing-room. The fashionable hour for dinner had gradually become later, from two o'clock in the early 18th century to half-past six or seven in the early 19th, although many provincial families lagged several hours behind. By that stage luncheon had been invented to fill the gap, but afternoon tea with bread and butter or cakes, taken before dinner, does not seem to have become a regular institution until the 1840s, when the movement of dinner to half-past seven or eight made another stop-gap necessary. The habit is said to have been started by Anna, wife of the seventh Duke of Bedford (1788–1861). Fanny Kemble recounted that she first experienced it at Belvoir Castle in 1842, and that it was then a novel practice.[40] Many people in the 18th century had taken tea at five o'clock, but this was because they had just finished dinner, and was not afternoon tea in the modern sense.

It is ironic that the most inventive period for the design of the British ceramic teapot, the period covered in these pages, closes just when the ritual most associated with it in the modern mind, that of afternoon tea, was becoming established. The social importance of tea-drinking in these years ensured that its utensils would be carefully made and their design subject to the rapid changes dictated by fashion. Jane Austen's readers were no doubt familiar with the sort of attitude displayed by General Tilney in *Northanger Abbey*:

> The elegance of the breakfast set forced itself on Catherine's notice when they were seated at table; and, luckily, it had been the General's choice. He was enchanted by her approbation of his taste, confessed it to be neat and simple, thought it right to encourage the manufacture of his country; and for his part, to his uncritical palate, the tea was as well flavoured from the clay of Staffordshire, as from that of Dresden or Seve. But this was quite an old set, purchased two years ago. The manufacture was much improved since that time; he had seen some beautiful specimens when last in town, and had he not been perfectly without vanity of that kind, might have been tempted to order a new set.

3

Supplying the Tea Equipage

Flying Teapots and the Challenge of China

In the newspaper *The Leeds Intelligencer* on 28 October 1760 the firm of Robinson and Rhodes advertised '. . . a good assortment of Foreign China and a great variety of useful English China of the newest improvement, which they engage will wear as well as foreign, and will change gratis if broke with hot water.'

Boiling water was a major challenge for early British porcelain teapots. As late as the 1780s the Derby factory was regularly receiving complaints from its London manager that he '. . . wished something could be done respecting the teapots to prevent them flying, for the disgrace is worse than anything, and it looses the sale of many sets.' The factory's only response was to suggest advising customers to warm the pot up gradually.

For most of the 18th century oriental porcelain was the favourite teaware, not only for its appropriate exotic associations but also because of its practical qualities. In his introductory advertisement for the newly founded Vauxhall porcelain factory, in the *Public Advertiser* in 1753, Nicholas Crisp compared Chinese porcelain with English delftware pottery:

> . . . the finest of our Manufacture in this kind, is no other than a coarse Earth, baked and glazed over with a thin Coat of vitrified Materials, so that the earth does neither unite into a solid body, nor admit the Glazing, with which it is covered, to adhere firmly to it; by this Means, not only any sudden Heat, but even the Moisture of the Air, will cause the Glazing to crack and flake off.

> The Porcelain Ware of China is free from these Imperfections, and is on this Account become of such general Use, that it must be considered as a great Acquisition to this Nation, could a domestic Manufacture be introduced, that might supply the place of this foreign Commodity.

> The essential properties of China-ware, besides the Beauty of its Colours, are these: That it is as smooth, and as easily cleaned as Glass, and at the same Time bears the hottest Liquors without danger of Breaking. And all the European Manufactures are fitted for general Use, in proportion as they come up to these Characters . . .[1]

Since the early part of the century the imports had poured in on a massive scale, but it was not until the 1740s that English factories succeeded in making porcelain. Inland China was barred to Europeans except for the Jesuits, and one such priest named d'Entrecolles wrote a tantalising account of the Chinese materials and manufacture. In 1738 this appeared in du Halde's book translated into English as *A Description of the Empire of China*,[2] and a good deal of effort was expended in trying to read between its lines (see p.31).

English factories first succeeded in producing porcelain of a kind, or rather several kinds, in the 1740s. The attempt 'to equal a foreign Nation', as an advertisement for Limehouse porcelain put it in 1747, became a matter of national pride.[3] Samuel Richardson's fourth edition of Defoe's *Tour of Great Britain* in 1748 describes '. . . Bow: where a large Manufactory of Porcelaine is lately set up. They have already made large quantities of Tea-cups, saucers, etc. which by some skilful persons are said to be little inferior to those which are brought from China. If they can work this so as to undersell the Foreign Porcelane, it may become a very profitable business to the Undertakers, and save great sums to the Public, which are annually sent abroad for this Commodity.'[4]

A writer in the *Public Advertiser* in 1753 noted:

> The Manufacture of Porcelaine improves but slowly, either for want of Skill, Stocks or Spirit in the Undertakers: this is a Commodity of great Demand, draws large Sums yearly out of the Kingdom, and is paid for wholly in ready Money. We want none of the Materials; and yet Bruges, Dresden and Paris, without any natural Advantages superior to England, have far outstripped us . . . At present the Manufacturers are only enabled to pursue the Art, through the Public Spirit and Generosity of those who think no Price too great for English Ingenuity.[5]

One commentator in 1774 summed up '. . . the capital Obstacle in their Way, by which I mean the moderate price of true [ie oriental] China, and the Necessity imposed thereby of selling cheap in order to force a Market.' He adds that '. . . these difficulties were encountered in the very Infancy of these several Manufactures; which however were carried on without any of those public Encouragements which were given to the Establishments in other Countries . . .'.[6]

Porcelain had already been made in continental Europe for some time, often under the patronage of governments. In Germany a young alchemist, Johann Friedrich Böttger, was thought by Augustus the Strong, Elector of Saxony, to have discovered the secret of the 'philosophers' stone', the elusive substance that would turn base metals into gold. This made Böttger hot property, and the Elector promptly locked him up in a castle at Meissen with instructions to get on with it. Undeterred by Böttger's failure, the Elector brought in an internationally famous physicist, Ehrenfried Walther, Graf von Tschirn-hausen, to see whether the two of them could produce precious stones by artificial means. Instead of the intended rubies they succeeded in 1707 in making fine red stoneware pottery, and within another two years they mastered the secret of making true porcelain like the Chinese. In 1710 the Meissen factory was born. Böttger put a wry notice over his door which read: 'God the Creator has transmuted a maker of gold into a maker of pots.'

The struggle to make porcelain had much the same excitement as the attempts of the alchemists to make gold. In an age when people thought rubies might be made artificially, it was easy to think of the mysterious white porcelain as equivalent to a semi-precious stone. Böttger and Tschirnhausen referred to their red stoneware as 'jasper', the same name Wedgwood later used for a kind of pottery which imitated the effect of ancient cameos carved from semi-precious stones. Samuel Bell of Newcastle-under-Lyme in Staffordshire was granted a patent in 1729 'for making red marbled stoneware with mineral earth found within this kingdom which being firmly united by fire will make it capable of receiving a gloss so beautiful as to imitate if not compare with ruby . . .'.[7] In their ignorance of the ingredients of porcelain, potters at first assumed it was simply a white equivalent of the red stoneware which came with it in the same ships from China, and referred to 'the red porcelain' as well as the white. Inspired by what they saw as 'semi-precious' qualities in these exotic wares, British potters attempted to rival them with new products appealing to the same scale of values and bearing names like 'agate', 'tortoise shell', 'pearl', 'basaltes' and 'chalcedony'.

Those who knew the arcane business of how to make porcelain, the 'arcanists', were in much the same position as a successful alchemist. Their services were certainly in demand, but strenuous attempts were made to prevent them from escaping and selling their secret elsewhere. An anonymous letter survives, written by three French porcelain makers to the second Duke of Richmond, perhaps in the late 1740s.[8] They were hoping to persuade him to finance them to set up a china factory in England, and provided a set of figures including some rather optimistic costs. They dared not give their names, and explain why: 'They respectfully ask that one should be discreet, otherwise they would run the risk, if they were found out, of being arrested at the frontier of the kingdom. Although they have made no promises to anyone and are their own masters, they would be delighted if this was done on the quiet.' The letter refers to prices at the royal factory of Vincennes, and it is known that one of the painters there, named Caillat, was indeed imprisoned for trying to escape to England with some recipes.[9]

Since the secret of porcelain was so valuable, it could be difficult to separate the genuine 'arcanist' from the charlatan or the deluded. George Psalmanazar was a French confidence trickster who specialised in this area, pretending to be Taiwanese, and apparently had some success in England.[10] The Journal Book of the Royal Society notes under 10 February 1743:

> Mr Bryand, a Stranger that was present, shew'd the Society several specimens of a sort of white ware made here by himself from native materials of our own Country, which appeared to be in all respects as good as any of the finest Porcelane or China ware: and he said it was much preferable for its fineness to the ware of Dresden, and seemed to answer the character of the true Japan . . .[11]

Three years later a Thomas Briand, painter, of Lane Delph in Staffordshire went into partnership with Joseph Farmer, a potter of the same place. The agreement recites 'that T.B. had found out the Art of making a beautifull Earthenware Little inferior to Porcelain or China Ware of which the said Joseph Ffarmer was convinced and thoroughly satisfied and the said T.B.

Had agreed . . . to take in the said J.Ff. as his Partner and Lay open the Secret etc. to the said J Ff. It's Covenanted to enter into Partnership from the date of the articles for 21 years at equal Profit and loss . . .'.[12]

Thomas Briand died not long after the partnership began, and in the ensuing dispute his widow and Joseph Farmer brought in arbitrators. John Wedgwood, nowadays less well known than his nephew Josiah, was picked by Farmer, and received an interesting letter from the London china dealers John Weatherby and John Crowther, who were closely associated with the porcelain factory at Bow. Thomas Briand had anticipated trouble from this quarter because his agreement with Farmer included 'A Covenant to indemnify T.B. against any accon or suit to be commenced against him by John Weatherby and John Crowther or either of them.' Their letter to Wedgwood expresses 'great concern to hear you are likely to meet with so much trouble with the Affair of Mr Farmers and Mrs Briand . . .', and reminded him:

> If you remember we told you in few words that we had nothing good to say of the deceased Briand (nor of his wife) that we had been greatly deceived by them, that they had from time to time made great promise to us of what they could do; and Mr Briand shew us several patterns of good China which he protested was of his making and that he would convince us he could make the like but upon trial all his promises ended in words he never performed any onething he proposed and it's our Opinion they knew nothing of what he pretended to know and we firmly believe the design of the deceased was only to make an advantage to himself of those he was concerned with . . .[13]

Whether or not Briand and Bryand were the same person, the latter's appearance before the Royal Society seems to have started a scramble among those who had been quietly experimenting in making porcelain but now saw the need to stake their claim before they were pre-empted. Just seventeen days later, on 28 February 1743, an application for a patent was filed by William Steers of Hoxton who 'by great labour, application and expense hath lately found out and invented the art of making Transparent Earthen Ware in imitation of Porcelain or China ware after a method entirely new . . .'.[14]

On 26 May Andrew Duché, a potter from Savannah in Georgia who is known to have been producing porcelain experimentally, arrived in England. He was probably the person of whom the Plymouth chemist William Cookworthy wrote two years later: 'I had lately with me, the person who has discovered the china earth. He had with him several samples of the china ware, which I think were equal to the Asiatic. It was found on the back of Virginia, where he was in quest of mines; and having read Du Halde, he discovered both the petunze [china stone] and kaolin [china clay]. It is this latter earth, which he says is essential to the success of the manufacture. He is gone for a cargo of it; having bought from the Indians, the whole country where it rises. They can import it for £13 a ton; and by that means afford their china as cheap as common stone ware; but they intend only to go 30 per cent under the company . . .' – by this he meant the East India Company's imported Chinese porcelains.[15]

On 8 October 1744 Edward Heylyn and Thomas Frye applied for a patent for 'a new method of manufacturing a certain material whereby a ware might be made of the same nature or kind, and equal to, if not exceeding in goodness and beauty, China or Porcelain imported from abroad . . . The material is an earth, the produce of the Chirokee nation in America, called by the natives unaker . . .'. The applicants, the future partners of the Bow factory, had evidently been talking to Duché. Three weeks later the earlier application of William Steers, which had been pending for a year and a half, was 'taken out' as unsuccessful. The patent for the future Bow factory, however, was granted within two months of application.

Steers went to Newcastle-under-Lyme in Staffordshire, and attempted to make porcelain at Samuel Bell's old pottery. Excavations on the site have unearthed porcelain wasters including a bowl dated 25 July 1746 in under-glaze blue. The venture was evidently unsuccessful. A newspaper cutting dated 1746 advertises 'A Very commodious House (late in the Occupation of Mr Bell, and now in the possession of Mr Steers) . . . sundry Warehouses, Workshops, Laths, Throwing Wheels, and other Utensils useful in making fine Earthenware or China; three Pot-Ovens, one lately built on Purpose to burn China . . .'.[16]

Both the oriental porcelain and that made at Meissen were composed of china clay (kaolin) and china stone (petuntse), and fired to a very high temperature. The English factories of the first generation did not know the secret of its manufacture. They therefore made imitations from different ingredients and fired at a lower temperature. These are known as 'soft-paste' porcelains, as opposed to the 'hard-paste' of Meissen and the Orient. Some soft-paste recipes were better for teawares than others. The three basic types of English soft-paste were all in production by 1750.

The glassy paste used at Chelsea was beautiful but not strong. Appearances were paramount with the fashionable customers of Chelsea, which was 'calculated rather for ornament than for use',[17] but all factories who used this type of paste faced serious problems. Even Chelsea had to change its paste, Derby's teapots 'flew' even after they had changed theirs twice, and the Longton Hall factory, which did not change, went out of business.

Bow in the eastern industrial suburbs was the first to strengthen the paste by adding bone-ash. This was a momentous invention for the future, since bone-ash is the ingredient which since about 1800 has distinguished English bone china from the porcelain of other countries. The factory's second patent of 1749 is for 'a certain ware which is not inferior in beauty and fineness and is rather superior in strength than the earthenware that is brought from the East Indies.' Samuel Richardson's sixth edition of Defoe's *Tour of Great Britain* in 1762 informs us that Bow porcelain 'though not so fine as some made at Chelsea, or as that brought from Dresden, is much stronger than either, and therefore better for common Use . . .'.[18] Bone-ash helped the porcelain to withstand knocks, but it was probably not as good at withstanding the thermal shock of boiling water as Chinese porcelain. There was also one unfortunate side-effect with bone-ash: it sometimes caused the porcelain to stain an orangey-brown colour where the paste was exposed by a gap or crack in the glaze. People certainly preferred Chinese porcelain if they could get it. Advertisements for sales in Norwich stated in 1755: 'No Bowe Manufactory in this collection', and six years later, 'All the above are Foreign China, and not Bow, as was here some Time before.'[19]

Alexander Lind of Gorgie near Edinburgh was perhaps being diplomatic when he wrote to Lord Milton in 1749: 'The China made at Bow must be vastly improven since I received the Specimen of it from Mr Fletcher, that I thought very little of it, being of the same kind made at St Cloud but not near so good, it has a pretty Glazing which sets it of, and that makes it appear good to those that look only at the out side, but to examine it throughly we must look at the inside and try it not only in the Furnace but likeways by its bearing hot water in cold weather, to see if it stands the sudden transitions from Cold to heat and from heat to cold as the Chinese Porcelain does . . .'.[20]

The third type of soft-paste included soapstone. This made the porcelain resistant to thermal shock, which meant that it would stand boiling water without cracking. The *Daily Advertiser* on 28 October 1747 mentions, '. . . great variety of useful and ornamental Goods in the New Limehouse Ware; which for strength and enduring the Fire, far exceeds China, or any other Ware hitherto invented.'[21] The porcelain wasters recently excavated on the Limehouse site are not, however, of soapstone type. It seems that the use of soapstone was developed by Benjamin Lund's short-lived Bristol factory and passed on to its successor at Worcester. The *Gentleman's Magazine* in 1763 compared those English porcelains which were cheaper than the Chinese and reported: '. . . except Worcester they all wear brown and are subject to crack, especially the glazing, by boiling water. The Worcester has a good body, scarce inferior to that of Eastern china, it is equally tough and its glazing never cracks or scales off . . .'.[22]

The best claim that a competitor using bone-ash could make was put forward by Richard Chaffers in *Williamson's Liverpool Advertiser* on 10 December 1756: 'All the ware is proved with boiling water before it is exposed for sale.' Unfortunately, it is not known how conscientious Chaffers' quality control was, how high the failure rate and whether the ware was warmed up first! Heat resistance was evidently understood at Worcester to be a major selling point, for even after 1800 the new factories in the town, making quite different types of porcelain, marked their teapots 'Chamberlain's Worcester Warranted' or 'Grainger & Co. Worcester Warranted'.

The first British hard-paste porcelain factory was set up by William Cookworthy at Bristol in 1765, thanks to his discovery of the necessary china clay and china stone in Cornwall.[23] The venture was not a success, and Cookworthy transferred operations first to his native Plymouth, and then back to Bristol again. His patent of 1768, covering the use of these vital ingredients, is a milestone in the history of British ceramics. He and his partner Richard Champion faced unprecedented production problems and a daunting rate of wastage because of the high temperature at which the glazed ware was fired. It was not until a consortium of Staffordshire potters bought the patent rights in 1781 and set up the New Hall factory to make a hybrid version of hard-paste porcelain that long-term commercial success was assured for English porcelain made with china clay and china stone. The key to New Hall's success was firing the glazed ware at a lower temperature than the unglazed.

When the patent expired in 1796, it was open to anyone to make porcelain with these materials. Their combination with bone-ash created bone china, which has been the standard English porcelain body ever since. These technical improvements no doubt caused a marked decrease in the number of cracked teapots and scalded hostesses. The less reliable soft-paste tewares were doomed to extinction, but the sensuous beauty of their materials could not be matched by harder wares and has become all the more alluring to collectors with the passage of time.

The story of this early porcelain is littered with failures, from the mysterious factories like Newcastle-under-Lyme and Stourbridge, which may never have reached production,[24] to the repeated attempts of entrepreneurs like William Littler and Nicholas Crisp (see pp.148 and 149–51 respectively). Josiah Wedgwood spent much of his life watching porcelain factories come to sticky ends, while his own manufacture of other new and improved types of pottery went from strength to strength. Soon after Crisp's death at Bovey Tracey in Devon, where he had failed in an attempt to produce porcelain, Wedgwood wrote: 'I have had too much experience of the delicacy and unaccountable uncertainty of these fine bodies to be sanguine in my expectations – and Crisp – Poor Crisp haunts my imagination Continually – Ever persuing – Just upon the point of overtaking – but never in the possession of his favourite subject! There are a good many lessons in the poor Man's life, labours and Catastrophe if we could profit by example.'[25] Like the genius of the Bow factory, Thomas Frye, whose epitaph relates that 'He spent fifteen years among Furnaces, Till his Constitution was near destroyed', Crisp was not alone in sacrificing everything to his obsession to make teapots of the perfect substance.

Inside the Pottery Trade

Imported Chinese teawares inspired not only the beginning of British porcelain but an industrial revolution throughout the whole pottery industry. Potters realised that they could create a new market for their own wares if they could match the hardness, delicacy and beauty of the imports, and responded by producing new types of pottery bodies, glazes and decoration, which often ended up quite unlike anything oriental. Once red teapots could be made in imitation of the Chinese, it was not difficult for Josiah Wedgwood to change the style to classical and rename the ware 'rosso antico' (see p.154).

In an industry undergoing a technological revolution, it was particularly profitable for a manufacturer to keep his own new materials and processes secret, while trying to discover those of his competitors. The Worcester factory in 1752 had a 'secret room', and Wedgwood referred to his materials by code numbers in case his letters were illicitly intercepted and read on their way to his partner Bentley. Despite such precautions, however, manufacturers seem to have been remarkably well informed about each other. No doubt the movement of skilled workers between factories accounted for much of this. The partnership agreement of the Worcester factory in 1751 included a special financial inducement to Robert Podmore to encourage his loyalty, but four years later he went to Liverpool and signed an agreement 'to instruct . . .

Richard Chaffers and Philip Christian in the Art and Mystery of making of
. . . Earthenware in imitation of or to resemble Chinaware.'[26] William Cookworthy wrote in December 1767 that he had just hired a modeller and a
painter who had been 'Employed for many years in the Chelsea, Bow and
Vauxhall China Potteries.'[27] Sitting at his desk in Plymouth, he could write
knowledgeably about the quality of the coal used for firing china in William
Littler's factory at West Pans in Scotland.[28]

The success of English pottery, as opposed to porcelain, in European markets
in the later 18th century led many continental factories to import skilled
English labour. In the Wedgwood archives is a letter which the firm evidently
intercepted, written by an employee, Samuel Jones, to Georges Bris of Douai
in 1784. It is addressed simply from the 'Staffordshire pottery':

> Sir, I take this opportunity of offering my service to you if you think it will
> be of any service to you I understand that you want some workmen in the
> Different Branches of the poting and I have it in my power to serve you if
> we can agree upon terms I can bring a turner a presser and handler
> a modeller and a man that can make as good a China glaze and Enamel
> coulers as any man in the country and both he and me are painters either in
> blue or enamel likewise his wife, and I can prepare the coulers for either or
> bring some of it with me if you will answer this letter to let us know how you
> like my proposals and what terms you wants us to come upon and you are
> willing for us to come we shall want some money which we should be glad if
> we could receive some in London to bair our expenses over or if you chuse
> I will come my self first and settle for every one of us and come back a gain
> to England for them if you will be at the expence of coming and going for
> all the rest of us are married except my self and I will run the hazard of any
> thing happening from the masters in this country and you must excuse my
> not dating my letter from any particular part of the pottery for I Do it for
> fear it should be broke open please answer this letter with all expedition
> and you will oblige yours at command Samuel Jones. Please direct for me to
> be left at Mr Tho. Alsop Alsops Bricklayer Ashbourn Derbyshire.[29]

At the other end of the social spectrum, some people with technical knowledge could, under the wing of an aristocratic patron, gain access to parts of a
factory which were normally restricted. Alexander Lind did this with the
Duke of Argyll, as he described in 1749: 'I have seen the china manufactures
at Bow and at Chelsea, his Grace was so good as [to] carry me to both where I
had an oppertunity of examining everything pretty minutely; I mean the
structure of their Furnaces, and the other parts of their manual operations,
which were what I wanted cheifly to see, as to the materials they use, those
they keep secret, as far as they can, but as I think I know them, and that my
own are prefferable, I am the less curious to be informed about them. I shoud
not have seen what I did, I mean their Furnaces &ct, if I had not have had the
honour to have been in company with the Duke of Argyll, whose favour and
approbation I see they all court . . .'.[30]

A standard tale of industrial espionage has been handed down in the
folk-history of several factories. A cunning man pretends to be stupid and so
obtains a job at the factory and in due course the confidence of his employers,
so that he is able to observe and record their secrets. He then puts these to

good use elsewhere. Wedgwood suggested a way of limiting this sort of commercial damage, in a letter to his partner Bentley in 1769:

> If we get these painters, and the figure makers, we shall do pretty well in those branches. But these new hands should if possible be kept by themselves 'till we are better acquainted with them, otherwise they may do us a great deal of mischief if we should be obliged to part with them soon. I have had some thoughts of building steps to the outside of some of the Chambers for that purpose. What think you of it? We cannot avoid taking in Strangers and shall be obliged sometimes to part with them again, we should therefore prevent as much as possible their taking any part of our business along with them. Every different class should if possible be kept by themselves, and have no connection with any other.[31]

Wedgwood could no doubt do unto others as they did unto him. Richard Champion of the Bristol factory wrote to the Marquess of Rockingham in 1775: 'I have been making new kilns, and several other alterations. My good friend Wedgwood however declares that he will produce china next year, he has purchased a great deal of the materials but I have not lost any workmen, though he did clandestinely get into my works. However, I do not think he did me much harm, or himself good.'[32] The details made public in the patent Champion had bought from Cookworthy were in one sense a gift to his competitors, as Thomas Pitt reminded him in the same year: 'Wedgwood says your specification is a lighthouse, teaching the trade precisely what they are to avoid, which will only bring them safely into port . . . he is gone now into Cornwall to visit and procure samples of the materials, which he will make experiments upon, and communicate the results to the whole trade.'[33] C.J. Mason was more ingenious when he patented a strengthened earthenware under the name 'ironstone china' in 1813. The patent specification gave ironstone as a major ingredient, but this was just to mislead competitors, for there is little or none in the ware.

A factory's fashionable designs were likely to be copied quite shamelessly by its rivals, for there was no effective form of design protection until 1839 (see p.301). The experiences Wedgwood recorded in 1768 were no doubt typical; he informs his London partner Bentley: '. . . Caravalla supplies Mr P[almer] with all my patterns as they arrive at my rooms in London, and Fogg does the same for Bagnall & Baker, and these last let any of the other potters have them, paying a share of the expence. You must try if you can recollect any particular Persons repeatedly buying a few pairs or single articles of your new patterns as they arrive, very probably it may be some sham Gentleman or Lady equipped for the purpose, with their footman or Maid to carry them home to prevent a discovery.'[34]

The delicate neoclassical relief designs modelled at Wedgwood's factory were particularly popular with other potters (see nos. 273 and 285). Josiah wrote in 1790 to his nephew Thomas Byerley, who had taken on the mantle of Bentley:

> Another disagreeable thing which has lately come to my knowledge is a plaster man, a journeyman to somebody in London or Birmingham, I know not which, keeps a room in the pottery [we should say 'the Potteries'] and engages to furnish them with casts of anything I make. One channel by which he is enabled to do this is the Mounters of cameos, who suffer casts to

be taken from those they have in their hands for a trifle. And you know that one of our people who was in our warehouse some time ago furnished a man of this sort in Oxford road or Holborn with casts from our own bas reliefs. . . . As most of our bas reliefs are undercut it will be discoverable whether casts have been taken from them or not, for it will be almost impossible to get the plaster perfectly clean out, but then they must be very narrowly examined. He engages to furnish the potters with casts from any one of our bas reliefs . . . and has already furnished them with many of our Sylphs. Pray let the Sylphs be carefully examined, and endeavour to recollect whom you have sold any to, for we have sold very few, not half so many as the plaster man has sold here. It is a provoking thing, after we have been at so much pains and expence in procuring new models, that we should be plundered with so much ease and security to the thieves who do it.

We have had several potters, particularly Ralph Wedgwood [see p.103], send to our works for pieces, apparently intended to take moulds from to supply our customers. I apprehend something of this kind is done in your Warehouse and I wish you to be on your guard as much as you can . . .[35]

A certain Thomas Appleton left the employment of Josiah Spode for that of William Mason, taking with him 'a parcel of moulds'. Spode managed to get a confession by Appleton published in the *Staffordshire Advertiser* on 9 March 1811. The Masons stoutly denied 'soliciting or obtaining in a clandestine manner from the said Mr Spode, his patterns, moulds or shapes', but probably did not help their case by adding that anyway the moulds 'were not worth sixpence'.[36]

When one finds identical moulded designs used by different potters (see for example p.165), it is tempting to assume such plagiarism, but in the absence of direct evidence it is perhaps just as likely that different firms bought identical master block moulds from a freelance modeller such as Benjamin Bentley of Hanley, who in 1812 supplied Chamberlain's factory at Worcester with a set of teapot models including moulds for a cream jug and sugar-box. The deliberate variations between superficially similar moulded designs, for example in white salt-glazed stoneware (see p.51), may have had a practical point to enable individual manufacturers to recognise their own wares. Even where identical body mouldings were used by two manufacturers, the knobs, spouts or handles might distinguish them (see p.187).

Wedgwood was copied from rather than copying because of his own huge commercial success and his partner Bentley's nose for fashionable taste. Other potters almost certainly saw the issue in a rather different light. When Spode was slow to comply with a minimum price agreement of the Staffordshire potters in 1814, his competitor John Davenport explained his fears:

> . . . With respect to Cream Colour we were not very anxious, it is a staple and will find its value, but with regard to Blue Printed Table ware we conceive the case very different for if Mr Spode's large stock of that article gets all at once into the Home Market which it would naturally do at reduced prices, the future supply would be wanted chiefly of his patterns, which, of course, other manufacturers must adopt at great expense of new [printing] plates . . .[37]

Manufacturers may therefore not have had very much choice about whether to copy a firm which dominated the market to the extent that, for example, Wedgwood did around 1780.

The absence of readily recognisable maker's marks from so much British pottery and porcelain is often the source of frustration and puzzlement. There was no incentive for a factory to begin marking its products unless the public had heard of them and wanted them. That is why Chelsea, whose wares had the reputation as the most fashionable, was the first factory regularly to use a mark. Worcester followed suit once it had established a reputation (see p.33), but many other factories did not. Like Bow, their standard ware was cheaper than imported Chinese porcelain, and they probably hoped to be mistaken for it. The extensive advertisements of Norwich china dealers in the local papers never once mention the porcelain made a few miles away at Lowestoft, although Norwich must have been a major market for it.[38]

A French visitor to the Lowestoft factory noted that he had seen their ware sold on the Continent as oriental, and the same thing is likely to have happened in this country with Lowestoft and many other English porcelains. Marks imitating Chinese characters were used on blue and white at Bow and also at Worcester, where they served as a thin disguise for less exotic numerals presumably needed for some internal accounting system. The would-be oriental decoration on much early English porcelain, especially blue and white, must have assisted deception.

The first manufacturer of other kinds of pottery who followed the leading porcelain factories in regularly marking his wares was Josiah Wedgwood. The practice certainly assisted his reputation to spread and encouraged brand loyalty; an order for creamware from the Netherlands in 1781 specified 'every article of the best quality, and all to be marked with your name.'[39] He did not, however, propose routine marking until 1772, after he had been 'Potter to Her Majesty' for some years and was already establishing a unique position for himself among British potters. Unlike the porcelain factories, he marked not with a symbol, but with his surname impressed into the unfired pot. His nephew Ralph Wedgwood, who had his own independent works, was therefore able quite legitimately to mark his own pots 'Wedgwood & Co.' (p.103), while the enterprising potter John Wood, with a keen eye to his son's future, actually christened him 'Wedg' (p.207).

Many makers continued not to mark their ware on a regular basis. Their names were not known to the public, and there was always the chance that unmarked ware might be passed off as Wedgwood or Turner, as some of it still is! Retailers often preferred to sell unmarked goods and keep secret their source of supply, in order to prevent their competitors and customers from buying them direct from the maker. As late as 1845 an important manufacturer like Herbert Minton was still leaving many of his best wares unmarked, for fear of the top London retailers, who might even put on a mark claiming that they were manufacturers.[40]

Another good reason for not marking was the potters' traditional habit of trading pots with each other. If you had an order which could not be completed from your own stock, you did not let your customer shop elsewhere, but tried to buy the goods in the trade. Thus the order book of Baddeley and Fletcher about 1770 includes the note 'To inquire of Astbury for Blue Teapotts.'[41] Wedgwood in a letter of 1767 offered his own ware but, using a familiar salesman's ploy, made it clear that he could buy in cheaper goods if the customer was prepared to sacrifice quality to price:

> I can serve you with Creamcolor teapots of 12 to 24 to the dozen . . . I will sell them to you at Warehouse price at 3s 6d each . . . There is an inferior sort made here at 3s each, but they are seldom half fired and would be cracked all to pieces by the time they got to any foreign market, and are in other respects such goods as I would not put my name to in a bill of parcels.[42]

Whether they were trading in pots, raw materials or anything else, the potters avoided paying cash, preferring to use their own products as a medium of exchange. There was not much point in marking one's own if everybody was making up mixed orders with everybody else's wares in them.

The curious dozens of 12 and 24 to which Wedgwood referred are potters' dozens. The system is explained in a pamphlet of 1804 called 'The Ruin of Potters and the Way to Avoid it, stated in the Plainest Manner, in the following lines, addressed, after thirty years experience, to the consideration of all in the Trade, by a Manufacturer':

> The rule of our forefathers presents itself to our view in the original standard of count, denominated by the size of a pint mug, by which we are to understand, that all articles that may be deemed hollow ware, of whatever shape, containing one pint, are counted 12 to the dozen. If they contain less, the quantity is increased; if more, the quantity is diminished. As when we reckon a vessel holding six pints at 2 to the dozen, to a coffee-can containing only one third of a pint, at 36 to the dozen. These things are so well known, that they require no further explanation.[43]

The different sizes were therefore known as 12s, 18s, and so on. From 1770 if not earlier, a group of Staffordshire potters held meetings in suitable hostelries at which they would agree minimum prices for standard types and sizes of ware.[44] Those who puzzle over the apparent lack of standard sizing among surviving pots should note that there was one very good way of getting round such agreements and maintaining a competitive edge: a letter of 1807 in the Wedgwood archives advises, 'To succeed in the Country trade we must not be niggardly in our sizes, the best makers act otherwise e.g. Spode's pint jug holds three half-pints . . . J. Ridgway makes larger ware than anyone.'[45] Josiah Wedgwood received a similar message from his cousin Thomas about 'cauliflower' teapots in 1763: 'I see some 18s in London almost as large as our 12s.' Such escalation did the trade no good, and periodic attempts were made to curb it. A committee meeting in 1796 noted:

> . . . so great a loss is sustained on Chamber-pots, Wash-hand Basons, Bowls and Tea-pots, owing to the excess in the size, as to prevent the manufacturing of those articles in the quantity necessary for the supply of the Trade . . . they propose, that Chamber-pots, Wash-hand Basons, Bowls and Tea-pots, of the respective sizes here-under mentioned, shall not in future contain more than the quantity specified opposite each article . . .

The maximum capacity of teapots 12, 18 and 24 to the dozen was to be respectively 1½, 1, and ¾ pint, so the pint teapot had already grown an extra half-pint![46]

Whether or not it has a maker's mark, there are other kinds of mark a pot may have. Some of these are tally-marks to enable particular batches of production or the work of different decorators to be identified. The Staffordshire potteries operated a notorious system known as 'good from oven', which meant that craftsmen were only paid for wares which emerged from the kiln in saleable condition. Circumstances outside their control, like clumsiness on the part of the kiln-packers or an accident in firing, could result in serious loss of earnings. It was important to know whose work was whose when it reached the warehouse.

Pattern numbers were applied at the Derby and New Hall porcelain factories from the 1780s, and the practice spread rapidly. The pattern number referred to the painted or printed decoration, not to the shape of the pot. It corresponded to a numbered pattern painted in the factory's pattern book. Most such books probably existed in more than one copy, since it would be just as important to have one in a London showroom as in the factory. Reference to a number would reduce the possibility of error when orders were transmitted from showroom to factory, and could save a lot of work when a customer wanted pieces to match a previous purchase. The study of pattern numbers is extremely important for identifying the work of individual factories, but is not without pitfalls. Apart from occasional instances of the wrong pattern number being inscribed on a piece by mistake, there is also the matter of replacements. A teapot bearing only a pattern number may be in the same service as a cup which has a maker's mark but no pattern number. The cup may have been made as a replacement by another manufacturer, copying the original pattern.

The original prices of pots are apt to make modern collectors' mouths water, but the minimum wholesale price of 9s 6d for a dozen blue-printed pottery teapots in 1795 needs to be set in the context of wages and prices of the period. A skilled male worker might earn ten or twelve shillings a week in a pottery, fourteen or more in a porcelain factory, while enamel painters, the aristocrats of the business, might earn twice as much. The Wedgwood teapot which Parson James Woodforde bought in 1783 for four shillings[48] therefore represented two days' wages to many people.

Unfortunately it was not until the 1880s that anyone bothered to record how ordinary people in the industry made ends meet. Then it is not some British official or social reformer but the United States' Consul in the Potteries, Edward Lane, who provides the information. At this time a flat-presser, making plates by press-moulding, might earn thirty shillings a week. He also cites a carpenter working in one of the collieries that supplied the fuel for the potteries, a man earning twenty-five shillings a week, with a wife and three children: 'I suppose if he wanted a kettle or a teapot he would have to go without meat or get in a little overtime. A doctor's bill for the wife or children would be a calamity.' There is no reason to suppose that life was much better a hundred years earlier.

It is sobering to consider what proportion of the early factories' teaware output survives today, when we read that 40,000 pieces of Worcester porcelain were sold in one sale at the Royal Exchange Coffee-house, Threadneedle Street, on 15 March 1754. It is even more daunting to realise that the survival rate for porcelain is much higher than that for earthenware. The reason is not only the greater fragility of earthenware, but also its everyday use, compared to the Sunday best porcelain which was preserved with greater care and was more likely to be handed on to the next generation. The most eloquent testimony to the respect in which porcelain and fine stoneware pots were held is the care with which they were repaired after breakage. Firms like Robinson and Rhodes of Leeds undertook to repair broken china with the aid of a flux by refiring, but one wonders how well the result would have endured the repeated impact of boiling water. Rivets in carefully drilled holes provided a strong repair, but with some risk of seepage. The most commonly seen early repairs on teapots are metal replacements for damaged spouts, knobs or handles. Loving care is indicated by a silver spout on a Chinese porcelain pot, or a cover for a basalt pot made in pewter to fit snugly in the grooves for the original sliding cover.

The period covered by this book witnessed the achievement of technical refinement, accuracy, durability and competitive prices in the British ceramics industry. The phrase 'Industrial Revolution' needs much qualification for an industry which still relied so much on hand craftsmanship. Machinery had most impact in the preparation of the materials. John Riley's notes of about 1820 on glazing earthenware make the point:

> The glaze ought at all events to be well ground together at a mill, for every article being very finely ground, must and does assist the vitrification, and produces a finer glazing. For satisfaction, try articles of glaze that are only course ground and mixed by a hand mill. Afterwards, try the same articles of glaze ground at a water or steam mill for 12 or 24 hours together, and you will plainly perceive the latter will produce a much finer glazing, and from this circumstance only of the mixture being finer ground.[49]

One should emphasise the importance of skilled hand and eye, craftsman's intuition and sheer trial and error, in the creation of these wares. Riley notes of a recipe for a glaze for creamware:

> This glaze I received from William Pedley, who made Mr Wilson's glaze of Hanley for many years. Says they had used to dip the ware thick and fire up the glost [ie glaze firing] very slow, with one load of Newhurst coals, and two loads of Burnwoods. The former coals are swift and good coals – the latter heat but slowly and on that account are not liable to blister the ware.[50]

The potters provided the market with what it wanted, smooth white porcelain and earthenware which looked as much like the porcelain as possible. This trend towards homogeneity contrasted with the contemporary Romantic Movement in the arts and its worship of the individual personality. By the middle of the 19th century, displays in shops were suggesting that the customer could choose from the variety of their goods something that would suit his or her own personality.[51] A multiplicity of competing shapes conflicted with the customer's traditional need for guidance, for standards of taste. Gone were the days when one shape of teapot had dominated the market for a decade (p.263). The growing market which the potters created for their ware was increasing in diversity as it grew, opening up supposedly fashionable design to less wealthy and less educated customers. In the second half of the 19th century, the tension between industrial homogeneity and artistic diversity was to break the tradition of the previous century and a half.

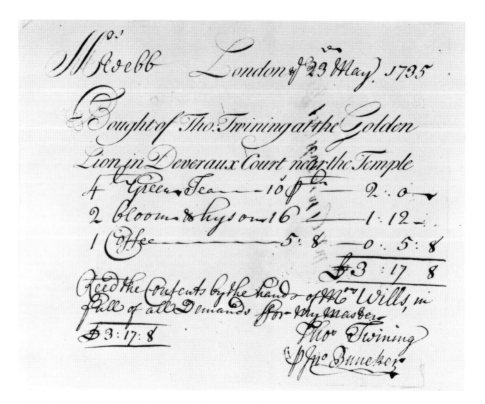

pl.13   A bill of 1735 for Twinings' teas – and a little of their coffee

Notes to Chapters 1–3

1 The Growth of Tea-Drinking

[1] Godden 1979, p.24.
[2] P. Thornton and M. Tomlin, *The Furnishing and Decoration of Ham House*, Furniture History Society, 1980, p.79, pp.83–5 and figs.87–8.
[3] *The Review*, vol.1 no.43, 8 January 1713.
[4] Godden 1979, p.104.
[5] Scarfe 1988, p.18.

2 The British Tea Ceremony

[1] Ribeiro 1984, pp.115–25.
[2] Robin 1784, p.23.
[3] Roberts 1947, p.266.
[4] Roth 1961, p.70.
[5] Scarfe 1988, p.18.
[6] Glanville 1987, p.67 fig.25.
[7] *Op.cit.* p.68.
[8] Clayton 1985, p.409 and pls.626–8.
[9] Oman 1965, pl.110.
[10] Godden 1979, p.120.
[11] Glanville 1987, p.95.
[12] Schroder 1988, p.173.
[13] Clayton 1985, pl.650.
[14] Butler 1978, pl.48.
[15] Clayton 1985, pl.633.
[16] Oman 1965, pl.116.
[17] Roberts 1947, p.266.
[18] Godden 1979, p.38.
[19] *Op.cit.* p.102.
[20] *Op.cit.* p.113.
[21] *Op.cit.* p.43.
[22] Art-Union, November 1846, p.296.
[23] Benson 1937, I, p.191.
[24] Zoffany 1977, no.100.
[25] Godden 1979, p.74.
[26] *Op.cit.* p.48.
[27] *Ibid.*
[28] Al-Tajir 1989, p.161 no.123.
[29] Godden 1980, pp.23–4.
[30] *Op.cit.* pp.49–50.
[31] Austin 1977.
[32] Whiter 1970, p.217.
[33] Pomfret 1988, p.83.
[34] Roth 1961, p.72.
[35] Cosnett 1823, p.113.

[36] Paulson 1975, p.15; Webster 1979, p.35.
[37] Glanville 1987, p.96.
[38] *Ibid.* pp.95–7.
[39] Cosnett 1823, p.113.
[40] Sitwell 1940, pp.129–30.

3 Supplying the Tea Equipage

[1] Valpy 1982, p.124.
[2] Burton 1906, pp.84–122.
[3] Valpy 1983, p.203.
[4] Tait 1963, p.197.
[5] Valpy 1982, p.125.
[6] Campbell 1774, II, p.18.
[7] Bemrose 1975, p.297.
[8] Haggar 1980, pp.248–59.
[9] Chavagnac and de Grollier 1906, p.133.
[10] Haggar 1960, p.374.
[11] Mountford 1969, p.87.
[12] *Op.cit.* p.88.
[13] *Op.cit.* p.92.
[14] Watney and Charleston 1966, p.58.
[15] Watney 1973, pp.10–11.
[16] *Op.cit.* p.53.
[17] *Gentleman's Magazine*, vol.XXXIII, 1763, p.191.
[18] Tait 1960, p.111.
[19] Smith 1974, p.206 and p.208.
[20] Charleston and Mallet 1971, p.114.
[21] *EPC* 1, 1928, p.20.
[22] *Gentleman's Magazine*, vol.XXXIII, p.191.
[23] Mallet 1974, pp.212–20.
[24] Watney 1981, p.35.
[25] Watney 1989, p.219.
[26] Boney 1957, p.193.
[27] Wills 1980, p.384.
[28] Wills 1981, p.33.
[29] Finer and Savage 1965, p.288.
[30] Charleston and Mallet 1971, pp.114–15.
[31] Finer and Savage 1965, p.76.
[32] Blake Roberts 1985, p.100.
[33] *Ibid.*
[34] Finer and Savage 1965, p.67.
[35] *Op.cit.* pp.329–30.
[36] Haggar 1952, pp.31–2.
[37] Lockett 1985A, pp.143–4.
[38] Smith 1974, p.210.
[39] Reilly 1989, I, p.91.
[40] Godden 1968, p.15.
[41] Mallet 1967, p.208.
[42] Farrer 1906, I, p.119.
[43] Whiter 1970, p.63.
[44] Mountford 1975, pp.3–14.
[45] Whiter 1970, p.63.
[46] Mountford 1975, p.11.
[47] Sandon 1981, p.3.
[48] Beresford 1924, II, p.95.
[49] Pomfret 1988, p.65.
[50] *Op.cit.* p.68.
[51] Sennett 1975, 144.

Plate 1   The dangers of not knowing the etiquette of the teaspoon, 1825.
(Reproduced by courtesy of Twinings)

Plate 2   . . . *one white Finger and a Thumb conspire*
To lift the Cup and make the World admire.
A portrait of about 1720.
(Reproduced by courtesy of the Worshipful Company of Goldsmiths, London)

Plate 3   Pious conversation, or tea and scandal? A portrait of about 1740. Note the
tea-chest at the lady's feet, and the servant at the door with the tea-kettle.
(Reproduced by courtesy of Christie's)

Plate 4   Creamware and redware, all lead-glazed, *c*.1730–80

122   90

39   87

106   28

Plate 5   White salt-glazed stoneware, c.1750–65

19   17

18   16

20   13

Plate 6   Lead-glazed earthenware, *c.*1740–70

35	32
26	25
42	43

Plate 7   Fruit and vegetables in lead-glazed earthenware, *c.*1760–5

49	cauliflower	44	cabbage
47	pear	46	apple
53	melon	50	pineapple

Plate 8 Creamware, all Wedgwood except for 98 (probably Derby), *c.*1765–75

66   65

62   64

98   61

Plate 9   William Greatbatch creamware, *c.*1770–82
'The Prodigal Son . . .' (75–77):

75 '. . . Receives his Patrimony'   76 '. . . in Excess'

77 '. . . returns Reclaim'd'   69

70   80

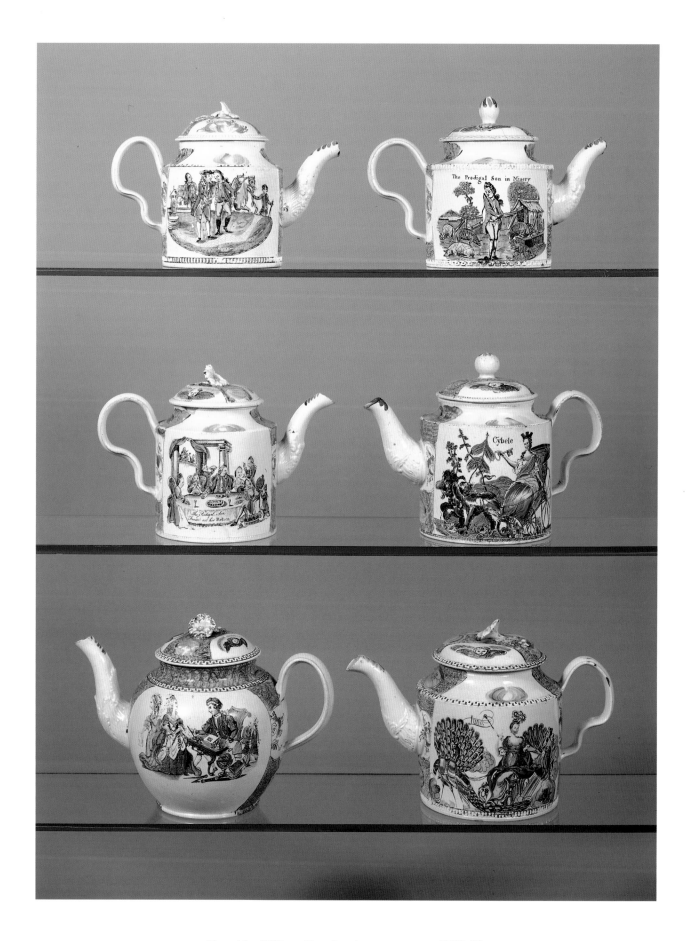

Plate 10   William Greatbatch creamware, *c.*1770–82
'The Prodigal Son . . .' (75–77):

75   his departure   76   '. . . in Misery'

77   '. . . Feasted on his Return'   79

81   78

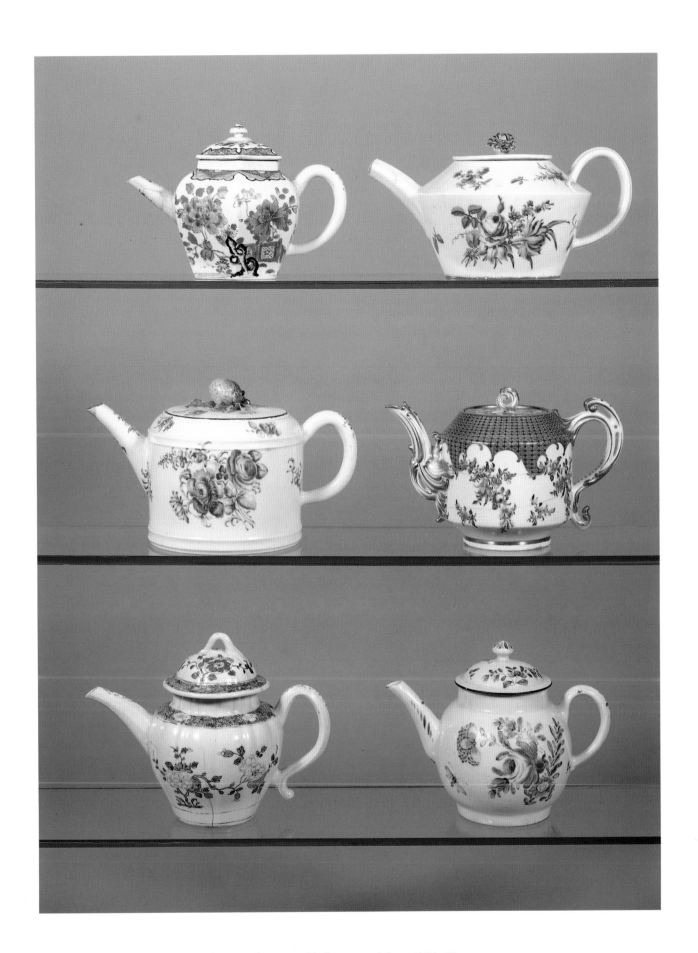

Plate 11   Chelsea porcelain, *c.*1750–65

141   143

144   145

Bow porcelain, *c.*1748–65

146   153

Plate 12   204   Vauxhall porcelain, 1753–64   203   Possibly Limehouse porcelain, 1747–8
Derby porcelain, *c*.1756–80
182   185
183   188

Plate 13   Worcester porcelain, *c.*1752–65

154   155

169   158

163   162

Plate 14   Worcester porcelain, *c*.1756–80

179 176
334 160
177 175

Plate 15   All Liverpool except for 208 (perhaps Baddeley and Littler), *c.*1760–85

195   193
197   200
208   199

Plate 16   Pearlware, two (246 and 272) painted in high-temperature underglaze colours, *c*.1800

272   Barker   252   Lakin and Poole
310   246   Hawley
309   282

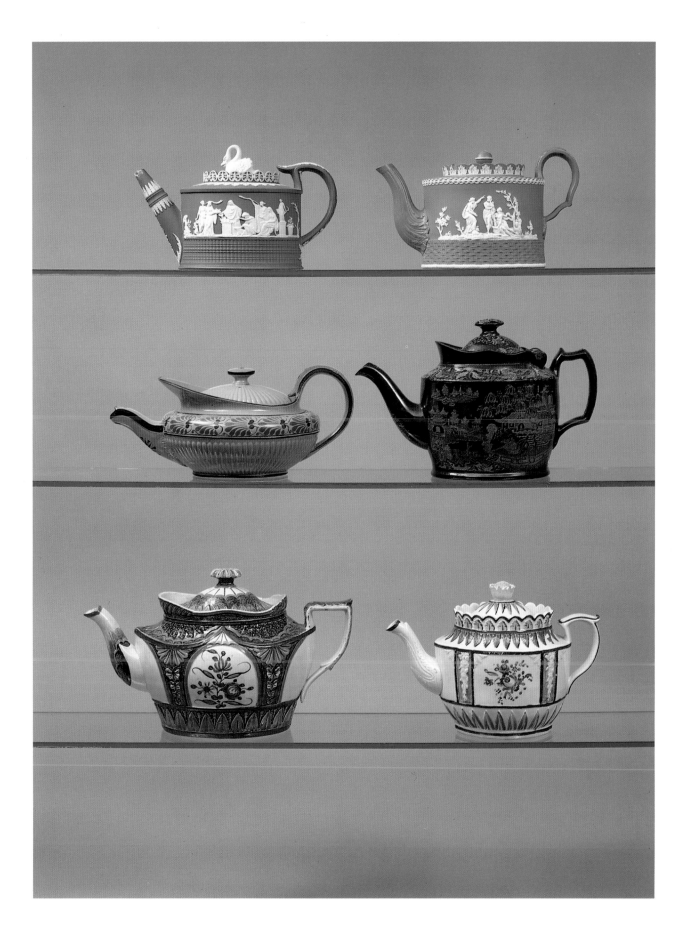

Plate 17   Jasperware, *c.*1780–1800

224   Adams   223   Neale

Earthenware, *c.*1800–10

323   Calcedony type   283   Printed in yellow

302   Painted in high-temperature   271   Barker
          underglaze colours

Plate 18   Porcelain, *c.*1790–1805

337   Caughley, painted at
        Chamberlain's, Worcester   345   Neale

366   Pinxton   365   Pinxton

369   Chamberlain's, Worcester   354   Factory Z, probably Wolfe

Plate 19   Porcelain, *c*.1805–15

425 Davenport	426 Spode
408 Davenport	384 Mason
415 Spode	416 Chamberlain's, Worcester

Plate 20   Porcelain, *c.*1810–20

447	Derby	437	Machin
454	Rathbone	452	Minton
459	Wedgwood	463	Unknown factory, possibly Hicks and Meigh

Plate 21   Porcelain, *c*.1820–5

471	Davenport	472	Davenport
469	New Hall	474	Charles Bourne
477	Coalport	478	Coalport

Plate 22   Porcelain, *c.*1820–30

490	Unknown factory	485	Hicks, Meigh and Johnson
499	Yates	487	Daniel
501	Alcock	480	Grainger's, Worcester

Plate 23   Porcelain, *c.*1830–5

520   Grainger's, Worcester   509   Coalport

534   Mason   510   Minton

533   Mason   535   Mason

Plate 24   Porcelain, *c.*1830–50

528	Daniel	530	Alcock
525	Grainger's, Worcester	526	Daniel
527	Daniel	540	Bowers

Catalogue

Introduction to the Catalogue

'Pot' means 'teapot' throughout unless otherwise specified. Some of the large pots, however, especially the early ones, were almost certainly used for punch rather than tea. Such pots cannot usually be distinguished by the absence of a strainer. Pots are described as though their handles were facing to the right, the position in which a pot would be placed ready for a right-handed person to pour. The side of the pot facing the pourer is described as the obverse, the other as the reverse. References to decoration are to the obverse of a pot unless otherwise specified. It is interesting to note how often the obverse of a pot bears more elaborate painted decoration than the reverse, evidently a sensible apportionment of resources for potters keen to attract the mistress of the house, who did the pouring. The front of the pot is used here to mean the spout end, the back to mean the handle end.

Pots already illustrated in Miller and Berthoud 1985 have been included here only if more comparative information or improved illustration was thought to be beneficial. Lowestoft porcelain teapots have been omitted because these are already covered in the two volumes of Sheenah Smith's *Lowestoft Porcelain in the Norwich Castle Museum* (1975 and 1985).

Heights are given in millimetres to the top of the knob unless another point is specified. The number in brackets following the height is a reference number for the pot, and the same system is used in the catalogue entries for referring to other pots in the museum's collections: those with a B preface are Bulwer pots, those with an M preface are Miller ones and refer to the plates in Miller and Berthoud 1985. Simple numbers between 1220 and 2000 refer to Miller pots which were not included in the latter book. Numbers divided by a decimal point indicate that the pot is from another source, of which details are given under 'Prov:', that is, provenance. The museum has the Bulwers' records of their collection, which list the source of their pots and the prices paid. For reasons of space, the provenance is given here only for pieces acquired from other private collections and from major auction sales such as Sotheby's. For the great majority of their pieces, only a dealer provenance is known. 'Ref:' means a publication in which the pot is illustrated and discussed. The short references given in the catalogue are enlarged upon in the bibliography.

Certain collections in other museums are mentioned so frequently that it seemed sensible to abbreviate their proper names. 'V&A' refers to the Victoria and Albert Museum, where the Schreiber collection may be found. The Glaisher collection is at the Fitzwilliam Museum, Cambridge. 'Stoke-on-Trent Museum' is more properly the City Museum and Art Gallery, situated in Bethesda Street, Hanley. 'Temple Newsam' refers to Temple Newsam House, which is one of the Leeds City Art Galleries. The Burnap collection is in the Nelson Gallery and Atkins Museum, Kansas City.

The decoration on other pots of the same shape as a catalogued example is described only if they bear a pattern number and were not illustrated in Miller and Berthoud 1985. New Hall patterns are not described because these already have an excellent book devoted to them (de Saye Hutton 1990).

Several other terms may require explanation. On a ribbed surface the convex curves are more prominent than concave ones: on a fluted surface vice versa. Spirally fluted surfaces are sometimes called 'shanked', a term used when they were popular around 1800. Mould-applied relief decoration was made by pressing an open mould filled with clay on to the pot: marks made by the edges of the mould around the relief can often be seen. This technique was popular only in the early part of the period covered by this book. Sprigged relief decoration was made by separating the clay relief from its mould before sticking it to the pot with liquid clay, known as slip. The applied reliefs on the pots in chapter six were all made by this process, which visitors can still see in action at the Wedgwood works today.

Instead of applying it afterwards, relief decoration could be made with the body of the object by press-moulding or slip-casting. Press-moulding involved pressing bats of clay into open moulds. An object like a spout or a teapot body had to be made in two halves, which were then carefully joined together. Slip-casting exploited the ability of a plaster mould to absorb water from slip poured into it. As the water was absorbed, a crust of solid clay gradually built up all over the inner surface of the mould, forming the body of the object. When the crust was thick enough, the clay that was still liquid was poured out. When the clay had dried, the mould was taken apart to reveal an object, such as the body of a teapot, formed in one piece. Press-moulding was more commonly employed than slip-casting until well into the 19th century, when deflocculents made slip-casting more economical by speeding up the drying process. Pots which are fired but not yet glazed are said to be in the biscuit state, and biscuit and glost firings are those respectively before and after glazing.

4

Early Pottery

Salt-Glazed Stoneware

Stoneware is pottery fired to a high temperature at which the ingredients fuse together, usually between 1200 and 1400°C. The early European stonewares were glazed by throwing salt into the hot kiln during firing. The soda in the salt combined with the silica and alumina in the clay to form a glaze so thin that it allowed modelling and relief ornament on a pot to remain sharp. The resulting surface is minutely pitted like orange peel.

The art of manufacturing salt-glazed stoneware was brought to Britain from the Rhineland. As early as 1614 an East India Company minute requested stone pots for Japan, referring to 'the house in Southwarke where they bee made . . .'.[1] The first English salt-glazed stonewares were brown, and the brown ware continued to be made for increasingly humble uses until it was elevated from drainpipes to 'Art Pottery' by Henry Doulton in the 1860s. In the late 17th century, however, John Dwight at Fulham was already trying to rival the whiteness and delicacy of porcelain, and by 1719 the Staffordshire potters were also making stoneware whitened with calcined flint. A two-handled cup incised '1720' in the Nelson Gallery and Atkins Museum, Kansas City, is the earliest known dated piece of white salt-glaze.[2] White clay from Dorset and Devon was preferred to local supplies, and was to remain the staple ingredient for white-bodied pottery of all kinds.

It has been traditional to attribute most pieces of white salt-glaze to Stafford-shire, but documentary evidence and excavations have shown that the ware was, in fact, made in most major potting centres including Liverpool, Derby, Yorkshire and Swansea. The absence of marks and the virtual impossibility of distinguishing the products of different potteries by their fabric makes identification extremely hazardous. White salt-glazed stoneware was ousted from the upper end of the pottery market by creamware in the 1770s (see p.71), but many humbler types of vessel were still being made in white salt-glaze in the 1790s. This pattern of survival was to be echoed by creamware in its turn.

[1] Godden 1979, p.302.
[2] Taggart 1967, p.74 no.182.

❦ **White Stoneware** ❦

1

Probably Staffordshire

*c.*1730–50
PLATE 14
92mm (B581)

The lion knob and mould-applied reliefs of prunus sprays directly imitate Chinese wares, not only the white Fukien porcelain but also the red stoneware of Yixing (see p.30). The shape of the lion knob is also found on agate wares (B502 and 110.922, and see nos. 25 and 26 below). The type of handle with two adjoining flat facets on top has been identified[1] with the 'white natched teapots' referred to in the 1740s in the crate-books of John and Thomas Wedgwood, and is found on the pots given by their descendants to the Stoke-on-Trent Museum. Pots displaying this feature have therefore been attributed to their works, the Big House, Burslem (but see entry for no.8 below). This piece retains traces of size gilding.

[1] Mountford 1971, p.42.

2

Painted with unfired enamel colours and size gilding

*c.*1730–50
PLATE 14
121mm (B435)

pl.14

1	3
2	4

The two bands of clay shreds have the remains of size gilding, and this clay technique may have been chosen to give the gilding a more secure foothold on the surface of the

pot. The remains of painting in enamels (apparently unfired) includes realistic flesh-colour for the face moulded on the spout. The incised lattice of lines on the body can be compared to a jug dated 1739.[1] Another teapot of this type (B505) has a slightly different knob and dolphin handle, and matches one in the Glaisher collection.[2]

[1] Earle 1915, p.48 no.60.
[2] Rackham 1935, no.505, II, pl.37C.

3

Probably Staffordshire

*c.*1740–60
PLATE 14
125mm (B458)
Prov: T. Boynton coll. no.676

The spout and handle are moulded as gnarled branches in the form known as 'crabstock'. This conceit was derived from Yixing red stoneware of the late 17th or early 18th century.[1] Mould-applied relief ornament of similar design is also found on creamware of about the 1750s (M85).[2]

[1] Lo 1986, p.80.
[2] Walton 1976, no.253.

4

Probably Staffordshire

*c.*1740–60
PLATE 14
128mm (B118)
Incised mark: cross
Prov: General Bulwer
Ref: Hodgson 1920, p.228 pl.I no.1

The relief ornament of figures, birds and animals was made in one piece with the body by the process called slip-casting (see p.46). The body was cast in a plaster mould taken in turn from a master block-mould. A block-mould of matching design is among the material given by the descendants of John and Thomas Wedgwood to Stoke-on-Trent Museum.[1] The pot also has the 'natched' handle associated with their work. A heart-shaped pot (M83) and a globular one moulded with shells and oak-leaves (B471) also match John and Thomas Wedgwood blocks.[2]

[1] Mountford 1971, pl.96.
[2] *Op.cit.* pls.94 and 92.

5

White-dipped, probably Staffordshire

*c.*1750–70
PLATE 15
163mm (B501)

The chipped surface reveals that the white clay is just a slip covering a grey body. This type has been identified as the 'dipped white' which was cheaper than white-bodied ware.[1] The body of this pot was press-moulded (see p.46) in two halves. The vigorous modelling of the leaves and crabstock handle suggests a date in the 1750s or '60s when realistic vegetable forms were popular in porcelain and earthenware. A pot of matching shape is in the Stoke-on-Trent Museum.[2]

[1] Mountford 1971, p.36.
[2] *Op.cit.* pl.126.

pl.15

6 7
8 5

6

Probably Staffordshire

*c.*1750
PLATE 15
127mm (B676)

Apart from the presence of a dormer in the roof, the slip-cast body matches another
pot in the collection (M80). The latter has a bird's head for a knob, and a dolphin
handle with incised slits for the mouth. This type of dolphin handle is also found on a
camel teapot (see next entry). Similar examples of this house teapot are at Stoke-on-
Trent Museum[1] and in the Glaisher collection.[2] A variant at Temple Newsam has the
elements of the house slightly rearranged.[3] All these houses have three stories on one
side and at the ends, but two stories on the other side. The Temple Newsam pot has a
lion knob and a different form of dolphin handle with slit mouth, both of which are
found on no.8 below. Another form of body, moulded with the arms of England on
one side and the Netherlands on the other, is seen on two other house teapots (B667
and 8.139.938), is found on a pot in the Schreiber collection[4] and is also on an
earthenware one decorated with coloured oxides in the Weldon collection.[5]

[1] Mountford 1971, pl.91.
[2] Rackham 1935, no.570, II, pl.41B.
[3] Walton 1976, no.103 illus. p.40.
[4] Rackham 1930, no.111 pl.20.
[5] Grigsby 1990, pl.87.

7

Probably Staffordshire

*c.*1750
PLATE 15
137mm (B662)

Also slip-cast, this has a modern knob, and matches a pot in the Schreiber collection.[1] A camel pot of another type (M79) matches one at Temple Newsam.[2]

[1] Rackham 1930, no.113, pl.20.
[2] Walton 1976, no.99, illus. p.39.

8

Probably Staffordshire

*c.*1750
PLATE 15
150mm (B346)
Ref: Hodgson 1920, p.228 pl.1 no.3

This has a slip-cast body and its design matches a pot in the Schreiber collection.[1] Block-moulds for similar bodies are different in their details,[2] as are the bodies of two other similar teapots (B445 and B422). It is possible that such variations may be explained by the same modeller supplying blocks to a number of firms, each wanting to be able to identify its own version of a popular design.[3]

The lion knob has jaws open in a vast gape and incised ridges going across both front paws at right angles to the way toes would be indicated. The combination of this knob and handle has been noted by Walton, who suggested that it may be specific to one factory.[4] On a lozenge-shaped solid agate teapot (16.139.938), however, this lion knob is combined with the 'natched' handle which usually accompanies a different lion knob (see no.1 above). This suggests that at least one of these two elements, the gaping lion knob and the 'natched' handle, is not specific to one factory.

[1] Rackham 1930, no.108 pl.21.
[2] Mountford 1971, pl.109; Luxmoore 1924, pl.58.
[3] Walton 1976, p.12.
[4] *Ibid*.

9

*c.*1750
PLATE 16
127mm (B452)

This pot belongs to a group with crude moulding and gadroons, including a jug moulded with the initials 'OB' at the Colonial Williamsburg Foundation, Virginia.[1] A related teapot is in the Glaisher collection.[2] The knob is modern.

[1] Godden 1974, pl.89.
[2] Rackham 1935, no.580, II, pl.36C.

10

With mould-applied reliefs stained with cobalt blue.
Probably Staffordshire

*c.*1750
PLATE 16
145mm (113.938)
Ref: Rackham and Read 1924, pl.LXXXVII, fig.155
Prov: Edward Sheldon no.984; Wallace Elliot no.55; Sotheby's 24 May 1938, lot 69; presented by
the Friends of the Norwich Museums, 1938.

Matching reliefs of birds are on a pot in the Glaisher collection.[1] A smaller pot with similar decoration (B672) is very like an example at Temple Newsam,[2] and was given to Bulwer as a birthday present by his principal dealer, W. Pease of Nottingham.

[1] Rackham 1935, no.528, II, pl.39C.
[2] Walton 1976, no.112, illus. p.41.

11

Decorated in 'scratch-blue'

*c.*1750–70
PLATE 16
87mm (B448)

Cobalt blue was rubbed into incised lines before the pot was fired. Dated examples of the technique range between 1742 and 1775.

12

Streaked with underglaze blue

*c.*1750
PLATE 17
109mm (B457)

The moulding of shells flanked by oak-leaves with acorns is related to that on pots of very different shape (see no.15 below). The streaks of cobalt have run and blistered where the pigment is thick. Such an unsuccessful method of decoration may have been relatively short-lived.[1] Very similar pots are in the Schreiber collection[2] and at Temple Newsam.[3]

[1] *Cf.* Luxmoore pl.34.
[2] Rackham 1930, no.132.
[3] Walton 1976, 42, no.118.

13

Decorated with 'Littler-Wedgwood' blue, probably Staffordshire

*c.*1760
COLOUR PLATE 5
119mm (B290)

Aaron Wedgwood, a cousin of John and Thomas Wedgwood of the Big House, shared a potworks at Brownhills, Burslem, with William Littler, and the Wedgwood brothers' sales-account book shows that in 1760 they were buying 'Blue Ware – Aarons'.[1] The blue was apparently achieved by dipping the unfired ware in a fusible mixture of cobalt, then firing and salt-glazing in the usual way. The resulting surface does not show the usual pitting of salt-glaze. Other examples of this type have feet (M7).

[1] Mountford 1971, 52.

Enamelled White Stoneware

The pottery traditions of Staffordshire in the first half of the 18th century did not include the painting of pots. Delftware, the one common form of painted pottery at the time, was not made there. The stimulus of rivalling porcelain encouraged the painting of white stoneware with enamel colours after its salt-glaze firing. In the absence of a painting tradition among the potters, many of the enamellers in the 1750s and '60s were specialist independent firms like William Duesbury in London, Messrs Robinson and Rhodes in Leeds, and in Staffordshire the Mr Courzen used by William Greatbatch. By 1770 creamware was beginning to oust salt-glaze as a type of ware smart enough for enamel painting.

14

*c.*1760
PLATE 16
108mm (B456)

Painted with Frederick the Great of Prussia, Britain's ally in the Seven Years War, and likely to date from that period. On the reverse is the Prussian eagle and the motto 'Semper Sublimis'. The ground is painted with the conventional representation for ermine, appropriate for a king. Another pot of this popular type is in the Schreiber collection.[1]

[1] Rackham 1930, no.209, pl.31.

15

*c.*1760
PLATE 21
147mm (11.941)
Prov: presented by Miss Richenda Bland, 1941

The little figure frequently painted on pots of this shape is sometimes interpreted as Prince Charles Edward Stuart, Bonnie Prince Charlie, but in the case of this pot and a similar one without feet (B120), there seems no good reason to assume that a particular individual was intended.

16–20

*c.*1760
COLOUR PLATE 5
100–111cm

The device of imitation, as used in white salt-glaze, extends from the use of enamel painting in an earnest attempt to match the qualities of porcelain, right through to the unlikely Chinaman of no.16 (B623), the playful imitation of shagreen on no.17 (B622) and the cabbage of no.18 (B460). The latter matches a lead-glazed earthenware example (see no.44 and col. pl.7) and has been associated with William Littler on the tenuous grounds that the porcelain he made at Longton Hall includes similar vegetable wares (see no.205).[1] The blue of no.19 (B583) differs from the usual Littler–Wedgwood blue (see no.13 above) in that it shows the normal pitted surface of salt-glaze.

[1] Towner 1963, p.190.

❦ Brown Stoneware ❦

21

Probably Nottingham

*c.*1760–70
PLATE 18
152mm (B549)

The date is suggested by the decoration with shreds of clay and incised wavy lines.[1] The thin white line between body and glaze, evident where the pot is chipped, is found on Nottingham ware and also on the similar products of Crich in Derbyshire.[2] A very similar pot is in the Glaisher collection.[3]

[1] Hughes and Oswald 1974, pp.164 and 160, fig.8.12; Oswald, Hildyard and Hughes 1982, p.126.
[2] *Op.cit.* p.106.
[3] No.1238, illus. Hildyard 1985, p.91 no.240.

Tin-Glazed Ware

Tin oxide is included in the lead glaze to render it white and opaque, concealing the buff clay pot beneath. In the 18th century English earthenware of this type was already known as delftware, because it was associated with Delft, the major centre of production in the Netherlands.

22

Tin-glazed earthenware painted in blue, red and yellow. London

about 1760
PLATE 18
83mm (64.974)
Prov: purchased with the help of a government grant-in-aid, 1974.

Surviving delftware teapots are relatively few. A correspondent in the *Gentleman's Magazine* supplies the most likely reason for this, advising that some pottery would not stand heat: '. . . the same cause that makes the glazing crack, makes it also scale off after it is cracked, which is universally the case with all earthenware, particularly that called Delft.'[1]

The painted pattern on this piece occurs in the same colours on a bowl in Bristol Museum,[2] and in blue only on a pair of flower-bricks in the Museum of London.[3]

[1] *Gentleman's Magazine*, April 1763, p.191.
[2] Britton 1982, p.112 no.8.6.
[3] Britton 1987, p.149, no.134.

23

Tin-glazed stoneware, painted in blue. Liverpool

about 1760
PLATE 18
108mm (B428)

This and a smaller teapot of very similar shape (B325) are examples of one of the rarest technical types in English pottery. A stoneware body was used for tin-glazing to overcome the problem of cracking. As with other examples of this type, areas on the base not covered by tin-glaze show the distinctive 'orange-peel' pitted texture of salt-glaze. Tests by the Ceramic Research Laboratory on one of the Merseyside Museum's pots of this type confirmed the presence of salt-glaze. On the analogy of 'Littler–Wedgwood blue' (see p.53), it has been conjectured that the biscuit-fired pots might have been coated with tin-glaze then fired in a salt-glaze kiln to a higher temperature than was usual for delftware.[1]

pl.18

The group has been convincingly attributed to Liverpool: a mug at Temple Newsam has a shape and a style of enamel painting with exotic birds which are found in Chaffers' Liverpool porcelain.[1] Fragments of tin-glazed stoneware were found on the site of Thomas Shaw's pottery in Liverpool, including a sherd with the pattern on the present pot.[2] A teapot very similar to the present example and painted with the same pattern is dated 1756.[3] Bristol Museum has a mug of this ware dated 1764.[4] The smaller teapot of the type (B325) is painted with a blue pattern seen on a tin-glazed stoneware jug,[5] with foliage of a type found on Chaffers' Liverpool porcelain.[6]

[1] Smith 1978, pp.14–19.
[2] Garner 1961, pl.72, bottom right.
[3] Horne 1987, no.171.
[4] Britton 1982, p.89, no.6.11.
[5] Stoke 1982, p.51, no.49a.
[6] Watney 1964, pl.252b.

Agate and Marbled Ware

Imported porcelain and red stoneware were regarded in the early 18th century as materials comparable to those used for *objets de vertu*, notably semi-precious stones. British potters therefore aspired to this scale of values for some of their own wares. Samuel Bell claimed, in the patent granted him in 1729, that his 'red marbled stoneware' was 'capable of receiving a gloss so beautiful as to imitate if not compare with ruby.'[1] The names the potters gave their wares – agate, marbled, tortoise-shell, basalt, jasper, pearl – reveal how important these ideas remained throughout the century.

An agate or marbled effect was achieved by mixing differently coloured or stained clays. The whole body might be made of this mixture, or it might be only a surface coating.

[1] Bemrose 1975, p.297.

24

Solid marbled. Probably Staffordshire

*c.*1730–50
PLATE 18
92mm (B376)

The knob is modern. The whole pot is made of the marbled clay mixture. Similar pots were found on the Pomona site from Samuel Bell's pottery, 1724–44, at Newcastle-under-Lyme, Staffs.[1] It has been suggested that Bell's patent, quoted above, may refer specifically to inlaid bands of marbling, of which examples were found on the Pomona site. Both these types of marbling were, however, similarly used by other potters, for examples were found also on the Fenton Low site, Staffs.[2]

[1] Bemrose 1975, pl.193d.
[2] Wasters in Norwich Castle Museum.

25

Surface agate. Probably Staffordshire

*c.*1740–50
COLOUR PLATE 6
106mm (B683)

The colouring is only a surface coating. It was difficult to preserve the definition of such an intricate mixture of coloured clays if the pot was thrown on the wheel. Instead, the carefully prepared bats of clay were pressed into separate moulds for the upper and lower halves of the body. The lion knob matches white salt-glaze examples (see no.1).

26

Solid agate. Probably Staffordshire

*c.*1750
COLOUR PLATE 6
161mm (B543)

The body was press-moulded. Closely similar shell shapes were made in white salt-glaze (B561). Block moulds also survive,[1] their slight differences suggesting that a block-maker was supplying a number of potters (see no.8).

[1] Luxmore 1924, pls.48 and 76.

Redware

Lead-glazed teapots in red earthenware appear to have been widely made in Staffordshire from around 1720–30. The unglazed red stoneware brought to the region by the Elers brothers in the late 17th century[1] does not seem to have been widely made there until almost the middle of the 18th. These were the 'red china' teapots in imitation of Chinese Yixing ware. For Josiah Wedgwood the 'red pot tea-pots', as he called them, came to represent the opposite to his 'un-pot-like' wares in fashionable neoclassical taste, for which he could charge 'un-pot-like' and fashionable prices. This may be a reason why red stoneware was not much used for neoclassical pottery, despite the plentiful existence of ancient Greek and Roman pottery of a similar colour.

[1] Macfarlane 1990.

27

Earthenware, decorated with bands of white slip and lead-glazed.
Probably Staffordshire

*c.*1720–50
PLATE 19
126mm (B507)

Wasters found on the site of Samuel Bell's pottery at Newcastle-under-Lyme and on a
site in Broad Street, Shelton are similarly decorated with bands of white slip.[1]

[1] Bemrose 1975, pl.192; Barker and Halfpenny 1990, p.24 nos.1 and 2 and plate on p.25
(accidentally transposed).

28

Earthenware, decorated with mould-applied reliefs in white clay,
and lead-glazed. Probably Staffordshire

*c.*1730–50
COLOUR PLATE 4
99mm (B503)

Wasters from the Fenton Low site are similar, but have slightly different versions of
the squirrel and scroll reliefs. Many Staffordshire potters probably produced wares of
this type.

29

Earthenware, hexagonal, lead-glazed. Probably Staffordshire

*c.*1740
PLATE 19
122mm (B585)

The moulded design is derived from a pot of the 1690s by John Philip and David
Elers,[1] including the form of lion knob. This knob is also found on porcelain of the
mysterious group marked with an 'A', and has been adduced as evidence of an English
origin for the group.[2] A block-mould with designs matching the present pot is in the
Delhom collection, Mint Museum of Art, Charlotte, North Carolina.[3] A pot in the
Weldon collection is virtually identical except that the spout and handle have been
placed in a different position around the body.[4]

A pot of similar design in white salt-glazed stoneware (B659) matches an example in an
American private collection.[5] It has different Chinoiserie scenes in the reserves, and
the body is undecorated outside the reserves. Portions of pots with similar plain bodies
but differently decorated reserves were found on the site of Samuel Bell's pottery in
Newcastle-under-Lyme[6] and in Broad Street, Shelton.[7] Fragments of moulds found
on the former site are not of plaster of paris but of fired clay, which explains the poor
quality of the moulding on wares of this type.

[1] Honey 1934, pl.3a; Wills 1969, p.83 fig.68; Macfarlane 1990, p.110.
[2] Mallet 1971, pls.65 and 66; Valpy 1987, p.96.
[3] Grigsby 1990, pp.19 and 257.
[4] *Ibid.*
[5] *ECC* 6,1, 1965, pl.43b.
[6] Bemrose 1975, pl.195; Barker and Halfpenny 1990, p.28 nos.8 and 9.
[7] City of Stoke-on-Trent Archaeological Society Reports no.7, 1975, p.36 no.17; Barker and
Halfpenny 1990, p.29 no.10.

30

Stoneware, decorated with mould-applied reliefs. Unglazed.
Probably Staffordshire

*c.*1760–70
PLATE 22
159mm (B185)
Prov: General Bulwer

The reliefs on both sides are a seated Chinaman with a lute, a standing lady holding an exotic bird, a larger exotic bird on a scrolled stand, and a large flower spray. The imitation Chinese seal-mark is a rare one, found also on a veilleuse and a piggin at the Colonial Williamsburg Foundation, Virginia.[1] The same reliefs are found on pots bearing different seal-marks.[2]

The collection includes other unglazed redwares: an exceptionally large pot (B186) has a seal-mark[3] applied unusually on the shoulder of the pot instead of the base. A cylindrical pot (B272) bears a relief of Britannia with '45' on her shield, a political slogan referring to John Wilkes (see p.77).[4] I am most grateful to David Barker for his help in compiling this entry.

[1] Price 1962, p.157 and pl.150 group X; Barker MS mark 30.
[2] *Op.cit.* marks 7, 11, 12, 21.
[3] Price 1962, p.163 and pl.150 group II(iv); Barker MS mark 7.
[4] Price 1959, group 2 p.3; Barker MS mark 2.

31

Stoneware, unglazed. Staffordshire

*c.*1760–65
PLATE 22
110mm (B666)
Ref: Reilly 1989, I, p.511 pl.743

The body is press-moulded rather than having reliefs applied separately. The reliefs of Chinese figures on the two sides are identical. The turning woman on the left and the leaping boy on the right with raised arms are found together on a hexagonal creamware pot in Manchester City Art Gallery which has the same spout and handle as the present pot.[1] The connection of hexagonal pots of this type with a block mould for '1 Chinese teapot', for which Wedgwood paid William Greatbatch 10s 6d in 1764, is purely hypothetical (see p.66). The handle is of a type found on the site of Thomas Whieldon's pottery at Fenton Vivian (see fig.1 on p.70), and both spout and handle match those on Wedgwood creamwares, but they were also used by other makers (see p.101).

[1] Reilly 1989, I, p.173 pl.145.

60

Lead-glazed earthenware with coloured bodies

32

Orange–brown body with sprigged reliefs in white clay, stained with underglaze oxides

*c.*1750–60
COLOUR PLATE 6
82mm (B643)
Prov: Micah Salt coll. no.124

The use of sprigged reliefs in the same colour clay as the handle and spout suggests that the 'stoukers' who applied handles may also have been responsible for the sprigging. A very similar pot was in the Stoller collection.[1]

[1] Charleston and Towner 1977, no.57.

33

Brownish–black body with sprigged reliefs in white clay

*c.*1750–60
PLATE 20
88mm (B589)

A similarly decorated pot is in the Victoria and Albert Museum,[1] and another was in the Stoller collection.[2]

[1] Rackham 1951, pl.61.
[2] Charleston and Towner 1977, no.56.

34

Blackware, decorated in low-fired gilding including the inscription 'Robt Fowler att Gainsborough August 21 1760'

PLATE 20 and see text figure on opposite page
96mm (1961)

The worn decoration (see figure on opposite page) shows an upholder or upholsterer holding a tack-hammer, with scissors and tacks before him on a tripod table; on the reverse are a version of the arms of the Upholders Company: on a chevron between three pavilions, three roses.

Black-glazed wares are often referred to as 'Jackfield', after the pottery of that name in Shropshire. They probably originated in Staffordshire, however, and were made in many places. The mention of Gainsborough, Lincolnshire on this example raises the possibility of manufacture in the south Yorkshire potting district. As the last town before the Trent enters the Humber estuary, however, Gainsborough was an important port of transhipment where cargoes on barges from Staffordshire were re-loaded on to sea-going vessels for the coastal voyage. Wedgwood wrote on 1 April 1775:

> We are packing all our Busts, Garden pots, and other heavy and cheap wares to go by sea, as we can have no dependence upon our Land Carriers. We propose to make out a Boat load with usefull ware, and send a Man along with the Cargo to Gainsbro, and hope they will go as safe, and in near as short a time as by Land.[1]

A customer in Gainsborough was therefore probably as well placed to order a specially decorated pot from Staffordshire as from south Yorkshire. Other glazed blackware pots of this type (B437) bear sprigged reliefs.

[1] Farrer 1906, II, p.224.

Tortoiseshell and Colour-Glazed Earthenware

The agate technique required coloured clays to be mixed together in the forming of a pot. It was much quicker to produce a variegated pot by just colouring the surface. Metallic oxides in the form of liquid slips were brushed or sponged on to the biscuit-fired pot. They tended to run into the clear lead glaze during the glost-firing, giving the ware a mottled, 'tortoiseshell' appearance. This term was used by Whieldon as early as 1749.[1] Although these wares have often been referred to generically as 'Whieldon', this is misleading since they were produced by many potters, not only in Staffordshire but in Yorkshire and elsewhere.

Colouring agents were being successfully included in a liquid lead glaze mixture by 1759, when Josiah Wedgwood recorded in his Experiment Book the successful production of a green glaze. The sales ledger of the quite separate firm of his cousin John Wedgwood, however, refers to 'green leaves' (ie leaf-shaped dishes) on 29 August in the previous year. This serves to warn us against assuming that Josiah did things first, just because we lack equivalent documentary evidence for other potters. Both types of surface colouring, glazes and underglaze oxides, were well suited for decorating pots made in plaster moulds, because the hills and hollows of the moulded design could be followed by semi-skilled decorators applying the colour.

The earthenware to which these colourings were applied is the pale-coloured body called creamware (see p.71). They were favourite forms of decoration in the early years of creamware from the 1740s to the 1760s, when the body was still a deep buff or yellowish colour and needed all the decorative help it could get. For convenience, these earlier wares are grouped together here, while some later, paler wares decorated in this way are included in the general sections on creamware (pp.81ff). Two tea-canisters decorated with underglaze oxides and dated 1779[2] serve as a reminder that, like other wares generally dated around the middle of the century, this type continued in production.

[1] Mountford 1972, p.172.
[2] Rackham 1951, pl.64; Grigsby 1990, pl.102.

35

Decorated with underglaze oxides, Staffs.

*c.*1750–60
COLOUR PLATE 6
92mm (B414)
Ref: Reilly 1989, I, p.151, pl.92

The sprigged designs are similar to but do not match those excavated on the site of Thomas Whieldon's pottery at Fenton Vivian, which he was working from 1747.[1] For many years it was thought that finds on the site of a pottery at Fenton Low (see p.57) represented Whieldon's production, but it is now known that it was worked by tenant potters. William Meir was there in 1750, and Edward Warburton from 1751 for at least a decade.[2] The upright flower knob with leaves around its base is one of the commonest types among tortoise-shell wares from the Fenton Vivian site.[3] It is evident, however, that similar sprigged details were used by other potters. A similar pot survives in biscuit state in the Wedgwood Museum, Barlaston.[4]

[1] Mountford 1972, p.167.
[2] Stoke 1986, p.16.
[3] Barker and Halfpenny 1990, p.41 no.22.
[4] Reilly 1989, I, p.45.

36

Decorated with underglaze oxides, Staffs.

*c.*1750–60
PLATE 23
157mm (B611)
Prov: Sotheby's, 17 December 1926

The sprigged leaves are similar to but do not match those on covers excavated on the Fenton Vivian site.[1] The latter match those on a similar creamware jug inscribed 'RH 1757' in the Stoke-on-Trent Museum, supposed to have been made by Whieldon for his milkman Ralph Hammersley.[2] See the previous entry.

[1] Mountford 1972, pl.122; Reilly 1989, I, p.149 pl.87.
[2] Barker and Halfpenny 1990, p.42 no.23.

37

Decorated with underglaze oxides, Thomas Whieldon

c.1750–60
PLATE 22
96mm (B123)
Ref: Hodgson 1920, p.230 pl.II no.3

The relief decoration is mould-applied apart from the main stems, which are sprigged. The distinctive pattern of crossing-over stems is found on wasters from the Fenton Vivian site. The leaves also match examples excavated on the site. A pot in the Weldon collection[1] has the same crossed-over stems with reliefs which are otherwise different from the present example. It must be borne in mind that moulds, workers and working practices can all be expected to have travelled between potteries. As is usual on pots with applied 'vineing', the stems are arranged to suggest that they are growing from the upper end of the 'crab tree' handle on either side. The cover is too large to fit into the recess for it, but its reliefs and colouring match the pot. At one point the body has a dent and a tear which is glazed over, and it is quite likely that damaged pots like this were matched up with any left-over covers and sold off as the 'seconds' and 'worse seconds' recorded in potters' invoices. A coffee-pot with reliefs apparently matching the present pot is at Temple Newsam.[2]

[1] Grigsby 1990, p.176 pl.82.
[2] Walton 1976, p.80 no.257.

pl.22

37	31
30	38

38

Decorated with underglaze manganese oxide, probably Staffs.

*c.*1755–65
PLATE 22
158mm (B382)
Ref: Reilly 1989, I, p.150 pl.90

The relief decoration is mould-applied. The handle is an elongated version of a shape (see fig 1, p.70) found on the Fenton Vivian site[1] and found also on early Wedgwood wares. It was being used by other potteries by the mid-1760s and quite possibly earlier (see p.101). The young Josiah Wedgwood was in partnership with Whieldon from 1754 to 1759, before beginning his own potteries in Burslem, first at the so-called Ivy House, then at the Brick House in 1763.

[1] Reilly 1989, I, pp.151 and 190.

39

Decorated with underglaze manganese oxide, probably Staffs.

*c.*1755–65
COLOUR PLATE 4
125mm (B516)

The relief decoration is sprigged. The stems are notable for the way they occasionally loop or coil away in daring fashion from the body of the pot. Very similar pots are in the Laver collection,[1] at Temple Newsam[2] and in the Schreiber collection.[3]

[1] Reilly 1989, I, pl.C8.
[2] *Op.cit.* p.150 pl.89.
[3] Rackham 1930, no.669 pl.46D.

40

Decorated with underglaze oxides, probably Staffs.

*c.*1760
PLATE 24
121mm (B669)
Prov: Brooke coll. no.267, sold Sotheby's 12 June 1929

Lozenge-shaped in plan. A closely similar pot is at Temple Newsam.[1]

[1] Walton 1976 no.268.

41

Decorated with underglaze oxides and coloured glazes, probably Staffs.

*c.*1765
PLATE 21 and cover illustration
150mm (B679)
Ref: Reilly 1989, I, p.175 pl.149

Sherds of this hexagonal moulded body have been found on several sites in Stoke-on-Trent including the Whieldon site at Fenton Vivian,[1] the William Greatbatch site[2] and the site of Humphrey Palmer's works in the Town Road, Hanley.[3] It was evidently made by many potteries, but some may have used spouts, knobs and handles which were distinctively their own. A green-glazed example (B645) with the same moulding on the body, including the shoulder, has a spikey dolphin handle: a pot of identical shape but for the knob is in the Weldon collection.[4] The handle is also found with pots of another shape.[5] A block-mould for a body of the present design is in the Victoria and Albert Museum.[6]

William Greatbatch was paid 10s 6d by Wedgwood in January 1764 for '1 Chinese Teapot', which at that price must mean a block-mould. There is no evidence, however, that the present body shape was the one concerned, and it may have been a completely different one.[7]

[1] Godden 1974, p.101 fig.125.
[2] Barker 1991, p.261.
[3] Barker and Halfpenny 1990, p.56 no.37.
[4] Grigsby 1990, p.198 pl.95.
[5] Parkinson 1971, pl.55a, and 1969, p.67 no.180.
[6] Rackham 1930, no.123 pl.18; Towner 1963, pl.176b.
[7] Barker 1991, pp.93–4.

42

Decorated with coloured glazes, probably Staffs.

c.1765

COLOUR PLATE 6
130mm (B122)
Prov: Solon coll.
Ref: Hodgson 1920, p.231 pl.III; Reilly 1989, I, p.174 pl.146

The pot has an early metal repair to the neck. The hexagonal shape with the diapered ground of squared-off scrolls is probably derived from Yixing stoneware.[1] Sherds decorated with this ground pattern were found on the Greatbatch site.[2] The same ground pattern and the same pattern on the shoulder, resembling Gothic tracery, are found with the same spout and handle on a pot decorated with Chinese figures instead of flowers.[3] The forms of spout and handle have been identified on the products of Wedgwood and of Cockpit Hill, Derby,[4] but were probably also made by other potteries.

[1] Godden 1979, p.39 pl.5.
[2] Reilly 1989, I, p.172.
[3] Grigsby 1990, p.196 pl.94.
[4] Towner 1978, p.191 pl. I.2 and p.198 pl.IV.5.

43

Decorated with coloured glazes, probably Staffs.

c.1770

COLOUR PLATE 6
114mm (B459)
Ref: Hodgson 1920, p.232 pl.IV

A similarly modelled pot was no.163 in Enoch Wood's gift to Dresden, described by him simply as 'Teapot stump of Tree'.[1] It has a more elaborate crabstock handle, matching another example in Manchester City Art Gallery[2] and one sold at Sotheby's in 1990.[3] A similar basalt teapot marked 'Astbury' in the British Museum[4] is likely to date from as late as the 1780s. Another similar pot in white salt-glazed stoneware is in the Metropolitan Museum of Art, New York.[5] It has been speculated that Jean Voyez may have modelled pots of this type.[6]

[1] Taggart 1967, pp.133 and 135.
[2] Parkinson 1971, pl.55b, and 1969, p.68 no.184.
[3] Sotheby's, London, 6 March 1990, lot 230.
[4] Godden 1966, p.10 pl.19.
[5] Mountford 1971, pl.182.
[6] Charleston 1963.

44

Decorated with coloured glazes, probably Staffs.

*c.*1760–70
COLOUR PLATE 7
97mm (B668)
Prov: Brooke coll.; Sotheby's 12 June 1929

A cabbage teapot with identical moulding, apart from the knob, is the salt-glazed stoneware one, no.18 (col. pl.5): another salt-glazed example is in the V&A,[1] and another colour-glazed one in the Nelson Gallery and Atkins Museum, Kansas City.[2] The distinctive form of spout is found on a melon teapot[3] (and see the next entry).

[1] Rackham 1930, no.189 pl.30.
[2] Taggart 1967, p.119 no.446.
[3] Towner 1963, pl.174c.

45

Decorated with coloured glazes, probably Staffs.

*c.*1760–70
PLATE 23
141mm (B593)

The body is rouletted. The distinctive outline of the spout matches the cabbage teapots nos.18 (colour pl.5) and 44 (see previous entry), and the double-scroll handle matches a melon teapot which has this spout.[1]

[1] Sandon 1973, pl.35; Charleston and Towner 1977, no.69.

46

Decorated with underglaze oxides, probably Staffs.

*c.*1760–70
COLOUR PLATE 7
119mm (B590)

Moulded in the form of an apple, complete with leaves, and the depressions at the stalk (upper) and flower (lower) ends. In an undated letter William Greatbatch wrote to Wedgwood: '. . . have sent you an apple teapot and should be glad to know if you would have leaves on the side the same as use to be.'[1] A similar pot was sold by Sotheby's in 1988.[2] An apple teapot of a quite different type is in the British Museum.[3]

[1] Barker 1991, p.90.
[2] Sotheby's, London, 14 June 1988, lot 327.
[3] Reilly 1989, I, p.154 pl.102.

47

Decorated with underglaze oxides, probably Staffs.

*c.*1760–70
COLOUR PLATE 7
123mm (B121)

Moulded as a pear, complete with a depression and scar at the flower (lower) end. The crabstock handle is continued on to the cover to form the knob.[1] The raised loop of the knob has been broken away and a new piece of twig inserted incorrectly. Similar sprigged leaves were found on the Town Road site in Hanley.[2] The wrapped-leaf spout is found on early Wedgwood wares. Another pear teapot with this spout (B413) has more crudely modelled leaves on the body.

[1] Cf. Towner 1963, pl.172b.
[2] Grigsby 1990, p.177.

pl.23

51	45
48	36

48

Decorated with green glaze, probably Staffs.

*c.*1760–70
PLATE 23
186mm (96.936)
Prov: presented by Mr A.J. Aldrick, 1936

It has often been supposed that Wedgwood's were the first cauliflower and pineapple teapots made in Staffordshire. His successful green glaze experiment was in 1759, and the bulk of his ware of these types is thought to have been made after his move to the Big House in 1763.[1] In that year, however, a merchant in the Netherlands was already importing cauliflower and pineapple ware from another source, and wrote to Wedgwood 'to make a tryal of your goods'. He insisted that 'all these must be in setts: a Teapot Milkjug Sugar dish and bowle: if not they wont sell here.'[2] The sales book of the quite separate firm of John and Thomas Wedgwood lists 'green leaves' (that is, leaf-shaped dishes) as early as August 1758. The assumption that Wedgwood's were the first cauliflower wares therefore seems open to question.

An example with matching but less crisp moulding (B497) is presumably from a worn mould. These pots do not match the block-mould at the Wedgwood Museum, Barlaston.[3] The modelling of the leaves on this block and on the tea-caddy inscribed 'JW' in the V&A[4] is flatter and less sculptural than on the present pot. Sherds of cauliflower ware found at Fenton Low are in the Fitzwilliam Museum, Cambridge.[5] Others were found at Fenton Vivian[6] and on the Greatbatch site.[7]

In 1766 Wedgwood complained that he was sick of 'Coloured ware' and was clearing his warehouse of it; it can be no coincidence that in the same year he traded 'Coly Flower Blocks' to the value of twelve guineas in part exchange to another potter, John Baddeley of Shelton.[8]

[1] Reilly 1989, I, p.49.
[2] *Op.cit.* p.89.
[3] *Op.cit.* p.164 pl.131.
[4] *Op.cit.* p.161 pl.119; Towner 1963, pl.173.
[5] *Op.cit.* p.185.
[6] Mountford 1972, pl.128.
[7] Barker 1991, p.255.
[8] Mallett 1967, p.210.

49

Decorated with green glaze, probably Staffs.

*c.*1760–70
COLOUR PLATE 7
105mm (B297)
Prov: Christie's, 1 March 1917, lot 47
Ref: Hodgson 1920, p.231 and pl.III.1

The body is again quite unlike the Wedgwood block-mould (see previous entry) although the handle is of a type (fig. 1, p.70) found on early Wedgwood ware.

50

Decorated with coloured glazes, probably Staffs.

*c.*1760–70
COLOUR PLATE 7
145mm (B312)
Ref: Hodgson 1920, p.231 pl.III.5; Reilly 1989, I, p.164

Modelled in the form of a pineapple. The moulding of the body does not match the block-mould in the Wedgwood Museum at Barlaston[1] or the sherds from the Greatbatch or the Whieldon sites.[2] The handle and spout match no.42 above. Wedgwood's successful experiment for a yellow glaze took place in 1760. He was already buying '1¾ Doz Pine Apple Ware' from John Baddeley of Shelton in 1762.[3] See the previous entry.

[1] Barnard 1924, p.65.
[2] Grigsby 1990, p.192; Mountford 1972, pl.129; Godden 1974, p.103.
[3] Mallett 1967, p.211.

51

Decorated with coloured glazes, probably Staffs.

*c.*1760–70
PLATE 23
117mm (30.927)
Prov: presented by the Friends of the Norwich Museums, 1927

Modelled in the form of a pineapple. A pot with matching moulded details is in the Weldon collection.[1] A biscuit-fired cover with matching moulded details was found on the Whieldon site at Fenton Vivian.[2] The dolphin handle matches the following pot.

[1] Grigsby 1990, p.193 pl.91.
[2] *Ibid.* p.192.

52

Decorated with coloured glazes, probably Staffs.

*c.*1760–70

PLATE 24

119mm (B580)

The pot is lozenge-shaped in plan. The dolphin handle matches the previous pot.

53

Decorated with brown and yellow glazes, possibly Wedgwood

*c.*1765

COLOUR PLATE 7

122mm (B535)

Prov: B.J. Harland coll. no.131

Ref: Reilly 1989, I, p.163

Figure 1

Wasters from similar rouletted melon wares have been found on the Fenton Vivian and Greatbatch sites. A rouletted green-glazed pot in the Fitzwilliam Museum, Cambridge, is dated 1765. The spout and handle (fig.1, p.70) are of types found on early Wedgwood wares, but also used by other potters. The handle is of a form found on the Fenton Vivian site.[1] The sprigged leaf and stem on the body were probably designed originally to accompany a crabstock handle.[2] A pot of matching form but for the handle, another type found on early Wedgwood wares (fig.2, p.76), and decorated in green and yellow glazes, is B485.

[1] Reilly 1989, I, p.151 pl.91 and p.190 pl.172.

[2] Walton 1976, p.82 no.270; Towner 1978, pl.7B.

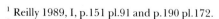

Creamware

The earthenware which in the 18th century was called simply 'the cream colour' has been described as England's greatest contribution in the history of ceramics. It was made with the ingredients of white salt-glazed stoneware, biscuit-fired, covered with a lead glaze and given a second firing. The earliest known dated piece is a bowl inscribed 1743 in the British Museum.[1] In a period when the white body of porcelain represented a ceramic ideal, creamware was the first really pale-bodied pottery fired at an ordinary earthenware temperature. Its colour, durability and refined potting conquered an international market, ousting the beautiful but less practical tin-glazed earthenwares (whether 'delftware' or 'faience') which were the staple of European potters. When the Castleford Pottery in Yorkshire published a catalogue in 1796, the text was in French and Spanish.[2] That of Whiteheads of Hanley, published two years later, was in German, Dutch and French.[3]

The deep colour of early creamware was gradually lightened, but progress was very variable, so that a possibly Yorkshire pot dated 1770 (no.89) is a much deeper tone than Wedgwood ones of the same period. In general the 'out-potteries' seem to have lagged considerably behind Staffordshire. The legal decision in 1775 that Cornish china clay and china stone could be used for pottery without infringing Richard Champion's patent rights over their use in porcelain (p.33) made these materials more readily available to creamware potters, and resulted in a general lightening of tone.

Creamware was made in many centres from Devon to Scotland. In contrast to the old tendency to attribute everything to Wedgwood or Leeds, there is now a mounting body of documentary evidence for creamware potteries to which sometimes not a single piece can yet be attributed, like that at Kidderminster, Worcestershire.[4]

[1] Towner 1978, pl.1.
[2] Castleford 1973; Edwards Roussel 1982.
[3] Whitehead.
[4] *NCSN* 72, 1988 and 74, 1989; *EEC* 14.1, 1990, p.109.

❦ Wedgwood ❦

Josiah Wedgwood takes the credit for making the first really light-coloured creamware. Since his ware was already in production in the early 1760s, it would be surprising if he had not planned this as a result of successful experiments during his partnership with Thomas Whieldon between 1754 and 1759. An equally important aspect of Wedgwood's commercial genius is revealed in his use of the royal family for marketing purposes. By naming his creamware 'Queensware', he succeeded in giving it a status to which humble earthenware had not previously aspired. In a letter of 1767 he mused:

> It is really amazing how rapidly the use of it has spread almost over the whole Globe, and how universally it is liked. How much of this general use, and estimation, is owing to the mode of its introduction and how much to its real utility and beauty? are questions in which we may be a good deal interested, for the government of our future Conduct. The reasons are too obvious to be longer dwelt upon. For instance, if a Royal, or Noble introduction be as necessary to the sale of an Article of Luxury, as real Elegance and beauty, then the Manufacturer, if he consults his own interest, will bestow as much pains, and expence too, if necessary, in gaining the former of these advantages, as he would in bestowing the latter. I had with me yesterday an East Indian Captain and another Gentleman and Lady from those parts who ordered a Good deal of my Ware, some of it, Printed and Gilt, to take with them for presents to their friends and for their own use. They told me it was allready in Use there, and in much higher estimation than the finest Porcellain, the Captain said he had dined off a very complete service just before he left India.

Thinking of the European Jesuit missionaries who recorded the mysterious art of porcelain manufacture in China, he adds jokingly: 'Dont you think we shall have some Chinese Missionaries come here soon to learn the art of making Creamcolour?'

The name Queensware began to be applied to creamware in general, and Wedgwood's own name became known to people outside the trade. In this respect he resembled the prestigious porcelain factories rather than other earthenware potters. As Chelsea and Worcester already did, he began regularly to mark his wares to assist his reputation to spread and encourage what would now be called brand loyalty. In the 1760s he occasionally marked his creamware, and in 1772 he announced in a letter: 'We are going upon a plan to mark the whole if practicable.' This policy paid off: in 1781 an order from a merchant in Amsterdam specified 'every article of the best quality, and all to be marked with your name.'[1]

The colour of Wedgwood's creamware changed rapidly in the early 1760s. John Sadler reported in 1764 that the new pale body was better liked than his previous deep yellow.[2] By 1768 china clay and china stone were apparently included in the body.[3] In the same year Wedgwood wrote: 'I cannot regularly make two cream-colours, a deep and a light shade, without having two works for that purpose.'[4] It should therefore be possible to date his ware by its progression from the deep colour of the early sixties (see no.54) to the pale colour of the late seventies.

As was normal in the industry, Wedgwood sold his creamware to other potters and bought in ware from them to fulfil any rush of orders for which his own production was insufficient. This habit probably helps to explain why it was difficult to institute the routine marking of all wares. Once Wedgwood's creamware was well-known, it was clearly in the interests of other potters to imitate it, and the wares Wedgwood bought in may have looked very like his own. Writing of these 'banks' of other potters' wares, he complained in 1765 that his nephew Thomas Byerley, who was making his way in the firm, could not tell the difference 'betwixt Mr Somebody's Teapots and mine.'[5] Over two centuries after the event it would probably be rash to assume – though it usually has been assumed – that we can necessarily do better than Thomas Byerley (see nos.105 and 108).

[1] Reilly 1989, I, p.91.
[2] *Op.cit.* p.214.
[3] *Op.cit.* p.184.
[4] Towner 1978, p.44.
[5] Reilly 1989, I, p.199.

Black Transfer-Printed Decoration
by Sadler & Green, Liverpool

54

Queen Charlotte and, on the reverse, Fame

*c.*1763
PLATE 24
127mm (B434)
Ref: Reilly 1989, I, p.222

Wedgwood sent creamware to be transfer-printed by the Liverpool firm of John Sadler and Guy Green as early as 1761.[1] The art of printing on ceramics had probably been practised for no more than eight years, but this firm was already very experienced in printing delftware tiles.[2] Wedgwood does not appear to have printed any ware in his own works, even on an experimental basis, before about 1780, preferring to use Sadler and Green. Sadler informed him in 1763: 'we never printed a Piece for any person but yourself.'[3] Sadler was enthusiastic about the suitability of Wedgwood's teapots for portraits. He wrote: 'I think they will never be mended [improved]. They are the last [best] shape for shewing Heads, or any other subject.'[4]

The portrait of Queen Charlotte copies the engraving by Thomas Frye published in May 1762, after his own painting. It is probably the 'new Queen' referred to by Sadler in a letter to Wedgwood in March 1763.[5] A very similar pot is in the Delhom collection at the Mint Museum of Art, Charlotte, North Carolina.[6] The engraving was perhaps executed by the Liverpool engraver Thomas Billinge, as the distinctive scrolls flanking it are found on signed examples of Billinge's work on Liverpool porcelain.[7] Billinge is recorded as a freelance engraver in Liverpool from 1766, but the range of other skills credited to him in subsequent directories has prompted the thought that these entries, which continue until 1816, might conceal the activities of two men of the same name. Sadler used a similar print on Worcester porcelain.[8]

The figure of Fame on the reverse of this pot is copied from *The Ladies Amusement*, Robert Sayer's publication, the second edition of which dates from 1762.[9]

The pot does not have the turned footring of the earliest Wedgwood creamwares, but still has the deep colour of the early wares. For the type of handle see p.76 fig.2.

[1] Reilly 1989, I, p.210.
[2] Ray 1973.
[3] Reilly 1989, I, p.209.
[4] *Op.cit.* p.214.
[5] Stretton 1970, p.225.
[6] *Op.cit.* pl.18c.
[7] Stretton 1983, p.25.
[8] V&A 1984, p.257 no.036.
[9] *The Ladies' Amusement* 1762, p.122.

55

*'An Opera Girl of Paris in the Character of Flora', and on reverse
'The Pretty Mantua Maker'*

*c.*1772–75
PLATE 25
224mm (B356)
Impressed workman's mark
Ref: Hodgson 1920, p.235 pl.VI no.1. Reilly 1989, I, p.242 (obverse)

The decoration is adapted from prints published by Sayer in 1771 from engravings by
Grignion after Michel-Vincent Brandoin. Both designs are found on Liverpool
printed tiles.[1] A version of the Opera Girl of Paris is found on a documentary bowl
inscribed 'Mary Bickford . . . Bushipstenton . . . 1776' (see Ref. to Reilly above) which
is probably from the Indio Pottery at Bovey Tracey in Devon.

[1] Ray 1973, pl.50 nos. D5–26 and D5–27.

56

'The Smoking Party', and on reverse 'The Pipe and Punch Party'

*c.*1775
PLATE 25
183mm (B548)
Impressed marks: 'WEDGWOOD' and workmen's marks
Prov: Mrs Randolph Berens coll.; Sotheby's, 21 May 1924
Ref: Reilly 1989, I, p.244 (both sides)

The design on the reverse is also found on Liverpool printed tiles.[1]

[1] Ray 1973, pl.49 no.D5–20.

57

'The Miller's Maid'

c.1775–80
PLATE 26
143mm (B671)
Impressed mark: 'WEDGWOOD'
Ref: Reilly 1989, I, p.233

On the obverse, old men being ground young in a hand-mill, and on the reverse the inscription:

The Millers Maid Grinding Old Men Young

Come Old, Decrepid, Lame or Blind,
Into my Mill to take a Grind,
See, see, one in the Hopper's got,
And thanks his Stars, 'tis first his Lot,
With Pipe, and Glass, he shews his joy,
That he once more may love and toy.

He laughs at those that are behind,
Who long as much as he to grind,
Observe the Priest, he kneels & prays,
To grind away his antient Days,
Like other Mortals he's inclin'd,
The Deaf, the Dumb, & all wou'd grind.

The Fair she turns the Mill about,
Whilst Age goes in, there's Youth comes out,
Then may we all with Jove prevail
That this Machine may never fail,
That when we're feeble and decay'd,
We'll grind, and with the Miller's Maid.

'Till we are freed from e'ery Pain,
We'll grind, and grind to Youth again,
And when we're young, as once before,
We'll love 'till we can love no more,
Then be content to end our days,
With Life wore out for Female praise.

Grinding with the miller's maid has a sexual double meaning. A later version of this popular subject, with the figures dressed in the fashion of c.1790, is found on a jug (16.58.923) where it is entitled 'Old Men Grinding Young' and accompanied by its female equivalent 'Old Women Being Ground Young'. A still later version is taken from an engraving of 1805 by the young George Cruikshank.[1]

[1] Stoke 1986, no.92.

58

Printed cartouche with painted inscription. On reverse a standing man with a book, and a woman apparently recoiling

c.1775–85
PLATE 26
132mm (B127)
Impressed marks: 'Wedgwood' and workmen's marks
Ref: Reilly 1989, I, p.239

The cover is not the original.

Decorated with Enamel Painting

59

Painted in iron-red, possibly at the Leeds enamelling shop of David Rhodes, with the Crucifixion and, on the reverse, the inscription 'Lett your conversation bee that becometh the Gospel of Christ'

*c.*1765
PLATE 24
128mm (B694)
Ref: Reilly 1989, I, p.254

Figure 2

By 1763 Rhodes had bought out his partner Jasper Robinson, who became an employee.[1] The earliest mention of creamware in his surviving correspondence with Wedgwood is in that year, and it was probably at about this time that Rhodes & Co. began regularly to enamel Wedgwood creamware.[2] The possibility of other enamellers painting on Wedgwood creamware in a style very similar to the Leeds shop should not be ignored. The handle is illustrated at fig.2. It is of a type used also by other manufacturers, e.g. William Greatbatch.[3]

[1] Reilly 1989, I, p.250.
[2] Towner 1959, p.7, and 1974, p.134.
[3] Barker 1991, p.173 fig.6.

60

Painted in iron-red and black, possibly in Rhodes' London studio or at the Leeds enamelling shop, with the inscription 'Wilkes and Liberty' and, on the reverse, 'No.45'

*c.*1768
PLATE 27
132mm (B709)
Prov: given by Commander D.H.C. Cooper (nephew of Mrs Bulwer) in 1944 when he inherited the C.H.B. Caldwell coll.
Ref: Reilly 1989, I, p.255

The radical politician John Wilkes wrote an attack on George III in issue 45 of the magazine *The North Briton*, published in 1763. For this he was imprisoned in the Tower, but almost instantly released since he could claim Parliamentary privilege. Popular support for him reached its height in 1768 when he was elected for Middlesex. The mob dragged the Spanish ambassador from his carriage, turned him upside down and chalked '45' on the soles of his shoes. The importance of political tea-parties is shown by the survival of a number of election teapots, despite the rapid obsolence of their decoration (see no.65).[1]

[1] Priestley 1987, pp.1304–13.

61

Painted possibly in Rhodes' London studio or at the Leeds enamelling shop

*c.*1770
COLOUR PLATE 8
142mm (B249)
Ref: Hodgson 1920, p.232 pl.V no.5; Reilly 1989, I, p.259

In 1768 David Rhodes entered into agreement with Wedgwood to enamel wares for him in London. He had been enticed to the capital in the previous year by a couple of 'China Men' but disappointed of his expectations. Rhodes was henceforth, until his death in 1777, in charge of Wedgwood's London decorating studio. Wedgwood may have continued to send some ware to Rhodes' former partner Jasper Robinson at Leeds for enamelling, because it is known that correspondence was passing between Wedgwood and Robinson in 1770.[1] It may not be possible therefore to distinguish between much of the painting done in London and that done in Leeds. Similar painting to the present pot is found on a pot identified as of Yorkshire manufacture, and likely therefore to have been painted at Leeds.[2]

[1] Towner 1974, p.135.
[2] Walton 1976, p.190 no.768.

62

*Painted possibly in Rhodes' London decorating studio or
at the Leeds enamelling shop*

*c.*1770

COLOUR PLATE 8

153mm (B358)

Incised workman's mark

Ref: Towner 1957 pl.79A; Towner 1959, pl.9a; Towner 1978, p.57 pl.18A; Reilly 1989, I, p.258

The refreshingly bold flower-painting is in a style developed for painting pottery rather than the more expensive porcelain. The lower price of pottery meant that not much time could be spent on painting each piece, and encouraged the use of swift, bold brushwork. Wedgwood, informing his partner Bentley that he had come to an agreement with an enameller from Yorkshire (unnamed, but Rhodes is meant), reported that 'he paints flowers and Landskips very prettily . . . and has a tolerable notion of Colours – He has an Apprentice and another hand.'[1]

[1] Towner 1959, p.8.

63

*Painted possibly in Rhodes' London decorating studio or
at the Leeds enamelling shop*

*c.*1770–75

PLATE 27

131mm (B528)

Prov: Sotheby's, 20 July 1923

Ref: Reilly 1989, I, p.262

The knob is modern

pl.27

| 66 | 60 |
| 65 | 63 |

See the previous entry.

64

Possibly painted in Rhodes' London decorating studio

*c.*1770
COLOUR PLATE 8
139mm (B87)
Impressed and painted workmen's marks
Prov: General Bulwer

The work attributed to Rhodes' London decorating studio shows increasing attempts to imitate porcelain painting. The bold effects of nos. 62 and 63 were toned down in favour of gentility, but it was not economically possible to take the time to achieve subtler effects with equal success. The Wedgwood form of double handle is distinguished from those of many other factories by having no separately applied terminals (but compare no.94). The rose knob is not of the more usual Wedgwood kind, simply press-moulded in two parts (see no.67), but is the more complex type constructed of separate rings of petals.[1]

[1] Reilly 1989, I, p.192 pl.178C left.

65

Possibly painted in Rhodes' London decorating studio. Inscription on the reverse: 'Success to Sir Charles Holte Esq.'

*c.*1774
COLOUR PLATE 8 and PLATE 27
137mm (B150)
Ref: Hodgson 1920 p.232 pl.V no.4; Towner 1957, pl.77B; Towner 1959, pl.7a; Towner 1978, p.56 pl.17A; Birmingham 1984; Reilly 1989, I, p.256

Sir Charles Holte of Aston Hall, Birmingham, was successful Parliamentary candidate for Birmingham in the election of 1774. This pot was therefore specially decorated for political entertaining (see also no.60 above). See also the following entry.

66

Possibly painted in Rhodes' London decorating studio

*c.*1775
COLOUR PLATE 8 and PLATE 27
121mm (B634)
Impressed mark: 'Wedgwood'
Prov: Hadley sale, Sotheby's, 1 March 1928
Ref: Reilly 1989, I, p.256

The distinctive style and colouring on this and the 'Holte' pot in the previous entry place them in a celebrated group of pieces attributed to Rhodes' studio. In 1773 Wedgwood wrote to Bentley: 'I think Mr Rhodes cannot be better employed than in painting Landskips.'[1] The girl with a rake was taken from her context in a print known as the 'Fortune Teller', which is found on Liverpool tin-glazed tiles and Wedgwood creamware and which is included on page 37 of a drawing-book published by John Bowles, dated 1756.[2] The same painter took a seated shepherdess from her context in a print to decorate a Wedgwood creamware pot at Temple Newsam.[3] The girl with the rake is painted with the fortune teller on a creamware pot in the British Museum.[4]

[1] Towner 1959, p.11.
[2] Watney 1972, pl.18 opp. p.822; Ray 1973, pl.31d; Stretton 1976, p.264.
[3] Walton 1976, p.171 no.701; Towner 1978, p.55 pl.16B; *ECC* 1,5, 1937, pl.XIIa for the print on a Worcester porcelain mug.
[4] Jay 1978, p.23 pl.6.

pl.28

71   68   67

72   67

Possibly painted in Rhodes' London decorating studio. Reverse also
painted with a Chinese figure

*c.*1775
PLATE 28
146mm (B327)
Impressed mark: 'WEDGWOOD'
Ref: Hodgson 1920, p.232 pl.V no.2
Ref: Reilly 1989, I, p.260

The form of rose knob, whose massive flower, press-moulded in two parts, contrasts
with thin stems and lank-looking leaves, is a distinctive Wedgwood type.[1]

[1] Walton 1976, p.277 fig.32; Towner 1978, p.205 pl.VII.8; Reilly 1989, I, p.192 pl.178A.

❦ William Greatbatch ❦

Such is the place of the Wedgwood archives in pottery studies that until
recently William Greatbatch was better known as a supplier of models to
Wedgwood than as a manufacturer on his own account. The excavation of the
waste dump from his pottery at Lower Lane, Fenton, Staffordshire has
changed all that.[1] Its stratification enables his production to be divided into
three phases. He began his works in 1762, continuing until his bankruptcy
twenty years later. See also the entry for no.128 in the Pearlware section.

[1] Barker 1991.

68

Decorated underglaze with green, brown, blue-grey and yellow metallic oxides

*c.*1770–82
PLATE 28
100mm (B312)
Ref: Hodgson 1920, p.230 pl.II no.5

Wares moulded in the form of a basket of fruit and with moulded details matching this pot were excavated on the Greatbatch site,[1] as were the forms of spout,[2] handle[3] and knob.[4] It is possible that the 'Basket worked Teapot' Greatbatch sent to Wedgwood on 21 January 1765 had a body of this design.[5] Greatbatch made this type of ware throughout the life of his factory, but the pale colour and type of handle and spout on this example indicate that it belongs in the last of the three phases into which his production has been divided. There is so far no evidence that basket of fruit wares were made by other potters. Another example of this shape (17.139.938) has a spout matching no.72 below.

[1] Barker 1991, pp.241–4.
[2] *Op.cit.* p.174 fig.28 type 6.
[3] *Op.cit.* p.173 fig.27 type 18.
[4] *Op.cit.* p.169 fig.24.
[5] *Op.cit.* p.90.

69

Painted with enamel colours and gilding

*c.*1770–82
COLOUR PLATE 9
121mm (B101)
Ref: Hodgson 1921, 146 pl.I; Barker 1991, 193 and pl.V

After lathe-turning to remove a central horizontal band, a band with floral sprigged ornament has been carefully inserted in short strips into the depression. The forms of spout,[1] knob,[2] handle (see previous entry) and floral band were all excavated on the Greatbatch site.

[1] Barker 1991, p.174 fig.28 type 1.
[2] *Op.cit.* p.168 fig.23 type 10.

70

Painted in enamel colours

*c.*1770–82
COLOUR PLATE 9
106mm (B266)
Ref: Hodgson 1921, pl.III. Towner 1957, pl.64B; Barker 1991, pls.VI and 94

The shape is unusual and the flower-painting is a fine example of a style seen on other Greatbatch wares.[1] The handle, spout and knob with its terminal match the previous pot.

[1] Barker 1991, pl.93.

71

Painted in enamel colours, with on the obverse the inscription
'Let your conversation/Be upon the/Gospell of Christ',
and on the reverse a floral spray

*c.*1770–82
PLATE 28
127mm (B351)
Ref: Barker 1991, pls.95 and 121

The spout matches no.69 above. The flower-painting on the reverse is in a fluent but simpler style than the previous pot.

72

Painted in enamel colours. Cover missing

*c.*1770–82
PLATE 28
124mm to rim (M201)
Ref: Barker 1991, p.187 and pl.64

The engine-turned vertical ribbing on the lower part of the body matches examples excavated on the Greatbatch site, as does the spout.[1] This spout also occurs on a cylindrical pot painted with exotic birds (B378).

[1] Barker 1991, p.174 fig.28 type 3.

pl.29
73
74

73

Painted in enamel colours, including 'MM/1775' in black enamel. The cover is not original to the pot, and is not of Greatbatch's manufacture

PLATE 29
123mm (B unnumbered)
Ref: Smith 1985, p.154 no.361; Bidgood and Walton 1990, no.41; Barker 1991, p.218 and pls.120 and 108

The spout matches no.72 above. This pot has been assigned to the Daniel Potter group on the basis of the decoration, particularly the lettering, surrounded by frothing scrollwork.[1] Several pieces decorated in this style bear addresses in Suffolk: the jug at Temple Newsam which gives its name to the group, inscribed 'Daniel Potter/Barton Mills/1775';[2] a jug in the Royal Pump Room Museum, Harrogate, inscribed 'John Avey/Welnetham/1775';[3] and a teapot in private hands, inscribed 'Thos Trip, Cooper/ Lowestif/1774'. It has been suggested[4] that these were decorated by Richard Phillips, who had painted in underglaze blue at the Lowestoft porcelain factory, signing the 'Ann Hammond' mug dated 1764 in the museum's collections.[5] The link is his signature on a creamware screw-top box lid in the museum's collections, inscribed 'Elizth/Meachin/1773'.[4]

Whether Phillips remained in Suffolk or simply continued to use his local contacts, the Daniel Potter group is clearly connected with the Greatbatch factory. Apart from the cover, which is not original, the present pot matches in all its forms with wasters from the Greatbatch site.

Others of the same shape and with lettering of the same type are an example at Temple Newsam inscribed 'CG/1775'[6] and one inscribed 'Ann Heath 1776' in the possession of a descendant.[7] The Chinese figures painted on the reverse of the present pot are very close to those on the 'John Avey' jug mentioned previously.

[1] Bidgood and Walton 1990.
[2] *Op.cit.* no.37; Walton 1976, p.173 no.706; Bidgood 1985, pp.16–20; Barker 1991, p.218 pl.119.
[3] Bidgood and Walton 1990, no.39.
[4] Smith 1985, p.154 no.360.
[5] Smith 1975, p.43.
[6] Walton 1976, p.199 no.807; Bidgood and Walton 1990, no.40.
[7] Barker 1991, pl.118.

74

Printed in black and painted over with enamel colours

*c.*1770–82
PLATE 29
119mm (B442)
Prov: Edward Sheldon coll. no.701

The spout matches no.69 above. The different prints of Chinese ladies on the two sides are found together on other examples.[1]

[1] Barker 1991, pls.XVII and 150.

75–77

Three pots printed in black with the story of the Prodigal Son and painted over in enamel colours

*c.*1770–82
COLOUR PLATES 9 and 10

75 'The Prodigal Son receives his Patrimony'; on reverse his departure

76 'The Prodigal Son in Excess'; on reverse 'The Prodigal Son in Misery'

77 'The Prodigal Son returns Reclaim'd';
on reverse 'The Prodigal Son feasted on his Return'

127–131mm (B447, B100, B223)
Ref: Hodgson 1921, p.146 pl.I (cat.76 and 77); Reilly 1989, I, p.304

The floral knobs and spouts are as no.69 above. In his *History of the Staffordshire Potteries*, published in 1829, Simeon Shaw connects one specific product with Greatbatch, relating that he 'for some time had a most rapid sale of teapots, on which was printed, in black, by Thomas Radford, the history of the Prodigal Son.'[1] Sherds bearing these Prodigal Son prints were excavated on the Greatbatch site.[2] The six scenes are derived from the set of six mezzotints by Richard Purcell after Sebastien le Clerc II, *c*.1752–55, which were still available in Sayer and Bennett's catalogue in 1775 and were evidently extremely popular.[3]

A narrative scheme of decoration which requires three teapots to complete it does not seem a brilliant piece of marketing. Was the customer expected to buy all three? Greatbatch had acknowledged when writing to Wedgwood in 1764 that 'you understand what will suit trade Better than me.'[4] The survival of numerous examples, however, indicates that Shaw was right about their popularity.

Thomas Radford's signed engravings on Cockpit Hill creamware are in a different style from the Prodigal Son scenes, but were not intended to be over-painted.

[1] Shaw 1829, p.190.
[2] Barker 1991, p.229.
[3] Dolmetsch 1979, pp.145–174; d'Oench 1990, p.325 fig.15.
[4] Barker 1991, p.52.

78

Printed in black with 'Juno', and on reverse the world, with sun, moon and stars, and painted over in enamel colours

c.1770–82
COLOUR PLATE 10
141mm (B98)
Ref: Hodgson 1921, p.146 pl.I; Barker 1991, pls.XVIII and XIX

The floral knob is as no.69 above. The form of spout was excavated on the Greatbatch site,[1] as were fragments of the prints. This spout is found on a cylindrical pot (B unnumbered) inscribed 'When this you See/Remember me tho/Many miles We/Distant be'.[2]

[1] Barker 1991, p.174 fig.28 type 2.
[2] *Op.cit.* pls.96 and 122.

79

Printed in black with 'Cybele', and on reverse the world, with sun, moon and stars, and painted over in enamel colours

c.1770–82
COLOUR PLATE 10
138mm (B99)
Ref: Hodgson 1921, p.146 pl.I

The spout is as the previous pot.

80

Printed in black with Harlequin and Columbine surprised by Pierrot, and on reverse a suitor, an old man with stick and a distraught woman; painted over in enamel colours

*c.*1770–82
COLOUR PLATE 9
114mm (B682)
Mark: print includes the signature 'GREATBATCH' at lower right
Ref: Reilly I, p.303

The spout matches no.69 above. The signature should be taken to indicate Greatbatch as the publisher of the print rather than its engraver.[1] Fragments of the Harlequin print were found in the excavation.[2] A similar version was used earlier on Liverpool tiles, and the source is a sheet dated 1756 in a drawing-book printed by John Bowles.[3] The two prints on the present pot are the normal pairing; on a cylindrical pot (B486) they are separated by underglaze blue bands.[4]

[1] Williams–Wood 1981, p.172.
[2] Barker 1991, p.232.
[3] Ray 1973, pl.31e and pl.45 no. D2–3.
[4] Barker 1991, pl.XV.

81

Printed in black with the Fortune Teller, and on reverse 'The XII Houses of Heaven', and painted over in enamel colours

*c.*1770–82
COLOUR PLATE 10
147mm (B313)
Ref: Hodgson 1921, 146 pl.I

The flower knob with its terminal matches no.69 above. The spout matches examples excavated on the site.[1] The two prints are normally paired with each other.[2]

[1] Barker 1991, p.174 fig.28 type 8.
[2] *Op.cit.* p.236 pl.148 and pl.XIII.

82

Decorated with stripes of green glaze

*c.*1770–80
PLATE 41
152mm (B603)

The spout is only slightly different from a type excavated on the Greatbatch site,[1] but the other features, including the flower knob with its thin, curling leaves are quite different and suggest that the pot is from another manufacturer.

[1] Barker 1991, p.174 fig.28 type 2a.

❦ Yorkshire and Related Wares ❦

A long-standing habit of attributing some types of early creamware to the Leeds Pottery was broken by the discovery that the pottery was not founded until 1770. Some pieces with features similar to Leeds (e.g. B82) may come from earlier and contemporary Yorkshire potteries about which little is known, like those at Holbeck, Rothwell and Rotherham.[1] Another accepted view, that a particular type of terminal (known as the 'Leeds classic', see p.115 fig.15) was found only on the products of the Leeds Pottery, also had to be

revised following the discovery of apparently identical terminals on the site of the Swinton Pottery. This should not have been so surprising, since John Green of the Leeds Pottery was a principal partner in the Swinton Pottery between 1785 and 1800, and there is documentary evidence that the two works had a very close relationship at that period.[2]

[1] See Lawrence 1974.
[2] Cox and Cox 1981, p.51, and 1983, p.50.

83

Painted in dark brown enamel. On reverse, houses in landscape

*c.*1765–70
PLATE 30
131mm (B399)

The knob is modern. The painting is in the style attributed to the Leeds enamelling shop of David Rhodes and Jasper Robinson.[1] After Rhodes' departure for London in 1767, Robinson continued the business, and was succeeded in turn by Leonard Hobson by 1779.[2] This pot is of a type frequently found with this style of enamelling, and may therefore be of Yorkshire origin. The two crossed dead branches slanting to the right, with the new growth springing up to their left, are widely regarded as a trademark of the Leeds enamelling shop, but were probably copied elsewhere (see no.116).

[1] Towner 1974, pl.70B.
[2] *Op.cit.* p.135.

84

Painted in black enamel, with red for the outline of the face and hands only. On reverse, houses in landscape

*c.*1770
PLATE 30
113mm (B609)

The moulded details have not been noted on any attributed pots. The ends of the double handle are modelled as cut ends of branches, so that the applied terminals represent side-shoots springing from them. The painting, in the style of the Leeds enamelling workshop, includes a typical seated man in profile. In this example he smokes a pipe; in others he plays one.[1]

[1] Towner 1974, pl.73a.

85

Painted in red and black enamel, the handle terminals picked out in blue, yellow and green

*c.*1770
PLATE 31
135mm (B705)
Prov: given by Commander D.H.C. Cooper (nephew of Mrs Bulwer) in 1944 when he inherited the C.H.B. Caldwell coll.

With a lathe-turned central band. The painting, in the style of the Leeds enamelling workshop, includes such typical features as the smoking chimneys of the cottages. The flower knob has four pointed leaves instead of the usual three. The handle terminals (fig.3) are different from the two closely related types illustrated by Towner as of

Figure 3

Leeds origin,[1] and it is possible that several potteries were using very similar moulded details. A pot of almost identical form but enamelled with geometric designs (B316) has the same terminals picked out in the same colours, but with the addition of red for the strawberry on each terminal.

[1] Towner 1978, p.209 pl.IX.1 and 2.

Figure 4a

Figure 4b

86

Undecorated

*c.*1770
PLATE 31
122mm (B82)
Ref: Hodgson 1921, p.150 pl.III

An ambitious pot. Parts of terminals matching the upper pair on the handle (fig.4a) are applied to the body between the handle terminals. A terminal matching the lower pair on the handle (fig.4b) is used on the knob and at the base of the spout. The junction of spout with body is carefully covered on all sides with parts of terminals of a third pattern (fig.4c). A pot with apparently matching moulded spout, handle and terminals at Temple Newsam has been attributed to the Rothwell Pottery,[1] but the terminals do not match the pot cited[2] and are more finely moulded than examples attributed to Rothwell. The pierced outer wall, derived from Chinese Yixing stoneware pots, is associated with Leeds creamware[3] but was evidently also used elsewhere.[4]

Figure 4c

[1] Walton 1976, p.154 no.60.
[2] *Op.cit.* p.275 fig.12.
[3] Towner 1978, pl.71B.
[4] Walton 1976, p.155 no.635.

pl.32

89	88
91	92

87

Decorated with green and purplish-brown oxides, possibly Rothwell Pottery

c.1770
COLOUR PLATE 4
140mm (B632)
Prov: Bliss coll.

Sherds decorated in a similarly patchy manner with sponged copper and manganese oxides were found on the site of John Smith's Rothwell Pottery.[1] The attribution of such wares to Rothwell is extremely tentative; matching moulded details were not found, and the manner of applying the oxides could easily have been copied, or copied from, elsewhere. Pots of this type seem united, however, by the distinctive wiry and rather crude moulding of their terminals and knobs. A pot of very similar shape is at the Colonial Williamsburg Foundation, Virginia.[2] The knob (as fig.6b) and handle terminals (fig.5) on the present pot differ from examples previously illustrated.[3]

Figure 5

[1] Walton and Lawrence 1973, pp.4–13.
[2] Walton 1980, pl.107b.
[3] Walton 1976, p.275 fig.12; Towner 1978, p.163 pl.87, p.211 pl.X.10.

88

Decorated with purplish-brown oxide, possibly Rothwell Pottery

c.1770
PLATE 32
113mm (B631)

Figure 6a

See the previous entry. The lower ends of the double handle branch out on to the body. The upper handle terminals (fig.6a) differ from examples previously illustrated. The knob and its terminals (fig.6b) match the previous pot.

89

Decorated with low-fired gilding

Dated 1770
PLATE 32
126mm (B524)

Figure 6b

Inscribed 'John & Ann Knott, 1770'; on reverse a man drawing ale from a barrel. The decoration suggests that John Knott was a tapster or publican. The knob and its terminals (fig.7a) are of a type which has been associated with Leeds.[1] The handle terminals (fig.7b) are superficially similar to but do not match a plaster mould from the Leeds Pottery in the Kidson collection, now at Temple Newsam.[2] The Leeds factory was only being built in 1770,[3] the date on this pot, and it was possibly made at one of the factory's little-known precursors nearby.

[1] Towner 1978, p.205 pl.VII.1a.
[2] Walton 1976, p.277 fig.24; Walton 1980, pl.105b (right).
[3] Towner 1964, p.263.

Figure 7a   *Figure 7b*

90

Green glazed, probably Leeds Pottery

*c.*1775
COLOUR PLATE 4
158mm (B124)
Prov: General Bulwer
Ref: Towner 1963A, pl.6a

Decorated with a roulette before glazing. The strawberry terminals are of a type used by the Leeds Pottery,[1] but also elsewhere in an extremely similar version (see no.115).

[1] Walton 1976, p.275 fig.1; Towner 1978, p.209 pl.IX.1.

91

Painted in enamel colours, probably Leeds Pottery

*c.*1780
PLATE 32
150mm (38.139.938)
Prov: bequeathed by Susanna Taylor, 1938

The knob and its terminals match no.89 above. The handle terminals with three berries or acorns have been associated with Leeds.[1]

[1] Towner 1978, p.209 pl.IX.4.

pl.33
95   94
93   118

92

Decorated with stripes of green glaze, Leeds Pottery

c.1780
PLATE 32
132mm (B83)
Prov: General Bulwer
Ref: Hodgson 1921, p.150 pl.III; Towner 1963A, pl.9a.ii

The type of spout[1] and flower knob[2] are found on marked Leeds examples. The fluted body, the stripes of green copper oxide, the pierced gallery and the knob with its terminal were all found on the Pottery Fields site at Leeds.[3]

[1] Towner 1978, p.193 pl.II.6.
[2] *Op.cit.* p.205, pl.VII.4.
[3] Walton 1980, pl.111a and pl.B.

93

Probably Leeds Pottery, painted in enamel colours in the Netherlands

c.1787
PLATE 33
106mm (B167)
Ref: Hodgson 1921, p.150 and pl.III

The handle terminals are of the Leeds classic type found on the Pottery Fields site in Leeds[1] and shown in the Leeds drawing-books[2] (see no.132, p.115 and fig.15). The knob with its terminal matches the previous pot. All these features were also found on the Swinton Pottery site.[3] The spout, however, matches sherds excavated at Pottery Fields in Leeds[4] (see no.96 below and fig.8 on p.92).

There are many examples of Leeds creamware which were exported to the Netherlands and painted there with distinctive, dry-looking enamel colours. This pot probably celebrates the occasion of Prince William V of Orange's return from exile in 1787. The inscription translates as: 'So long as the sun and moon shall shine, so long shall the house of Orange reign'.[5]

[1] Walton 1980, pl.B fig.1.
[2] *Op.cit.* pl.111b; Walton 1976, p.275 fig.3.
[3] Cox and Cox 1981, pls. 25d and 23c; Cox and Cox 1983, p.239 fig.23, p.238 fig.18.
[4] Walton 1980, p.228 and pl.110a.
[5] *Cf.* Hirsch 1986, pl.170.

94

Probably Leeds Pottery, painted in black enamel in the Netherlands

c.1790
PLATE 33
116mm (B375)
Prov: A.E. Clarke, Wisbech

The spout is of a type found on marked Leeds Pottery examples.[1] The knob with its terminal matches no.92. The double handle is a multi-reeded type without applied terminals.[2] The decoration on both sides shows Samuel anointing Saul, and is inscribed with the biblical reference 'I. Samuel 10.1'. A similarly decorated plate is at Temple Newsam.[3]

[1] Towner 1978, p.193 pl.II.6.
[2] But different from Towner 1963A, p.148 fig.7, 8 and 9.
[3] Walton 1976, p.204 no.841.

95

Painted in underglaze manganese brown, possibly Leeds Pottery

*c.*1780
PLATE 33
122mm (B90)
Prov: Caldwell
Ref: Hodgson 1921, p.150 pl.III

The spout (see no.121 below) is of a type used at Leeds.[1] The painting is in a nervous, trembly hand.

[1] Towner 1978, p.193 pl.II.4.

96

*Decorated with orange-brown slip, applied reliefs and underglaze blue.
Possibly Leeds Pottery*

*c.*1790
PLATE 46
129mm (B349)

Figure 8

The decoration is of a type practised at Leeds and elsewhere. The spout (fig.8) matches no.93 above.

❧ Derbyshire and Related Creamware ❧

The creamware of the pottery at Cockpit Hill, Derby, has been identified by the characteristics of pots whose printed decoration includes the words 'Derby Pot Works' or 'Pot Works in Derby'.[1]

Limited excavations at Furnace Farm, Melbourne, yielded wasters which were used to identify complete pieces as of Melbourne manufacture. Working outwards by comparison with these complete pieces, a wide range of cream-ware was attributed to Melbourne, some of it quite unlike the wasters.[2] The weakness of this chain of inference was shown up by the discovery that some items attributed to Melbourne in fact matched wasters from the site of the Swinton Pottery in Yorkshire.[3]

Melbourne poses two yet more serious problems. Firstly, the site was an ironworks until 1773, and the only known piece of documentary evidence for the existence of a creamware pottery there is an item in the *Derby Mercury* for 18 March 1776: 'Wanted a journeyman potter at Melbourne, Derbyshire that can throw and turn cream-coloured ware . . .'. Secondly, the Furnace Farm site now has the Staunton Harold reservoir on top of it. Further excavation would require underwater archaeology.

The absence of any other documentary evidence makes it clear that Melbourne was not the major creamware producer which it once seemed.[4] Two things at least are clear: in the first place, the creamware sherds must have been made in the area, because the difficulties of transport at this period would have dissuaded anyone from carrying pottery wasters far as hardcore. In the second place, the use of closely similar moulded details by different potteries (see p.105) means that complete pieces have to be compared very critically with the Furnace Farm sherds (see no.100 below).

A reasonable working hypothesis in the present state of knowledge might be as follows: in about 1776 an attempt was made to manufacture creamware near Melbourne, perhaps at the Furnace Farm site or nearby. Some wasters were dumped at Furnace Farm, but the manufacture of creamware was quickly abandoned. Comparison between the wasters and complete pieces (see no.100 below) shows that some moulded details, while similar, are not identical. This does not indicate that these complete pieces were made at the same pottery as the wasters, but the pottery which produced the complete pieces may have been the source of expertise in potting creamware for the enterprise which produced the wasters found near Melbourne. In view of the demonstrated links between this group and the Swinton Pottery, a source in south Yorkshire seems at least as likely as one in Derbyshire.

[1] Towner 1967.
[2] Thorpe and Barrett 1962; Towner 1971.
[3] Cox and Cox 1983, pp.33 and 35 fig.10; Lockett 1985, p.77.
[4] Brown 1978–9, pp.95–9.

Cockpit Hill, Derby

97

Undecorated

*c.*1770
PLATE 43
202mm (B280)
Prov: bought from W. Larcombe, Derby, 1916
Ref: Hodgson 1920, p.235 pl.VI no.3

The simply modelled flower knob and terminals in conjunction with the plain straps to the double handle are typical of Cockpit Hill ware.[1]

[1] Towner 1967, pls.190.5 and 192.5.

98

Painted in enamel colours to resemble fossil limestone

*c.*1770
COLOUR PLATE 8
129mm (B586)

The underside of the pot has a central depression and patches of glaze, bright lemon-yellow where it has pooled. The spout is moulded with basketwork and a strawberry with its leaves on the lower part on both sides. The handle resembles a Wedgwood form (fig 2, see p.76) but lacks the moulded leaves.[1] All the features enumerated are characteristic of Cockpit Hill ware. The lower terminal of the handle is missing. The knob is modern. Similar painting is found on white salt-glazed stoneware.[2]

[1] Towner 1978, p.197 pl.IV.3b; Towner 1967, pls.163.2 and 190.4.
[2] Taggart 1967, no.237.

pl.35 Terminal excavated at Melbourne

99

Painted in enamel colours

*c.*1770
PLATE 42
118mm (B361)
Ref: Towner 1967, pl.173a; Bradley 1978, no.387

The faceted spout and handle and the form of pierced button knob are distinctive to Cockpit Hill.[1] The painting is in Venetian red and pale green. Another pot of similar shape is decorated only with gilding (M173).

[1] Towner 1978, p.191 pls.I.3, VI.4, VIII.16.

'Melbourne' group

100

Painted in red and black enamel

*c.*1770
PLATE 34
152mm (B446)
Ref: Towner 1971, p.28 and pl.32; Towner 1978, p.110 and pl.53B; Bradley 1978, no.409;
Lockett 1985, p.78

The trellis pattern painted in red and black enamel is derived from the pierced outer wall used on teapots of similar shape at Leeds and other potteries (see no.86).[1]

This pot and the following one were key pieces in Towner's comparison with the Melbourne sherds. Features on these pots which were not linked with the sherds, such as the form of convolvulus knob with its three leaves (fig.9a)[2] or the lower terminals to the handle (fig.9b),[3] were then used to identify other pots as Melbourne.

Towner compared the upper terminals on the handle of this pot (fig.9c and compare pl.36) with several Melbourne sherds which show a similar type.[4] Comparison with the best-preserved of these sherds, in a private collection (pl.35), shows that the basic arrangement of berry, crossed stems and long corrugated leaf to the left, is the same. On this and the other sherds, however, the hollow-lobed leaves above and to the right of the crossed stems are different from those on the present pot. The pot also has beading with alternate convex and concave diamonds, a type found on the Melbourne sherds, but used by other potters including William Bacchus at Fenton. The only other link with the sherds is a handle profile with a central depression, found not on the present pot but on other pots which have terminals matching it.[5] The most important point of comparison is therefore the terminals, which do not suggest that the present pot is from the same pottery as the sherds found at Melbourne. The general similarity between the terminals might, however, reflect the origin of a creamware potter working for the enterprise which made the sherds found at Melbourne (see p.92).

[1] Towner 1978, pl.71B; Walton 1976, nos.634–5.
[2] Towner 1978, p.205 pl.VII.6.
[3] *Op.cit.* p.209 pl.IX.12.
[4] Towner 1971, p.27 and fig.4.
[5] *Op.cit.* p.26 and pl.30.

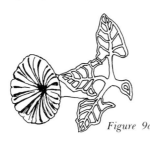

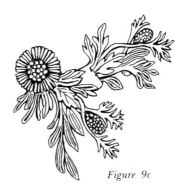

Figure 9a   *Figure 9b*   *Figure 9c*

pl.36 Handle terminal from no.101

pl.37
102
103

101

Painted in red and black enamels

*c.*1770

PLATES 34 and 36
124mm (B633)
Prov: Hadley sale, Sotheby's, 1 March 1928
Ref: Towner 1971, p.27 and pl.31; Towner 1974, pl.76; Towner 1978, p.110 and pl.53A;
Bradley 1978, no.407; Lockett 1985, p.78

The four applied handle terminals are exactly as on the previous pot, as are the beading and the form of convolvulus knob with its three leaves. The spout is what Towner christened the upside-down type, because the leaves at its base grow downwards not upwards.[1] He used its presence on this pot to attribute other pots with this feature to Melbourne. This feature was not, however, found on the Melbourne sherds, and see the previous entry. Towner's supposition that the painted building on the present pot represents Melbourne church is difficult to support.

[1] Towner 1978, p.195 pl.III.4.

102

Painted in enamel colours

*c.*1775

PLATE 37
130mm (B547)
Ref: Bradley 1978, no.411

The spout and flower knob with its terminal match those of the previous pot. The handle terminals are of a type not found on the Melbourne site, but common on pots of the 'Melbourne' group (fig.10).[1] Chinese figures painted in a similar style in bright red, yellow, green, blue and black are found on other pots with matching moulded details.[2]

[1] Towner 1971, p.29 fig.6.16.
[2] *Op.cit.* pl.35a.

Figure 10

103

Painted in enamel colours

*c.*1775

PLATE 37
149mm (54.207.976)
Prov: bequeathed by Major Hitchin, 1976

The lathe-turned central band is reminiscent of Yorkshire creamware (see no.85). The palette of the painting, as well as all the moulded details, are identical to the previous pot.

Related Wares

104

Painted in enamel colours

*c.*1770

PLATE 38
128mm (B88)
Prov: General Bulwer

The painting in light red, yellow, green and black is similar in colouring and style to that found on some Cockpit Hill creamware[1] and on some white salt-glazed stoneware, a type of ware known to have been manufactured at Cockpit Hill.[2] Towner in 1974

made a verbal attribution of this pot to Cockpit Hill. Its potting characteristics are, however, not typical of proven Cockpit Hill ware, and since painters were mobile and painting in a Cockpit Hill style is found on the ware of other factories, caution is necessary. The cover is probably not the original.

[1] Towner 1967, pl.171B.
[2] *Op.cit.* p.255 and pl.185A.

105

Painted in enamel colours

*c.*1765–70
PLATE 38
128mm (B169)
Ref: Reilly 1989, I, p.261 pl.310

The painting in Indian red, green, blue, yellow and black is similar in colouring and style to that found on some Cockpit Hill creamware.[1] The potting characteristics are, however, not typical of proven Cockpit Hill ware. The forms are similar to Wedgwood's, but may have been employed by other potters.

[1] Towner 1967, pl.164B.

❦ **Other Creamware Potteries** ❦

106

Decorated with mould-applied reliefs in light brown

*c.*1760–70
COLOUR PLATE 4
85mm (B644)
Ref: Towner 1963A, pl.8a,ii; Towner 1964, pl.241b

The spout matches a coffee-pot[1] with applied handle terminals of a type used at the Leeds Pottery (see no.90). Another pot (B440) is decorated with reliefs matching those on the present pot but in a darker brown (also illustrated at the references above). The reliefs match a coffee-pot at Temple Newsam[2] and a small teapot whose form also matches the present pot.[3] The reliefs are also found on salt-glazed stoneware.[4]

[1] Towner 1963B, pl.22b.ii; Towner 1964, pl.241a.
[2] Walton 1976, p.78 no.253.
[3] Sotheby's, London, 17 October 1989, lot 375.
[4] Sotheby's, London, 3 June 1980, lot 95.

107

Transfer-printed in black with strawberries and flowers

*c.*1765
PLATE 39
107mm (B407)
Prov: Caldwell

The lemon-yellow glaze, which partially covers the base, and its tendency to craze in horizontal lines suggest the Cockpit Hill factory at Derby. A Staffordshire origin, however, perhaps remains equally likely.

108

Transfer-printed in red with a sheep and, on the reverse, a cow

*c.*1765
PLATE 39
108mm (B492)
Ref: Reilly 1989, I, p.231 pls.251 A and B (both sides)

Apart from the lack of crazing, the fabric and glaze are very similar to the previous
pot. An attribution to Wedgwood is tempting, but the glaze is yellower than on other
early examples of his making (see no.54, p.00). The prints are derived from *The Ladies'
Amusement*, plates 150 (centre, left) and 151 (bottom, centre) in the 1762 edition.

109

*Transfer-printed in black with George III and, on reverse,
Queen Charlotte. Staffordshire or Liverpool*

*c.*1765
PLATE 40
133mm (B91)

The form of this pot, including the distinctive handle with large thumb-rest and curled
lower terminal, matches a pot which bears a print signed by the engraver Thomas
Rothwell.[1] Rothwell is known to have been in Liverpool in 1762, is said by Simeon
Shaw to have worked subsequently for Humphrey Palmer in Hanley, but was in
Birmingham by 1773. Since a signed print of his is found on a pot which may have
been made as far afield as Cockpit Hill, Derby,[2] a Liverpool attribution for the present
pot is very tentative. Liverpool potteries known to have produced creamware include

the Flint Mug Works at the corner of Flint Street and Parliament Street, which had in stock 'a large assortment of cream colour or Queensware, manufactured at the said work' when the business was advertised for sale in 1773.[3]

[1] Stretton 1967, pls.151b, 152a; compare *ECC* 8,2, 1972, pl.186a.
[2] Stretton 1967, p.250 and pl.152b.
[3] Smith 1970, p.10.

110

Transfer-printed in black with a boy and girl dancing and, on reverse, a gentlemen touching a country girl on the chin while an old countryman looks on. Staffordshire or Liverpool

*c.*1770
PLATE 43
221mm (B241)
Ref: Hodgson 1920, p.235 pl.VI.2

The handle is a type used by Wedgwood (see p.70 fig.1) but Wedgwood would certainly not have combined it with a crabstock spout as here! The main prints are found on Liverpool printed tiles,[1] and that on the obverse is also found on Liverpool porcelain, including a mug dated 1768.[2] Six of the eight subsidiary prints of birds, butterflies and flowers on the body of the pot are found in *The Ladies' Amusement* of 1762, four of them on plates signed by Hancock as engraver (for Hancock see p.133).[3]

[1] Ray 1973, pl.48 nos. D5–4 and D5–12.
[2] Sotheby's, 26 May 1938 lot 342; see also Boney 1957, pl.36d.
[3] *The Ladies' Amusement* 1762, pls.8,11,15,68,70.

111

Transfer-printed in black with the Freemasons' Arms, and on reverse further Masonic symbols. Staffordshire or Liverpool

*c.*1765–70
PLATE 40
111mm (B168)

This pot might be supposed of Wedgwood origin, for spout and handle are forms used by Wedgwood (see no.59). The form of knob is unusual, however. The glazing is very patchy and has left part of the body and most of the base uncovered. The engraving may be by Jeremiah Evans, who was himself a Freemason, and when in London in 1753 produced a booklet called *Freemasons' Lodges*.[1] Its frontispiece is engraved in similar style and inscribed 'Engraved and Published by Brother Evans in Bear Street, Leicester Fields'. In June 1757 an advertisement appeared in the *Liverpool Chronicle*: 'J. Evans, engraver, from London, at his house in Williamson's Field, Liverpool, executes Copper Plates, Seals and other Engraving in the most elegant manner, and teaches young Gentlemen, &c. to draw on moderate terms . . .'.[2]

The same prints, with the addition of scrolled cartouches surrounding them, are found on a Wedgwood teapot in the British Museum.[3] The print of the 'Masons' Arms' is first mentioned in a letter from Sadler to Wedgwood in 1763.[4] A very similar print to that on the obverse is found on a porcelain mug from Philip Christian's factory in Liverpool, and is signed by Sadler as the printer.[5] Evans might have been engraving for him as a freelance or as an employee. Another very similar print is known on a porcelain plate which was thought to be Bow.[6]

[1] Print Room, V&A.
[2] Stretton 1983, pp.23–4.
[3] Towner 1978, p.47 pl.11B (obverse); Dawson 1984, p.22 fig.11 (reverse).
[4] Reilly 1989, I, p.235.
[5] Stretton 1983, p.23 fig.3.
[6] *ECC* 3,4, 1955, pl.70a.

112

*Transfer-printed with 'the Virtuous Woman' and, on reverse,
'the Virtuous Man', both signed 'Rd Abbey sculp',
'Josh Johnson Liverpool'. Cover missing. Probably Liverpool*

*c.*1790
PLATE 41
137mm to rim (B626)

The prints are adapted from engravings published by Carrington Bowles in 1785. Below the female figure on the obverse is: 'The virtuous woman is a crown to her husband'. Around her is: 'Attend unto this simple fact as thro this life you rove, that virtuous and prudent ways will gain esteem and love'. The compass is inscribed: 'Fear God/Know thyself'. The four scenes beyond the compass indicate the fate of the woman who does not keep within compass: vanity (looking in a mirror) and extravagance (burning candles although it is daylight and the curtain is open) lead to arrest (being led away by two constables) and hard labour in the workhouse.

Below the male figure on the reverse is: 'The end of the upright man is peace'. Around him is 'By honest and industrious means we live a life of ease, then let the compass be your guide and go where ere you please'. The compass is inscribed as on the obverse. The four scenes beyond indicate the fate of the man who does not keep within compass: lust (toying with a woman on a sofa) and dissipation (seated at a table with drink) lead to moral disaster (a shipwreck) and prison (scene behind bars).

The female figure is dressed in the fashion of the 1780s. Another pot with these signed prints is in the collections of the Colonial Williamsburg Foundation, Virginia.[1] The signature on this pot is 'Jph' rather than 'Josh' Johnson, but is otherwise the same. Richard Abbey was an apprentice with Sadler and Green from 1767 until 1773, when at the age of nineteen he set up his own business as engraver and printer at 11 Cleveland Square, Liverpool. He evidently worked as a freelance engraver to the trade. Joseph Mayer stated in 1855 that he was an occupant of the site of the Herculaneum Pottery immediately before its foundation in 1796.[2]

A jug in the Harris Museum, Preston, has a print of Bidston Hill Signals signed 'Printed by Joseph Johnson Liverpool', dated 1789. This printer has not been found in the Liverpool directories or town records. An advertisement in Williamson's *Liverpool Advertiser* for 21 January 1793 reads: 'CLAY/Lately discovered within Parbold township sundry BEDS of CLAY, of excellent qualities which have been proved by Joseph Johnson, manufacturer of Earthenware, at NEWBURGH.' A Joseph Johnson born in 1779, son of a Newburgh 'mugman', must be a different person since he was only fourteen at the time of the advertisement. Newburgh is about fifteen miles from Liverpool. A connection is likely with the London publisher Joseph Johnson (1738–1809) who was born at Everton near Liverpool and whose nephew of the same name was listed as a Liverpool gentleman from 1813 to 1829.[3]

Richard Abbey's former master Guy Green printed a very similar version of these 'Keep within Compass' subjects on Wedgwood creamware.[4] For a version signed by John Aynsley see no.127. A much simpler version was printed by Thomas Fletcher of Shelton.[5]

[1] Smith 1970, pl.26.
[2] *Op.cit.* p.15.
[3] *Op.cit.* pp.36–7.
[4] Reilly 1989, I, p.236 pls.264, 264A.
[5] Stoke 1986, p.85 no.107.

113

Transfer-printed in black on the obverse with the verse: 'When this you see/remember me,/And bear me in your Mind;/Let all the World/say what they will,/Speak of me as you find'; and on the reverse with a sailor's farewell. Cover missing. Ralph Wedgwood. Probably Burslem, Staffs.

1789–96
PLATE 43
120mm to rim (B612)
Impressed mark: 'WEDGWOOD & CO.'

Ralph Wedgwood's father Thomas was Josiah Wedgwood's partner for the production of 'useful wares' and as such is one of the unsung heroes of English pottery.[1] Thomas died in 1788, and Ralph became involved in the setting up of the Hill Pottery, Burslem, which he ran from 1790 until he became bankrupt in 1796. In 1798 he was taken into partnership at the Knottingley Pottery, Ferrybridge, Yorkshire, enabling the firm legitimately to mark their wares as Wedgwood & Co. This venture did not last, for in January 1801 he was bought out.[2]

The form of handle moulded with overlapping leaves is superficially like Josiah Wedgwood's type (see no.55), but Ralph's leaves are of trefoil form including the lowest one;[3] Josiah's are not, except for the lowest leaf which spreads out on to the body of the pot. An oval basalt pot (M760) has the impressed mark 'WEDGWOOD' and may also be by Ralph Wedgwood.

[1] Niblett 1984.
[2] des Fontaines 1983A; Holdaway 1986.
[3] Towner 1978, p.203 pl.VI.5.

114

Decorated in low-fired gilding with the inscription 'Margt Nichole'. Tyneside or Sunderland

c.1780
PLATE 44
159mm (B271)

The distinctive form of spout (fig.11a) and the applied handle terminals which are eight-petalled flowerheads without leaves (fig.11b) appear to match the Ann Watson teapot dated 1777 at the Abbey House Museum, Leeds, and the Ann Fenwick coffee-pot at the Laing Art Gallery, Newcastle. The applied terminal on the knob is shown in fig.11c. The Ann Watson group has been convincingly linked with the area of Tyneside and Sunderland.[1] Another pot with moulded details matching the present pot and low-fired gilding (B500) is inscribed 'John and Jane Dent', 'It's love alone Makes too but One' and, on reverse, 'God Speed the Plough'.

[1] Bidgood and Walton 1990, nos.55 and 57.

Figure 11a   *Figure 11b*   *Figure 11c*

pl.41

82	120
112	116

115

Decorated in low-fired gilding with the inscription 'Success to our hopes
& Injoyments to our wishes, Ann Acton'.
Probably Tyneside or Sunderland

*c.*1780
PLATE 44
159mm (B570)

The fabric and glaze of this pot, which appears a brilliant cream with a tinge of green
where the glaze has pooled, match the previous pot. The distinctive spout, moulded
with hollow leaves on the upper but not the lower part, matches a green-glazed pot
(B670) inscribed in low-fired gilding apparently by the same hand 'M. Britiff Johnson,
Bayfield, 177[?]' and, on the reverse, 'Success to ye Lover/Honnour to ye Brave/health
to ye Sick/& Freedom to ye Slave'. Bayfield is near Holt in north Norfolk. The
existence of a jug decorated in low-fired gilding and inscribed apparently also by the
same hand 'Wm & Martha Decaux Norwich 1774' (Norwich Castle Museum 166.933)
raises the possibility of an East Anglian decorator for this group. It is also possible,
however, that the decoration was commissioned by East Anglian customers from the
pottery in Sunderland or Tyneside. That this was the practice in the early 19th century
is attested by Sunderland and Tyneside jugs in Norwich Castle Museum. The
commercial links between East Anglia and the North-East were well-developed
because of the important coastal trade in Sunderland and Tyneside coal. It is tempting
to connect the present group with an advertisement in the Norwich *Mercury* on 27 July
1782: 'Earthenware – Paul Jackson, Merchant in Newcastle upon Tyne, sells Wholesale
and Retail at his manufactory on Gateshead Common, adjoining the Durham Road,
about two miles from the Tyne Bridge, the greatest variety of Earthen Ware, equal to

any in Staffordshire. The prices are so low as to be very encouraging to the Dealers in that Article – He deals for ready money only and gives 5% discount.' Jackson is known to have been active from at least 1773.[1]

Figure 12

The applied terminals on the handle and cover of the present pot (fig.12) are basically of a type associated with Leeds,[2] but are also found on the 'George Wray 1778' mug at the Laing Art gallery, Newcastle, which belongs to the Ann Watson group associated with Tyneside or Sunderland.[3]

[1] Smith *NCSN* 31, 1978, p.29; Bell 1971, p.66.
[2] Towner 1978, p.209 pl.IX.1.
[3] Bidgood and Walton 1990, no.58.

116

Painted in iron-red enamel with a countryman and woman and, on reverse, a landscape. Probably Tyneside or Sunderland

*c.*1780
PLATE 41
184mm (B341)

The spout is a larger version of that on the previous pot. The fabric and glaze also match. The handle, with a fat central roll flanked by a substantial roll at either side, matches the Bayfield pot mentioned in the previous entry. The painting includes crossed-over dead branches leaning to the right, with new growth springing to the left, a motif of the Leeds enamelling shop (see no.83), but this painting does not appear to be quite in the Leeds style.

117

Painted in enamel colours with the inscription 'My heart is pure/And will endure' and, on reverse, a landscape in cartouche.
Sunderland or Tyneside

*c.*1780
PLATE 45
140mm (B597)

The distinctive spout, moulded on either side with four channels and a flowerhead and a leaf rising from it, matches the 'Wm and Mary Holyday' teapot at Scarborough Museum and the 'Hannah Mary Bainbridge' teapot at Temple Newsam,[1] which belong to the Ann Watson group associated with Tyneside or Sunderland. The sloppy painting in red, green, purple and black (with a little chalky pale blue) is typical of the group.

[1] Bidgood and Walton 1990, nos.59 and 60.

118

Decorated with orange slip, painting in underglaze blue, and low-fired gilding with the inscription 'When we drink our tea, let us merry be', possibly Tyneside or Sunderland

*c.*1785
PLATE 33
143mm (B85)

A similarly decorated pot (M218) is inscribed 'Joseph Nutman born on the 20th June in the year 1786'.

119

Painted in enamel colours and inscribed 'Elizth. Barker/Richmond, Yorkshire/1794'. Sunderland or Tyneside

PLATE 43
137mm (32.129.949)
Prov: bequeathed by Mr H.B. Broadbent, 1949
Ref: Bidgood and Walton 1990, no.64

This pot has been linked with the Ann Watson group on the basis of its decoration [see Ref.]. For a customer in Richmond the Sunderland or Tyneside potteries were more accessible than those in south Yorkshire.

120

Decorated with stripes of green glaze. With stand

*c.*1780
PLATE 41
147mm (B571)

Apparently identical to a pot at Manchester City Art Gallery,[1] and attributed by Towner to the 'Melbourne' group (see p.92).[2] The handle is, however, different from 'Melbourne' group examples,[3] while the spout (see next entry and fig.13) is known on marked examples from the Leeds Pottery.[4]

[1] Towner 1978, pl.56B.
[2] Towner 1971, pp.29–30.
[3] *Op.cit.* pls.36B and 37.
[4] Towner 1978, p.193 pl.II.5.

121

Painted in enamel colours

*c.*1770–80
PLATE 42
118mm (B86)
Prov: Solon coll.
Ref: Hodgson 1920, p.232 pl.V.6; Reilly 1989, I, p.302 pl.371

The spout (fig.13) matches that on the previous pot. The figure has been described as Aurora but seems more likely to be Apollo. The reverse is painted with a sunrise or sunset. The painting has been attributed to Rhodes' London decorating studio, but very similar decoration is found on pots by William Greatbatch[1] (an example lacking its handle and cover is 1672; for Greatbatch see p.80) which are more likely to have been decorated further north. The painted design does not match closely the prints of Aurora on Greatbatch creamware (see no.128).

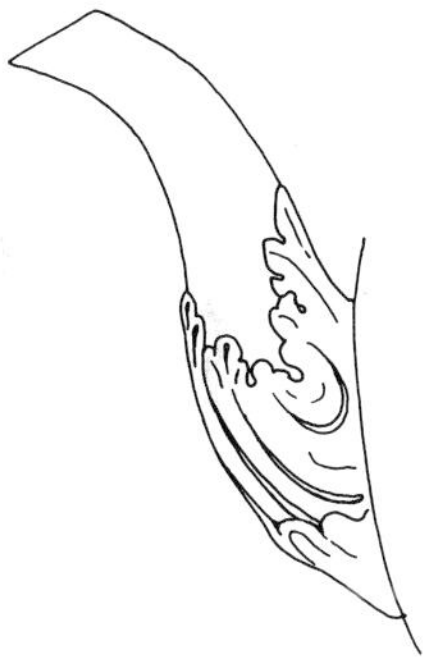

[1] Towner 1978, pl.80A; Walton 1976, p.199 no.807; Bidgood and Walton 1990, no.40.

Figure 13

122

Decorated with green glaze

*c.*1780
COLOUR PLATE 4
156mm (B444)
Prov: Caldwell

There is a general resemblance to jugs in the form of heads, which may bear names such as that of Admiral Rodney (victor of the Battle of the Saintes in 1782),[1] but it seems unlikely that the customer who bought this pot was expected to recognise the face as anyone in particular.

[1] *Country Life*, 15 December 1966, p.1625.

123

Decorated with underglaze oxides in green, brown, yellow and pale blue

*c.*1780
PLATE 45
132mm (B432)
Ref: Towner 1963A, pl.9a,i

Figure 14

An applied terminal on the handle is shown in fig.14.

124

Decorated with beige-yellow slip and painted in red and black enamel

*c.*1790
PLATE 47
139mm (B532)

The spout has a distinctive moulding: at the upper end is a beaded band from which acanthus leaves grow both upwards and downwards.

125

Fluted shape decorated with dark brown slip

*c.*1790
PLATE 46
123mm (B225)
Incised mark: '2'
Ref: Hodgson 1921, p.150 pl.III

126

Painted in underglaze blue

*c.*1780
PLATE 47
146mm (B152)
Prov: General Bulwer

The greenish or yellowish glaze of creamware prevented underglaze blue from achieving a clear colour. The muted tone may appeal to modern taste, but the type was short-lived, being replaced by the whiter pearlware with its brighter blue.

❦ Pearlware ❦

Pearlware is the modern name given to an earthenware developed from creamware, distinguished by its bluish glaze tinged with cobalt. The blue compensated for any tendency towards yellow or buff in the colour of the whitish body. This ware was usually known at the time as 'the china glaze', which indicates clearly that it was an attempt to make earthenware look more like porcelain. As with cream colour and Queensware (see p.71), Wedgwood gave his china glaze the brand name 'Pearl White'. Such has been the preponderance of Wedgwood in ceramic studies that the whole class is now referred to as pearlware.

Wedgwood's Pearl White was launched in 1779. His correspondence over the new ware, however, reveals not an eager pioneer but merely one who sees the

need to keep abreast of his competitors. Writing in 1772, he says that if he continues cream, his rivals will go white.[1] In March 1779 he asks his partner Bentley to help him 'to give the brat a name'. Most revealing are the remarks in a letter of 6 August:

> Your idea of the creamcolour having the merit of an original, and the pearl white being considered as an imitation of some of the blue and white fabriques, either earthenware or porcelain, is perfectly right, and I should not hesitate a moment in preferring the former if I consulted my own taste and sentiments: but you know what Lady Dartmouth told us, that she and her friends were tired of creamcolor, and so they would of Angels if they were shewn for sale in every chandlers shop through the town. The pearl white must be considered as a change rather than an improvement, and I must have something ready to succeed it when the public eye is palled, or it comes upon the town.[2]

It has been argued that the only earthenware 'blue and white fabriques' worth imitating at this period, after the eclipse of delftware, were china glaze wares, which must therefore already have been in production by other potters.[3] A jug in Stoke-on-Trent Museum, the earliest known dated piece of china glaze, has the painted inscription in underglaze blue: 'Tidmarsh's Original Staffordshire Warehouse N 1775'.[4] An important catalyst for the development of the new ware may have been the legal ruling in the same year that china clay and china stone could be used for pottery without infringing Richard Champion's patent for their use in porcelain.

Wedgwood's marketing skills timed the launch of his Pearl White ware with a royal visit to the firm's London showroom, and he was able to report in June 1779: 'I thank her majesty for the honor she has done to the Pearl White, and hope it will have due influence upon all her loyal subjects. The dishes etc. to complete the service are gone today . . .'. Despite this he does not appear to have made much of the ware, for which he evidently had little enthusiasm.

Pearlware enabled potters to produce successful imitations of porcelain which, despite their lack of translucency, continue to deceive inexperienced collectors. Nos.131 and 134 are direct imitations respectively of New Hall and Caughley porcelain patterns, in the latter case including even the mark! The ability to imitate porcelain extended of course to underglaze blue decoration. Underglaze blue painting was not popular on creamware (see no.126 above), presumably because the colour tended to look muddy through the green or yellow tint of the glaze. Pearlware lent itself also to underglaze printing, which had been practised on porcelain since its introduction in the late 1750s at Worcester. Wedgwood's reluctance to develop his Pearl White left to others like Josiah Spode the creation of the blue-printed earthenware which was to dominate the market for the next hundred years.

The new ware made underglaze decoration in other colours practicable. The range was restricted to those colours which would stand the temperature at which the glaze was fired. Whereas enamel colours would not be fired above about 700°C, these might have to stand temperatures in the region of 1000 degrees. This range of rich but muted earth colours – cobalt blue, antimony yellow, copper green, iron brown and manganese purple – is so appealing to

modern taste that it is easy to forget that its selection owed more to technical than to aesthetic reasons. Wares decorated in this way are often referred to as Prattware because the first marked piece to come to critical notice was marked 'Pratt'.[5] The type was made by many other potters, and the term Prattware is additionally confusing since it is occasionally used to denote the multi-coloured printing employed by a Pratt of a later generation on pot-lids and similar wares from the 1840s onwards.

Many pearlwares are included in Section Six rather than the present one because their shapes are related to the fashionable stonewares in neoclassical taste.

[1] Reilly 1989, I, p.317.
[2] Finer and Savage 1965, p.237.
[3] Stoke 1986, p.46.

[4] Adams 1975–6, pp.31–7; Lewis 1985, p.134.
[5] Lewis 1984, p.13.

127

John Aynsley, Lane End, Staffs. Transfer-printed on both sides with scenes inscribed 'KEEP WITHIN COMPASS', hand-coloured in puce, blue, yellow and red

c.1800
PLATE 48
162mm (B420)
Marked within the prints: 'J Aynsley Lane End'

On the obverse a female figure holding a book inscribed 'The Pleasures of Imagination Realized' standing beside an open jewellery chest inscribed 'The reward of Virtue': above her 'FEAR GOD', around her 'KEEP WITHIN COMPASS AND YOU SHALL BE SURE TO AVOID MANY TROUBLES WHICH OTHERS ENDURE', to the left 'Attend unto this simple fact As thro this Life you rove', to the right 'That virtuous and prudent ways Will gain esteem and love' and below her 'Prudence brings Esteem'. The four scenes beyond the compass indicate the fate of the woman who does not keep within compass: idleness (with playing cards scattered on the ground) and dissipation (raising a glass and dropping a baby) lead to arrest (being led away by two constables) and hard labour in the workhouse.

On the reverse a male figure: above and around him inscriptions as obverse, to the left 'By honest and industrious means We live a life of ease', to the right 'Then let the Compass be your guide And go where e'er you please' and below him 'Industry Produceth Wealth'. The four scenes beyond the compass indicate the fate of the man who does not keep within compass: idleness (seated, gaming?) and lust (seated with a woman on his knee) lead to moral disaster (a shipwreck) and prison (scene behind bars).

John Aynsley was described as an enameller at Lane End, Longton, Staffs., in 1790, and as a manufacturer in 1796 and 1802. A man of the same name in Lane End is described as an engraver in 1822. A plate with a very similar print to that on the obverse, is in the Willett collection at Brighton Museum and Art Gallery, and is signed by M. Shelley, Lane End. He also signed a 'male' print of this type on a mug belonging to Leicester Museum and Art Gallery. From about 1774 until his death in 1788 Michael Shelley occupied the site of the present Gladstone Pottery Museum, to which the latter piece is on loan. The presence of different marks on such similar prints suggests that the engraved copper plates were supplied to Aynsley and Shelley as potters by a third party, an engraver who remains anonymous.[1] For similar decoration see no.112.

[1] *NCSN* 74, 1989, p.31.

128

Transfer-printed with Aurora and, on reverse, the world with sun, moon and stars, painted over in enamel colours

*c.*1780
PLATE 48
181mm (B606)

The prints appear to match examples on William Greatbatch's creamware.[1] In this version the rear horse turns back his head; in another version found on Wedgwood creamware the front horse does this.[2] Unlike another pearlware pot in the collection painted in underglaze blue (1677), the details of potting on the present piece do not tie up with the wasters excavated on the Greatbatch site. Identifying prints from the same engraved plate is fraught with difficulty because plates were regularly re-engraved as parts became worn. Greatbatch's engraver may have worked for others, or perhaps Greatbatch was buying in undecorated ware from another potter to complete an order (see p.39). Another possibility is that following his bankruptcy in 1782 his engraved copper plates had changed hands and were in use elsewhere. Other prints extremely close to those on Greatbatch creamware have been noted on pottery of different but unknown origin:[3] 'the Fortune Teller' (see no.81)[4] and 'Juno' (see no.78).[5]

[1] Barker 1991, p.233 and pl.XI.
[2] Towner 1978, pl.23B.
[3] Barker 1991, pp.236 and 240.
[4] Towner 1978, p.153 pl.80B.
[5] Seligmann 1975, p.87.

pl.50
130

129

Painted in enamel colours including inscription 'God give us grace to drink/Our tea with bread and butter plenty/With sugar store & water more/to fill the pot when empty'. Flower sprays on the reverse.
Probably Leeds Pottery

*c.*1800–05
PLATE 49
141mm (B387)

The painting is in the style of 'the T decorator group', some examples being marked with a 'T' in red enamel. The style seems to be confined to products of the Leeds Pottery.[1] A pot of similar shape decorated in this style in the Yorkshire Museum is dated 1802.[2]

[1] Bidgood and Walton 1990, nos.79–103.
[2] Miller and Berthoud 1985, pls.403–4.

130

Painted in enamel colours including the inscription 'ROSE LOW 1797'

PLATE 50
168mm (B470)

131

Painted in enamel colours

*c.*1790
PLATE 49
156mm (B74)
Ref: Hodgson 1921, p.149 pl.II

The painting is a close copy of the New Hall porcelain factory's pattern 22 (M360).

132

Painted in underglaze blue, red enamel and gilding, probably Leeds Pottery

*c.*1790
PLATE 51
112mm (B480)

For the 'Leeds classic' handle terminals (fig.15) and flower knob, see no.93.[1] The spout matches no.96, p.92 and fig.8.

[1] Towner 1978, p.209 pl.IX.11, p.205 pl.VII.4.

Figure 15

pl.51

132	135
134	133

pl.52

136

137

133

Decorated in underglaze blue with transfer-prints, and painted flower sprays and inscription 'Mary Lee Born July 19 1787/Millton Oxfordshire/When This you see/Remember me Though/Many Miles Wee Distant/Bee'

PLATE 51
162mm (B149)

The chinoiserie print on the reverse is very similar but not identical to the 'Conversation' pattern found on wares impressed 'IH' and thought to have been made by Joshua Heath.[1]

[1] Coysh 1974, pl.8.

134

Transfer-printed in underglaze blue with the 'Fence' pattern

*c.*1790
PLATE 51
140mm (B564)
Printed mark: 'C'
Prov: Caldwell

Both the pattern and the mark are direct imitations of Caughley porcelain (see also no.181).[1]

[1] Godden 1969, pl.262.

135

Painted in high-temperature underglaze colours

*c.*1800
PLATE 51
114mm (B330)
Prov: Caldwell
Ref: Hodgson 1921, p.149 pl.II

This may have been made as a toy or for humble customers who still could not afford to drink tea in large quantities. Three other pots of similar size in the collection have this type of decoration (B95, B77 and B379).

136

Decorated with brown and black marbled slip

*c.*1800
PLATE 52
93mm (B409)

Excavations at pottery sites show this type of decoration to have been common in the late 18th and early 19th centuries, but relatively few examples have survived, presumably because such wares were cheap and not the 'Sunday best' teapots which people preserved. In 1786 Wedgwood referred to 'a little marbling or mixture of the clays, of which great quantities of our cheap wares are now made . . .'.[1]

[1] Finer and Savage 1965, p.297.

137

Decorated with underglaze oxides: mottled grey, and green on the turned bands

*c.*1800
PLATE 52
153mm (B453)

This type of decoration also was relatively inexpensive, but has survived less frequently than 'Sunday best' varieties. Identical decoration is found on a round pearlware pot (B394) of the 'sweep neck' shape (for the shape see no.287) and similar decoration on a creamware pot (B468).

138

Decorated with inlaid bands of multi-coloured clays

*c.*1800
PLATE 53
111mm (B510)

The inlay is a very thin layer composed of clay shreds, the shreds themselves being composed of different coloured and stained clays banded together. A block made of such shreds was probably sliced into thin slices which were then laid on to the pot. This technique was sometimes combined with chequered inlays of the kind found on the following pot.[1] It is possible that inlay of this kind is the 'terra tersia' (i.e. intarsia) ware being sold by Ralph Wedgwood in 1794.[2]

[1] Towner 1978, p.158 pl.85B(ii).
[2] Valpy 1991, p.231; *cf.* Holdaway 1986, pls.158a and 159a for another possibility.

pl.53
138
139

139

Decorated with blue slip, black and white inlays, and painted in black enamel and gilding including inscriptions: on the obverse 'Sarah Blowers 1795', on the reverse 'Joy's many, sorrows few,/Love sincere, and/ Friendship true'

PLATE 53
159mm (B479)
Prov: Caldwell (Christmas present 1921)

A type of decoration made by many potters. A cylindrical pot similarly decorated with blue slip and black and white chequered inlays but lacking its cover (1653) is marked 'NEALE & Co.' and has applied terminals (fig.16a) superficially similar to the Leeds classic type (see no.132 above and fig.15). See fig.16b for the spout. For Neale & Co. see nos.223 and 221.

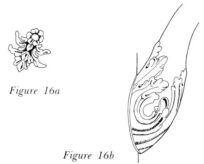

Figure 16a

Figure 16b

5

Early Porcelain

Chelsea

The following notice appeared in the *Daily Advertiser* on 5 March 1745: 'We hear that the China made at Chelsea is arrived to such Perfection, as to equal if not surpass the finest old Japan, allowed so by the most approved Judges here; and that the same is in so high Esteem of the Nobility, and the Demand so great, that a sufficient Quantity can hardly be made to answer the Call for it.' The factory, recently founded by the Huguenot silversmith Nicholas Sprimont, enjoyed the patronage of courtiers and aristocrats but went into decline when Sprimont's health failed. It was taken over by William Duesbury in 1769 and became an adjunct of the Derby factory before being closed down.

140

Undecorated

c.1747–9
PLATE 54
126mm (B512)
Incised mark: triangle
Prov: Caldwell (as an 'Easter Egg', 1923)

The metal mounts and chain are probably 18th-century. Another undecorated example is in the British Museum,[1] and an example painted with flowers and insects in enamel colours is in the Victoria and Albert Museum.[2] Following suggestions of a French source for this moulded design,[3] it was discovered on a Chantilly cream-jug.[4] Chelsea may also have derived from Chantilly or other French porcelain the use of tin oxide to whiten the glaze, which is evident on the present piece.

Sprimont may have been exploiting an existing English taste for the sensuous beauty of undecorated soft-pastes. The Duc de Luynes, writing of the Vincennes factory in 1749, commented: 'The English only want undecorated porcelain, but as they could add painted decoration, we sell them this undecorated porcelain at the same price as though it were painted.'[5]

Chelsea was able to keep abreast of developments in French and German porcelain thanks to its aristocratic patrons. In 1752 Lord Chesterfield, the leader of fashionable taste in London, wrote to thank the Marquise de Montconseil in Paris for some porcelain which is 'charming, perfect and will make our manufacture here blush. I showed it to the manager who was very struck with it and asked me as a favour to lend it to him for a few days in order to use it as a model, which I could not refuse him – particularly as I ordered two or three of the same for use . . .'[6].

[1] Mackenna 1948, no.6 pl.3.
[2] Op.cit. no.19 pl.8.
[3] Clarke 1959, p.49.
[4] Mallet 1965, p.16 and pl.24b; for other Chelsea pieces of the type see Austin 1977, p.41.
[5] Clarke 1959, p.47.
[6] Op.cit. p.48.

141

Painted in enamel colours

c.1750–2
COLOUR PLATE 11
118mm (B696)
Prov: Hignett sale, Sotheby's, 27 October 1932

This hexagonal pot[1] has a glaze whitened with tin oxide, and a flat base which is mostly unglazed and has three pad marks caused by the kiln supports. The painting imitates Chinese 'famille rose' enamels.

[1] Cf. Mackenna 1948, p.83, no.46 and pl.20; V&A 1948, no.212 pl.45.

142

Painted in enamel colours

c.1750–2
PLATE 55
99mm to rim (B601)
Cover missing

This octagonal pot has a blue-tinted glaze, and is of a shape often found with the raised anchor mark. A hexagonal teapot is decorated with a variant of this pattern, in which the turquoisey blue is replaced by deep green.[1] The pattern has been identified as the 'lady pattern' of the Chelsea 1755 sale catalogue[2] and the 'old japan lady pattern' of the 1756 catalogue.[3] The pattern is copied from Japanese porcelain, which had been extensively imported into Britain around 1700 but had become unobtainable after about 1720.[4] Patterns of Japanese origin were therefore described by the 1750s as 'old'. Lady Cavendish in 1756 lent a 'Japan Octogon cup and saucer lady pattern' to the Bow factory.[5] Bow duly produced its own version, an example of which is on a dish in the Victoria and Albert Museum.[6]

[1] Christie's London, 13 November 1972, lot 108; Sotheby's London, 6 June 1989, lot 366.
[2] 5th day lot 55: see facsimile in Austin 1977.
[3] 9th day lot 55: see reprint in Savage 1952.
[4] Mallett 1965, p.17 and pl.26a.
[5] Jewitt 1878, I, p.210.
[6] Mallett 1965, pl.26b.

143

Painted in enamel colours

*c.*1752–6
COLOUR PLATE 11
110mm (B160)
Prov: General Bulwer
Ref: Hodgson 1923, p.24 illus. 1e

The tip of the spout has subsequently been ground off, presumably because it was chipped. The base is flat and unglazed, with three pad marks caused by the kiln supports. The knob is made of four separately cut rows of petals. This shape is found having a cover without raised edges and with an open form of knob.[1]

[1] Mackenna 1951, no.31 pl.16; Sotheby's 10 March 1964, lot 84.

144

Painted in purple monochrome, but with the strawberry knob painted in its natural colours

c.1756–8
COLOUR PLATE 11
127mm (B567)
Prov: Bellamy Gardner

Chelsea began to include bone-ash in the body of their porcelain between about 1756 and 1758, and the similarity in body between this and the following example suggests that bone-ash may already be present. The use of purple monochrome was probably inspired by Meissen. At Wentworth Woodhouse is a receipted invoice from Sprimont dated 16 January 1754 which includes 'Six Nurled plates in purple'.[1]

[1] Cox and Cox 1980, p.202.

145

Painted in enamel colours, with a cell border in pink, purple and gilding

1758–65
COLOUR PLATE 11
124mm (M271)
Mark: anchor painted in gold

The tip of the knob is missing. In the late 1750s Chelsea developed a number of ground colours, mostly inspired by Sèvres porcelain. The spring advertisement of 1760 mentioned 'a few pieces of some new Colours which have been found this year by Mr Sprimont, the Proprietor, at a very large Expence, incredible Labour, and close Application, all highly finished, and heightened with the Gold peculiar to that fine and distinguished Manufactory . . .'. The elaborate forms of spout, knob and handle represent the swan-song of the rococo, which was soon to yield the high ground of fashion to the neoclassical taste. A particularly well-decorated example of this shape is in the National Gallery of Victoria, Melbourne.[1]

[1] Legge 1984, p.80 no.177.

Bow

The *Daily Advertiser* announced on 26 August 1748: 'BOW CHINA / GREAT Variety of useful and ornamental CHINA to be sold at Mr Mitchell's Toyshop, at the Dial and King's Arms in Cornhill, near the Royal Exchange.'

Bow was already described as a 'large Manufactory' soon after it was set up (see p.29). In 1755 the buildings were insured for £2,750 and the utensils and stock, including that in the warehouse in the City of London, for £5,900. The comparable figures for the Worcester factory two years later are £1,000 for buildings and £2,000 for utensils and stock.[1] In 1851 a box was discovered in a cupboard in the British Museum: it contained a bowl, and inside the lid was a statement dated 1790. It begins: 'This bowl was made at the Bow China Manufactory at Stratford-le-Bow, Essex, about the year 1760, and painted there by me, Thomas Craft . . .'. After narrating the history of the bowl and reflecting that it 'may meet with the same fate that the manufactory where it was made has done, and like the famous cities of Troy, Carthage, etc . . .', he tells us that the factory 'employed 300 persons; about 90 painters (of whom I was one), and about 200 turners, throwers, etc, were employed under one roof. The model of the building was taken from that of Canton in China . . .'.[2]

The factory styled itself 'New Canton' on a series of inkpots dated 1750 to 1752,[3] and the building was perhaps intended to resemble the East India Company's warehouse on the Canton waterfront. Nicholas Sprimont of Chelsea said that Bow differed from his own concern in making 'the more ordinary sort of wares for common uses'.[4]

[1] Adams and Redstone 1981, p.214.
[2] *Op.cit.* pp.45–6.
[3] *Op.cit.* p.106, p.122.
[4] 'The Case of the Undertaker of the Manufacture of Chelsea Ware', *c.*1752, quoted in Adams 1987, p.93.

146

Painted in enamel colours

*c.*1748–50
COLOUR PLATE 11
140mm (B701)
Prov: Sotheby's 2 November 1933, lot 190 (part)
Ref: Charleston 1965, p.100; *ECC* 1, 3, 1935, p.14 and pl.5a

The piece has the drab greyish-white appearance which has been identified as distinguishing some of the earliest products of the factory, made before the white pieces of 1750 which are the first dated Bow porcelains.[1] The enamelling, outlined in

pl.56
147
148

iron-red and black, is in turquoisey blue, a thick eggy yellow showing many burst bubbles, a leaf green which has misfired in places to olive, a thin and insubstantial attempt at white, and a distinctive maroon. This colouring connects the pot with triple-shell dishes of early type.[2] The unsucessful attempt at white enamel was probably inspired by Chinese porcelain.

When the present pot was shown at a Miscellany meeting of the English Ceramic Circle in 1933 (see Ref. in *ECC* above), opinion was divided as to its origin, with the late Jim Kiddell noting shrewdly that its spout was of Bow type. Another pot of the same shape, decorated with 'famille rose' enamels, was listed as Chelsea in error.[3]

[1] Tait 1963, p.214.
[2] *Op.cit.* pls.190 and 191; Adams and Redstone 1981, pl.C opp. p.64.
[3] *ECC* 6,2, 1966, pl.58a; compare also Sotheby's 7 March 1961, lot 160 and 10 March 1964, lot 98 for similar decoration.

147

Painted in underglaze blue

*c.*1750
PLATE 56
120mm (B655)

The pot is of an early type distinguished by having what appears to be a 'double glazing'.[1] A bubbly upper layer has pooled thickly in patches around the lower part of the body and the base. At the edges of the base, just inside the foot-rim, the upper layer has been removed by running a tool around, presumably to prevent thick glaze from running down in the kiln and sticking the pot to its support. (A glaze-free margin is best-known on Worcester porcelain, where it is normal from the late 1750s onwards.) Both here and where the patchy upper layer of glaze has failed to flow over the body, a thinner layer of glaze without bubbles is visible beneath. It is known that at Worcester the underglaze blue decoration was given a first 'hardening-on' firing before glazing, to avoid the blue from running in the glaze during the glost firing. It has been suggested that the first, thin layer of glaze on these early Bow wares was used to protect the painting during such a hardening-on firing, before the full glaze was applied.[2] The painting is in the bright royal blue typical of the earliest Bow blue and white.

[1] Watney 1973, p.15.
[2] Adams and Redstone 1981, p.100.

148

Painted in underglaze blue

*c.*1750
PLATE 56
125mm (B698)
Incised mark: a line

Another example of the 'double glazing' seen on the previous pot. Here the upper layer of glaze has flowed over the body more evenly and pooled and bubbled less. Interestingly, however, the upper layer has been removed with a tool from those parts of the pot where it was thought most likely to run and pool: in vertical lines down below the spout, down the body inside the handle, down below the handle; and around part of the edge of the base inside the foot-rim. The painting is in a slightly paler tone of bright blue than the previous pot. The cover is painted with the same pattern as the previous pot, and probably does not belong.

pl.57
149

149

Painted in underglaze blue, red enamel and gilding

*c.*1752–4
PLATE 57
129mm (73.207.976)
Painted mark in underglaze blue: '4'
Prov: bequeathed by Major Hitchin, 1976

In the 1720s Japanese porcelain had become difficult to obtain, and the Chinese began to produce a version of the decoration in underglaze blue, red enamel and gilding which was so popular with Japan's Western customers, and which is nowadays loosely termed 'Imari' after the Japanese port of export. The colour combination required the minimum possible number of firings for enamelled and gilt ware, and was at once flashy and economical to produce. It was made specifically for export to suit European taste. The design on this Bow pot seems to be following a Chinese rather than a Japanese model.[1] A more typical type of Chinese export porcelain decoration is the flower painting in 'famille rose' style found on a Bow pot of about 1752–4 (B143) and on a piece in the Freeman collection.[2]

[1] Klaber and Klaber 1978, no.40.
[2] Gabszewicz 1982, no.13.

150

Undecorated

*c.*1755
PLATE 54
110mm (B675)

Uncoloured porcelain decorated only with sprigging was inspired by the ware known in Europe as 'blanc-de-chine', made at Dehua in the Fukien province of China. At Bow it became something of a speciality for tearwares, showing off the creamy white glaze which seems to have been developed during 1750.

151

Transfer-printed in brick-red with, on the obverse, the 'Tea Party No.1',[1] on the reverse the 'Wheeling Chair', and on the cover the 'Bird on a String' and 'Lady with a Basket of Flowers'

*c.*1754–7
PLATE 11, p.25
88mm (B689)
Prov: Sotheby's 2 July 1931

It no longer seems necessary to suppose the presence of Hancock at Bow in order to account for the presence of his designs on the factory's ware. It is also likely that the 'smoky primitive' prints on Worcester porcelain pre-date the inception of transfer-printing at Bow. This pot, with its painted trefoil-loop border, belongs to the second classified group of Bow transfer-printed wares.[2]

[1] Cook 1948, no.104.
[2] Watney 1972A, p.218, type B.5, pls.160a,c and d, and 161b.

152

Transfer-printed in outline in dark brown with 'the Mating Chickens', painted over in puce, mauve, green, yellow and blue enamels

*c.*1760–5
PLATE 55
132mm (B656)
Prov: Sotheby's 13 July 1928, lot 14 (part)

The use of outline prints which could be cheaply coloured by hand was probably derived from Worcester. These are the fourth classified group of Bow transfer-printed wares.[1]

[1] Watney 1972A, p.222, type D.2 and pl.174b.

153

Painted in enamel colours

*c.*1760–5
COLOUR PLATE 11
133mm (B529)

The palette is characteristic and matches the previous pot. From the late 1750s Bow followed the lead of Chelsea and Worcester in introducing naturalistic flower-painting, inspired by Meissen ('deutsche blumen'), as opposed to the more stylised flowers derived from oriental porcelain ('indianische blumen'). A similar pot is in the Freeman collection.[1]

[1] Gabszewicz 1982, no.167.

Worcester

The Worcester factory was in production by 1752, having taken over the soapstone formula for soft-paste porcelain from Benjamin Lund's short-lived factory at Bristol. Worcester was the most successful British producer of porcelain teapots until the founding of the New Hall factory thirty years later (see p.33).

154

Painted in enamel colours

1752–5
COLOUR PLATE 13
116mm (B412)

This octagonal shape seems to have been used at Worcester earlier than the plain, thrown, globular shape (see no.157 below). The moulding forms a reserve divided into three compartments on either side of the pot. The moulding forming the divisions is different on the two sides, one having asymmetrical scrollwork and the other having paired leaves above a column-shaft. The enamelling on this pot imitates Chinese 'famille verte', in an unusual, early palette of both dark jade and bright apple green, turquoisey blue, greyish blue, iron-red, mauve and greenish yellow, with brown outlining. A similar pot is in the Victoria and Albert Museum.[1] An undated price card for the factory's London warehouse, probably produced not long after it opened in 1756, lists 'Tea pots, Fluted panneled and Octagon' at thirty shillings a dozen wholesale price.[2]

[1] Barrett 1953, pl.8B.
[2] Sandon 1969, p.8.

155

Painted in enamel colours

1752–5
COLOUR PLATE 13
112mm (B163)

The moulded shape matches the previous pot. The elongated Chinese figures and utensils are frequently seen in Worcester decoration of this period. A very similar pot is in the Marshall collection at the Ashmolean Museum, Oxford.[1] The figure on the reverse holds a fan.[2]

[1] V&A 1948, pl.80 no.366; Marshall 1954, pl.4 no.366.
[2] *Cf.* Spero 1984, p.38 no.30.

156

Painted in underglaze blue

1754–8
PLATE 58
126mm (B164)
Ref: Hodgson 1923, p.24 pl.I

The moulded shape matches the previous two pots, with the exception of the knob. The cover has a particularly deep flange, and can be matched not only on another teapot bearing an identical pattern, but also with a waster excavated on the factory site.[1] The pattern on the obverse is the 'Captive Bird'.[2]

[1] Sandon 1969, pl.10.
[2] Branyan, French and Sandon 1981, I.A.33.

157

Painted in underglaze blue

*c.*1753–5
PLATE 68
145mm to rim (B431)

The cover is missing. The pattern on the obverse is the so-called 'Man with a Lunchbox'.[1] The only other known example of this pattern is in the Godden Reference collection. Both sides of the present pot are illustrated in the standard work on Worcester blue and white patterns, the pattern on the reverse being the 'Crescent Moon'.[2]

[1] Branyan, French and Sandon 1981, I.A.24.
[2] *Op.cit.* I.B.4.

158

Painted in enamel colours

*c.*1755–8
COLOUR PLATE 13
132mm (B298)
Ref: Hodgson 1923, p.24 pl.I

The decoration is inspired by the naturalistic flower-painting at Meissen, known as 'deutsche blumen' to distinguish it from stylised flowers in imitation of oriental porcelain, 'indianische blumen'. A leaf-dish painted in similar style is at the Cecil Higgins Museum, Bedford.[1]

[1] Barrett 1953, pl.23A.

159

Painted in underglaze blue

*c.*1755–8
PLATE 60
116mm (B243)
Painted workman's mark
Prov: Mrs G. Eaton, Garboldisham; Mr G. Cubitt, Norwich

Globular teapots do not appear to have been made at Worcester before 1753 or 1754. The 'Prunus Root' pattern was popular at Worcester, being used through the first two decades of the factory's life, and also at Bow, Longton Hall and Lowestoft.[1] Two of the painted branches on the body continue on to the cover, but only when the cover is in one position. A third branch on the cover comes to the edge but leads nowhere!

[1] Branyan, French and Sandon 1981, 1.D.27; Watney 1973, pls. 18A, 41D and 83C respectively.

160

Painted in enamel colours

*c.*1756–60
COLOUR PLATE 14
158mm (B498)

The pattern on the obverse is the 'Beckoning Chinaman', which is also found on Liverpool porcelain from the Shaw's Brow factory of Philip Christian.[1] The pattern on the reverse is its usual accompaniment, a child with raised arms approaching a standing figure which holds an inverted fan. A pot of similar shape (B499) bears the same patterns painted on a smaller scale.

[1] Wills 1969, p.303 pl.44.

161

Painted in black enamel

*c.*1756–60
PLATE 59
116mm (B469)
Painted mark: cross within a circle
Prov: Boynton coll. no.408; Christie, 28 April 1920

The 'Boy on a Buffalo' pattern. A pencil in the 18th century meant a very fine brush consisting of only a few hairs, and decoration of this kind is known as pencilling. It was inspired by Chinese porcelain painted in monochrome, and a Chinese example is known with a very similar pattern.[1] The design occurs as an underglaze blue print on Bow and Derby porcelain.[2]

[1] Klaber and Klaber 1978, no.61A.
[2] Watney 1972A, pl.176a and b.

162

Painted in puce enamel

*c.*1756–60
COLOUR PLATE 13
130mm (B652)
Prov: Sotheby's 13 July 1928, lot 52

This pattern is found on a leaf-dish of 'Blind Earl' type.[1] It is also known on Derby porcelain.

[1] Barrett 1953, pl.31B.

pl.61
166

163

Painted in enamel colours

*c.*1756–60
COLOUR PLATE 13
120mm (B629)
Prov: Dr W.S. Hadley, Master of Pembroke College, Cambridge; given to Bulwer by his widow

The reverse is painted with two birds perched on a flowering prunus branch. A globular pot bearing both these patterns, except for the absence of the right-hand figure on the obverse, was formerly in the Selwyn Parkinson collection.[1]

[1] Albert Amor Ltd., *Exhibition of First Period Worcester Porcelain 1751–84*, 1973, no.26.

164

Painted in enamel colours and gilding

*c.*1760–65
PLATE 59
109mm (B321)
Ref: Hodgson 1923, p.27 pl.III

The painting picks out the details of the moulded relief decoration: that on the reverse is a flower spray. A very similar pot is in the Klepser collection.[1] An undecorated example of this moulded shape is B309.

[1] Spero 1984, p.47 no.39.

165

Painted in underglaze blue

*c.*1755–60
PLATE 60
123mm (B621)

The flutes on the body are modelled as though they were pleated. The painting in the reserves is the 'Fisherman and Willow Pavilion' pattern.[1] A very similar pot is B348.

[1] Branyan, French and Sandon 1981, I.B.21.

166

Transfer-printed in black enamel

*c.*1760
PLATE 61
119mm (B555)

The print of a cock, hen and chickens on the obverse is a different one from that usually encountered,[1] and is known on a Worcester saucer.[2] The reverse bears a print of a group of lapwings,[3] and these two prints are also found together on a Worcester mug.[4] The source of the designs is Pierce Tempest's engravings of 'Various Birds and Beasts Drawn from the Life by Francis Barlow.'

[1] Cook 1948, no.23.
[2] Capell 1953, p.167.
[3] Spero 1984, p.163 no.193.
[4] Capell 1962, p.163 fig.8.

167

Transfer-printed in black enamel

*c.*1760–5
PLATE 7, p.18
112mm (B408)
Signed in the print on the obverse at the bottom left corner: 'R. Hancock fecit'

The print on the obverse is the 'Tea Party No.3'.[1] The engraving is by Robert Hancock. The design was adapted from an indoor scene in an illustration to Warburton's *Works of Alexander Pope*, I, 1751, pl.3 facing page 131, illustrating 'The Rape of the Lock'.[2] The print on the reverse is the 'Maid and Page No.1',[3] showing the maid carrying a bread and butter plate and the page carrying a tea-kettle.

[1] Cook 1948, no.106.
[2] Watney 1966, pl.34 opp. p.410.
[3] Cook 1948, no.63.

168

Transfer-printed in black enamel

*c.*1760
PLATE 62
130mm (B703)
Signed in the print on the obverse at the bottom right corner with RH in monogram,
'Worcester' and an anchor

The print on the obverse is 'L'Amour',[1] that on the reverse the 'Minuet'.[2] Both prints are thought to have been engraved by Robert Hancock, although signed examples of the latter have not been recorded. 'L'Amour' derives from an engraving, probably by W. Eliott, after C.N. Cochin the Younger.[3] The 'Minuet' was re-used on page 118 of Robert Sayer's 1775 edition of *The Ladies Amusement*.

Richard and Josiah Holdship were principal partners in the Worcester factory, and the anchor is evidently a rebus for one of them. It has been debated whether the RH monogram was devised by Robert Hancock or Richard Holdship. Since Richard Holdship directed the production of printed ware after his removal to Derby in 1764, he must have been involved in this at Worcester. The initials RH occur on Bow and Battersea prints which must relate to Hancock rather than Holdship, and at Derby Holdship used the anchor but not the RH in monogram. It appears that in the use of this mark at Worcester there was a conflict of interest between Hancock and Holdship. The following verse is found in a poem 'On seeing an armed Bust of the King of Prussia curiously imprinted on a Porcelain Cup of the Worcester Manufacture . . .', which appeared in the *Gentleman's Magazine* for December 1757, giving Josiah Holdship the credit for its decoration:

> What praise, ingenious Holdship! is thy due,
> Who first on porcelain the fair portrait drew!
> Who first alone to full perfection brought,
> The curious art, by rival numbers sought!

The claim in the second line was toned down when the poem was reprinted in *Berrow's Worcester Journal* in January 1758:

> What praise is thine, ingenious Holdship! who
> on the fair porcelain, the portrait drew?
> To thee, who first, in thy judicious mind,
> A perfect model of the art designed;
> An art which, long by curious artists sought,
> By thee alone to great perfection's brought.

An extra couplet was also appended:

pl.62
168

> Hancock, my friend, don't grieve, tho Holdship has the praise,
> 'Tis yours to execute, 'Tis his to wear the bays.

Unfortunately little is known about the Holdships' role on the production side at the Worcester factory.

[1] Cook 1948, no.2 fig.1.
[2] *Op.cit.* no.75.
[3] Toppin 1948, pl.XCVII.

169

Painted in enamel colours

*c.*1760–5
COLOUR PLATE 13
136mm (B255)

On the obverse is a bearded man in a blue robe seated on a rock with a fishing rod planted upright, and a small boy in a red jacket offering a fish; on the reverse is the same small boy without the fish, which is now brandished by a woman dressed in puce and green on the left, while another woman dressed in blue and puce stands on the right. The pattern, including the colouring, copies a Chinese original.[1] In the Chinese version the small boy is approaching the seated man, but the Worcester painter has rearranged them so that they turn their backs on each other! A Chinese saucer with this pattern in the museum's collections omits the standing woman on the right. The Worcester version was copied at Christian's Liverpool factory, see no.198.

[1] Marshall 1957, p.38 no.49 and pl.4d; Klaber and Klaber 1978, no.28.

170

Painted in enamel colours and gilding

*c.*1765
PLATE 58
141mm (B347)
Ref: Hodgson 1923, p.24 pl.I

This pattern also has a Chinese counterpart, but in the Chinese version the divisions between the panels are in underglaze blue, as are the flowers in alternate panels.[1] In the Worcester version the divisions between the panels are in gold. Lowestoft's very similar version is known as the 'Jodrell' pattern.[2]

[1] Marshall 1957, p.27 no.13 and pl.4b; Klaber and Klaber 1978, no.18.
[2] Smith 1985, pp.40 and 55 no.8.

171

Painted in enamel colours and gilding

*c.*1770
PLATE 63
137mm (B654)
Prov: Sotheby's 13 July 1928, lot 53

The 'Black Quail' pattern. On the obverse is a second quail seated on a branch-like rock. The pattern is painted in black outlines, with the flowering plants picked out in green, puce, blue and yellow. The border is in iron-red and gold. Another teapot of the pattern shows both birds on the obverse.[1] This pattern is also derived from Chinese porcelain, including the colouring.[2] The present pot was probably decorated at the factory, but one version has been attributed to the London workshop of James Giles[3] (see no.175).

[1] Barrett 1953, pl.31A.
[2] Marshall 1957, p.27 no.12 and pl.4c; Klaber and Klaber 1978, no.22.
[3] Spero 1984, p.144 no.166.

pl.63

174	173
172	171

172

Painted in enamel colours and gilding

*c.*1770
PLATE 63
143mm (B285)
Ref: Hodgson 1923, p.33 pl.VI

The decoration on the obverse is the 'Staghunt' pattern and on the reverse, its usual complement, two figures conversing in a landscape, with a building to the left. The pattern is derived from Chinese porcelain, and it has been suggested that this version was painted in the London workshop of James Giles.[1] The pattern is also found on Liverpool and Lowestoft porcelain.

[1] McNeile 1990, pp.12–23 and no.22.

173

Painted in underglaze blue

*c.*1770–80
PLATE 63
130mm (B472)
Painted mark: open crescent.
Prov: C.H.B. Caldwell

The pattern is the 'Rock Strata Island'.[1] This painted pattern was also used at Caughley, and a printed pattern derived from it was used at Lowestoft.[2]

[1] Branyan, French and Sandon 1981, I.D.8.
[2] Howell 1970, p.216 and pl.186a.

174

Painted in underglaze blue

*c.*1770

PLATE 63
144mm (B49)
Painted mark: open crescent
Prov: General Bulwer
Ref: Hodgson 1923, p.30 pl.V; Branyan, French and Sandon 1981, I.A.16

The pattern is the very rare 'Arabesque Reserve', of which a biscuit fragment was found during an early excavation on the Worcester site (see Ref. to Branyan, *et al.*, above).

175

Painted in enamel colours and gilding, probably in the London workshop of James Giles

*c.*1770

COLOUR PLATE 14
156mm (B236)
Painted mark in underglaze blue: crossed swords and '9' followed by a dot
Ref: Hodgson 1923, p.27 pl.III

From December 1767 James Giles advertised his independent decorating establishment in Soho as the 'Worcester Porcelain Warehouse'. The following month he stated '. . . the Enamelling Branch is performed in London by the said J. Giles, and under his Inspection . . .'.[1] The Worcester proprietors responded with an advertisement stating that at the factory they had engaged the best painters from Chelsea, that orders would be executed in the highest taste and much cheaper than could be afforded by any painters in London.[2] By November 1768 Giles' advertisements no longer refer to him as 'the enamelling branch', perhaps as a result of pressure from the factory, although they continued to sell him glazed, undecorated porcelain at 15 per cent discount until 1771.[3] By this time they had probably decided that his superior enamelling and gilding were too dangerous a rival for their own ambitions at the smart end of the trade. Giles' business survived until 1776. See also the next entry.

This pattern is an attributed Giles one.[4] Mr Christie's sale of Giles' stock in 1774 included on the third day, 23 March, as lot 45, 'a complete set tea china in festoon flowers – 36 pieces', which was apparently sold for four pounds.[5] This Giles style of flower-painting has more freedom than much of the work done at the Worcester factory (see no.177 below), and the gilding which extends most of the way down the handle in graduated dots is also a feature of Giles' products.

[1] Coke 1983, p.106.
[2] *Op.cit.* no.5.
[3] Valpy 1985, pp.180–1.
[4] Coke 1983, Appendix H, A.1.30; Marshall 1954, pl.16 no.291.
[5] Coke 1983, p.134.

176

Chinese porcelain, with stand, painted in enamel colours, probably in the London workshop of James Giles

*c.*1772–6

COLOUR PLATE 14
133mm (B7)

When his special arrangement with the Worcester factory ended, so did Giles' discount. A note in his ledger against a purchase on 27 July 1772 states 'from this date no disc: allowed on white'. The increased price of white porcelain was a financial handicap which probably contributed to the failure of Giles' business.[1] After March 1773 he began to fall behind with his bills,[2] and three years later the business failed. It was probably in a desperate attempt to reduce his costs that he bought poorer quality porcelain and seconds for decorating.[3] The present pot, with its bumpy and unevenly made handle, contrasts strangely with the accomplished painting of exotic birds. The latter are typical of Giles' workshop, including the cheese-like yellow rocks on which some of them stand.[4]

[1] *ECC* 6,3, 1967, p.297.
[2] Coke 1983, p.22.
[3] *Op.cit.* pp.64–6.
[4] *Op.cit.* p.100.

177

Painted with green borders and other enamel colours and gilding

*c.*1770
COLOUR PLATE 14
172mm (B490)
Painted mark in underglaze blue: crossed swords and '9' followed by a dot

The tight style of flower-painting, for example the use of concentric circular patterns to decorate frontally placed blooms, is distinctive of work done at the Worcester factory rather than at Giles' workshop. The pattern is known as 'The Marchioness of Huntley' after the provenance of a service sold in the 19th century, but there were evidently numerous services of this pattern.

pl.64

180	184
181	178

178

Painted in blue enamel

c.1770
PLATE 64
144mm (B536)

This form of monochrome painting is known from its appearance as 'dry blue'. The style of this example indicates that it is the work of the factory rather than of Giles' workshop.

179

Painted in enamel colours

c.1770
COLOUR PLATE 14
128mm (B61)
Prov: General Bulwer

The pattern, known as the 'Spinning Maiden', was copied from an engraving in the second volume of Du Halde's *Description de la Chine*, 1736, p.717.[1] This book was an important early source of information for Europeans about Chinese porcelain manufacture. There is an earlier pattern with the same name.[2] The knob on the cover of the present pot is modern.

[1] Watney 1966, p.406 and pl.14.
[2] Spero 1984, p.80 no.83.

180

Printed in black outline and painted in enamel colours and gilding

c.1770
PLATE 64
143mm (B235)

The 'paint over print' type of decoration, which Worcester was the first to use in the mid 1750s, was not fully exploited until the end of the century. At a period when printing could conveniently be done only in a single colour, multi-coloured decoration was necessarily painted (apart from a small group of printed porcelain now thought to be from the Vauxhall factory).[1] An outline print coloured in by hand would look as smart to many purchasers as freehand painting, but enabled cheap, unskilled labour – probably young girls – to be used for the colouring, and costs could be kept down.

[1] Neild 1935, p.71; Watney 1960, p.43; Watney 1989, p.212.

181

Printed in underglaze blue

c.1775–85
PLATE 64
142mm (B51)
Printed mark: hatched crescent

The 'Fence' pattern[1] was the most popular Worcester pattern in the late 1770s, as excavations on the factory site have confirmed.[2] Its popularity caused it to be copied by Caughley,[3] Derby[4] and Lowestoft.[5] A Lowestoft example in the museum's collection even includes a painted version of the Worcester hatched crescent mark.[6] A copy of the pattern in pearlware, which includes the 'C' mark of the Caughley porcelain factory, is no.134.

[1] Branyan, French and Sandon 1981, II.B.9.   [4] Watney 1973, pl.67C.
[2] Sandon 1981, p.3.   [5] *Op.cit.* pl.85C.
[3] Godden 1969, pl.262A.   [6] Smith 1975, p.213 no.561.

pl.65
187   189
190   186

Derby

A porcelain factory was founded in Derby about 1750, apparently by Andrew Planché, but few teapots seem to have been made until William Duesbury became a principal partner in 1756. As the self-styled 'New Dresden', they laid more emphasis on decorative than useful wares, and their porcelain body was still not very practical for teapots even in the 1780s (see p.28).

182

Painted in enamel colours and gilding

about 1756
COLOUR PLATE 12
140mm (B677)
Prov: Mrs Manning-Lee coll.
Ref: Bradley 1978, no.47

A pot of the same shape and pattern but lacking its cover is in the Cecil Higgins Museum, Bedford, and bears the incised date 1756 on the base.[1] The reverse shows a man, flanked by vases and other objects, reaching up towards a butterfly. This is the earliest identified Duesbury Derby teapot shape, with a moulded shell or leaf at the tip, and a distinctive handle with curled upper and lower terminals, found also on jugs, mugs and coffee-pots.

[1] Bradley 1978, no.48.

183

Painted in enamel colours

about 1756–8
COLOUR PLATE 12
134mm (B284)
Prov: Lt. Col. Hopton Bassett Scott coll.; Christie's 29–30 November 1916
Ref: Hodgson 1923, p.24 pl.I; Barrett and Thorpe 1971, pl.35; Bradley 1978, no.50

A ribbed version of the same shape. A very similar example is known with a more pointed knob.[1] The flower-painting is in the so-called 'cotton-stem' style, following the naturalistic 'deutsche blumen', of Meissen rather than the stylised 'indianische blumen', which imitated oriental porcelain. The sales of Derby porcelain in 1756–8 referred to such pieces as 'finely enamelled in Dresden flowers'.[2]

[1] Rice 1983, pl.Jb.
[2] Barrett and Thorpe 1971, pp.20 and 22.

184

Painted in enamel colours and gilding

c.1760–5
PLATE 64
129mm (B592)

The shape of handle, keeled on the upper and lower faces, is also known on coffee-pots. The vent hole beneath the lower terminal is a feature of Derby porcelain at this period. The pattern on the obverse is found on a coffee-pot in Derby Museum and Art Gallery,[1] and is also known on Derby creamware from the Cockpit Hill factory.[2] The pattern on the reverse is a seated man with a parasol, squatting with legs apart in an uncomfortable-looking position.[3]

[1] Bradley 1978, no.61.
[2] Walton 1976, p.192 no.777.
[3] *Cf.* Bradley 1978, no.62.

185

Painted in pink enamel and gilding

c.1775
COLOUR PLATE 12
109mm (91.139.938)
Prov: bequeathed by Susanna Taylor, 1938

The 'wishbone' handle imitates a Meissen shape, of which an example is M268. The painting in different tones of the same colour ('en camaieu') is in the style attributed to Richard Askew, who painted for Chelsea and went to Derby in 1772. He returned to London in 1780 and worked freelance as a 'miniature enamel portrait painter'. After a spell in Dublin he moved to Birmingham, and a bill of July 1794 shows him working by the day for Derby. Work of this quality was time consuming and very expensive: for painting '2 coffe cans, with cupeds, tow Days & a half' his charge was 13s 1d. A month later he signed an agreement to work for the factory by the piece. He undertook to paint 'in quantity and effect equal to the Cupids on Two Flower Pots by James Banford having Richard Askew's name written upon them (to prevent a mistake in alluding to them)'.[1] This is a reminder that while individual artists specialised in particular types of subject, they were often quite capable of painting in another artist's style. Caution is therefore necessary about making definite attributions on the basis of style alone! Askew died at Bilston, Staffordshire, in 1798.

[1] Barret and Thorpe 1971, p.72.

pl.66

194	196
191	192

186

Painted in enamel colours and gilding

*c.*1770–80
PLATE 65
142mm (B665)
Painted mark in gold: anchor and D combined

The border is salmon-pink. The handle is of a different wishbone shape from the previous pot, and has a divided upper terminal. Another pot of this shape is M267.

187

With quadrilobed stand. Painted in enamel colours and gilding

*c.*1775–82
PLATE 65
132mm (B227)
Painted mark in gold (on pot only): anchor and D combined

The shape is adapted from Sevres and marks the arrival of neoclassicism in British porcelain. The sphinx knob proclaims its classical aspirations, backed up by the wreath around the spout and the rope of overlapping husks which hangs down the body inside the handle. The borders and the hollows of the gadroons are picked out in 'Smith's blue' enamel, a favourite Derby colour at this period, inspired by the Sevres 'bleu de roi'. A pot decorated with the initials 'MB' (B484) is in a plain version of the shape, without the gadrooning.[1]

[1] Bradley 1978, p.146 no.232.

188

With quadrilobed stand. Painted in enamel colours and gilding

1770–82
COLOUR PLATE 12
159mm (B680)
Prov: J.H. Taylor coll.; Sotheby's 12 November 1930
Ref: Bradley 1978, p.146 no.231

The borders are in turquoise enamel and gilding. The spiral flutes contain in each hollow a moulded acanthus leaf which follows the line of the fluting. They grow upwards on the body and downwards on the cover. This idea was imitated on the porcelain of Neale & Co. (see nos.345 and 346).

189

Painted in enamel colours and gilding

1773–82
PLATE 65
123mm (B390)
Painted mark in blue enamel: crown over D
Prov: Col. Parker coll., Grantham

The collection also includes two pots of this quadrilobed shape decorated with borders in 'Smith's blue' enamel, B221 and B148.[1]

[1] *Cf.* Twitchett 1980, p.141 pl.155.

190

Painted in green enamel with red spots, black outlining and gilding

*c.*1770–80
PLATE 65
140mm (M275)

The cylindrical shape is unusual in Derby porcelain at this date, and shows a neoclassical purity of form despite the older fashion of the intertwined double strap handle.

191

Printed in underglaze blue, possibly Derbyshire

*c.*1775–80
PLATE 66
149mm (B415)
Prov: Lord Carnarvon's sale, Bretby Park, Derbyshire, 1918
Ref: Bradley 1978, p.298 no.457

The surface on the obverse is a mass of black specks, and all over the pot there are numerous blisters, two of which have burst leaving unglazed craters. The printed pattern is also known on saucers which have similar firing faults (see Ref.). The shape and the very translucent white paste suggest a Derby connection. Bulwer at first identified the pot as from the mysterious factory at Church Gresley, on the grounds that Lord Chesterfield, who formerly owned Bretby, was interested in the factory and was a friend of the Gresleys of Drakelowe. The factory was certainly making pottery in about the 1790s,[1] but the present pot appears too early for the factory's recorded dates of operation. After the closure in 1779 of the Cockpit Hill factory in Derby, the stock in trade advertised for sale included an assortment of enamelled and blue and white useful china,[2] and Philip Gell's Wirksworth factory was producing porcelain between 1772 and 1777.[3]

[1] *NCSN* 78, 1990, p.40.
[2] Bradley 1978, p.234.
[3] *Op.cit.* pp.230–2; Lockett 1972–3, pp.45–57; Brown and Cox 1984, pp.33–51.

Liverpool: Shaw's Brow

Richard Chaffers began porcelain production about 1755, and at his death in 1765 his partner Philip Christian continued the works. After the first couple of years, Chaffers' porcelain was of soapstone type modelled on that of Worcester (see p.34).

192

Printed in black enamel with, on the obverse the 'Tea Party', and on the reverse the 'Shepherd Boy', Chaffers

*c.*1760–5
PLATE 66
138mm (B212)

The printing was done in Liverpool by Sadler and Green and is in their distinctive brownish black. They also printed Liverpool delftware tiles and Wedgwood's cream-ware (B355) with both these prints. A very similar print is found on a creamware pot which is not of Wedgwood's manufacture (B493). The Tea Party print differs from the most similar of the several versions used at Worcester.[1] The cover of the present pot is probably not the original, and may be of Worcester origin.

[1] Cook 1948, no.104.

193

Painted in enamel colours, Chaffers

*c.*1760–5
COLOUR PLATE 15
138mm (B214)

The pattern imitates a 'famille rose' one on Chinese porcelain.[1] The white enamel, used on the stork and the leaf above him, has misfired, crawling and shrinking in the heat of the muffle-kiln. The Chinese use of white on white porcelain evidently appealed to Chaffers' painters, who would have been familiar with its use on Liverpool delftware pottery. This pattern is recorded on a bowl.[2]

[1] Marshall 1957, pl.IVa.
[2] Boney 1957, pl.13f.

194

Painted in enamel colours and gilding, Chaffers

*c.*1760–5
PLATE 66
121mm (B693)

The footring is shallow on the inside and the base is slightly dished. Because the glaze on the base has pooled thickly, it is heavily pitted from escaping gas bubbles. The painting, in imitation of Chinese 'famille rose', includes blossoms in white enamel, which has misfired. This enamel is thin, unlike the thick white on the previous pot. The gilding, on the knob, the borders and the body of the bird, is thin and has mostly come off.

195

Painted in enamel colours and gilding, Chaffers or Christian

*c.*1765
COLOUR PLATE 15 and back cover
120mm (B640)

The potting characteristics and the gilding are very similar to the previous piece. On one side the shoulder has sagged in the kiln during firing. The painting shows a cockfight between two very inoffensive-looking birds placed on either side of the lower handle terminal (see the illustration on the back cover). Cockfights seem to have been a popular decoration at the Shaw's Brow factory:[1] a letter of 1854 states that Chaffers produced for Lord Strange punchbowls 'blazed with representations of the gallant battles of the spurred favourites of the noble lord'.[2] A bowl in the museum's collections, painted in the same attractive style, is of similar date and shows Chinese figures with another lively bird, this time a vain but stupid-looking peacock.

[1] Boney 1957, pl.1b.
[2] *Op.cit.* p.198.

196

Probably Christian, painted in underglaze blue

*c.*1765
PLATE 66
141mm (B377)

The pleated moulding follows a Worcester design (see no.165) and is also recorded on coffee-pots.[1] The painting with its masses of dots is typical of Chaffers and Christian, and the glaze has crawled where the cobalt blue has been thickly applied. There is no footrim, the base being slightly dished and partly covered with patches of glaze.

[1] Boney 1957, pl.15b.

197

Painted with enamel colours and gilding, Christian

*c.*1770
COLOUR PLATE 15
148mm (B275)
Painted mark in grey enamel: cross
Prov: Trapnell coll. no.408[1]
Ref: Hodgson 1923, p.29 pl.IV

The attractive colouring is predominantly in reddish-brown, grey and brownish-mauve, with small touches of yellow, green and blue. On both sides of the pot the unlikely creature towards which the boy gestures looks as though it has stepped out of Edward Lear's Nonsense Verse!

[1] Oxford 1912, p.48 and pl.37.

198

Painted in underglaze blue and enamel colours, Christian

*c.*1770
PLATE 67
138mm (B292)

The pattern on the obverse is a version of one found on Worcester and derived from Chinese porcelain (see no.169). In the Liverpool version the seated man has taken his hat off. It follows the Worcester copy rather than the Chinese original, because the man sits facing the handle, with his back turned to the other figure. The design has

pl.67

198   201
209   202

been further altered, in that the second figure holding the fish is no longer the little boy, but is now the standing woman from the reverse side of the Worcester pot. The reverse of the Liverpool pot is painted with three Chinese figures accompanying a red bull. The same two patterns on this piece are recorded on a bowl.[1]

[1] Boney 1957, pl.19b.

199

Painted in enamel colours, Christian

*c.*1770
COLOUR PLATE 15
171mm (B326)

The flower-painting, in rather dry, pale colours compared to Worcester, is typical of Christian's ware, and is also found on a coffee-pot in the museum's collections.

200

Painted in underglaze blue, enamel colours and gilding, Christian

*c.*1770
COLOUR PLATE 15
139mm (B663)
Prov: Sotheby's, 19 April 1929

An interesting but not very successful attempt to produce a 'gros bleu' or 'mazarine' blue ground like Worcester. The brush-strokes are only too visible, giving a typically streaky effect. The thin gilding around the edges of the reserved panels is typical of the factory.

Liverpool: The Penningtons

John Pennington is thought to have set up his business as an independent manufacturer of porcelain at Copperas Hill in about 1769, moving to Folly Lane in 1779. Upon his death in 1786, his widow Jane continued the business until 1794.[1] John's brother Seth Pennington took over the Shaw's Brow factory of Philip Christian in 1778.[2] Both brothers produced bone-ash porcelain, but John's products have only recently begun to be differentiated from those of Seth,[1] and most of their wares cannot yet be distinguished.

[1] Hillis 1987, pp.1–21.
[2] Hillis 1984, pp.29–35.

201

Painted in underglaze blue

c.1770–80
PLATE 67
76mm to rim (1734)
Cover missing

A pot of most unusual shape. The neat potting, pale straw translucency, glossy glaze and dark greyish tone of blue suggest a relatively early date in the Pennington output. The contrast between neat potting and sloppy underglaze painting is still more marked on a covered sugar dish in the museum's collections.

202

Painted in enamel colours, probably Seth Pennington

c.1780–90
PLATE 67
196mm (B286)
Ref: Hodgson 1923, p.25 pl.II

A Christian's example of this moulded shape, with reserves created by a row of arching-over palm trees, is M321. It is therefore likely that the moulds for it were acquired by Seth Pennington along with the Shaw's Brow factory. The moulded shape of the cover is correct for the pot, but the pattern is incorrect, and it has evidently come from another pot of the same shape.

Limehouse

The excavations on the site of the Limehouse porcelain factory in East London, and the resulting identification of its surviving products in collections, are one of the most exciting recent ceramic events. For over half a century collectors had been trying to identify the products of this short-lived factory (1746–8). When in 1959 the wares now thought[1] to be Limehouse were first identified as a group of common origin, the wish was expressed that they might turn out to be Limehouse, but the idea seemed almost too good to be true, and at that time a possible attribution to William Reid at Liverpool was mooted.

[1] Watney 1990, p.123.

203

Possibly Limehouse. Painted in underglaze blue, enamel colours and gilding

1747–8
COLOUR PLATE 12
119mm (B419)

The heavy potting, greyish-blue glaze and poor translucency are typical of much porcelain formerly attributed to Reid, as is the acorn knob.[1] (See no.206.) The broad blue leaves painted either side of the spout and handle are also typical. The enamel colours were probably added to conceal as much as possible of the badly run underglaze blue. They include pink painted over white, a device regularly used on porcelain of this group to imitate Chinese 'famille rose' enamels.

[1] Watney 1959, pp.15–16 and pl.8b.

Vauxhall

The excavations on the site of Nicholas Crisp and John Sanders' Vauxhall porcelain factory (1753–64) and the identification of their wares in collections have created another recent stir in the ceramics world. These wares had until recently been attributed very tentatively to William Ball in Liverpool.

204

Painted in underglaze blue, red enamel and gilding

1753–64
COLOUR PLATE 12
111mm (B386)

This pattern of a man on a bridge was one of the most popular multi-coloured patterns used on porcelain of this group. Pots of similar shape and bearing this pattern have a variety of slightly different rococo handles,[1] and one example bears the date 1764.[2] The Longton Hall factory's figure of Hercules and the Lion has a separate stand painted with a similar man on a bridge.[3] It has been suggested that Nicholas Crisp may have bought undecorated figures at the London sale following the closure of the Longton Hall factory in 1760, and had them decorated by painters from Vauxhall.[4] Another pot of this group, M152, has a plain loop handle with projecting thumb-rest, and is painted with another popular multi-coloured pattern, a bird on a branch in the same colours as the present pot.

[1] Watney 1960, pl.32f.
[2] *Connoisseur*, vol.XX no.77, January 1908, pp.62–3.
[3] Watney 1957, pl.39A.
[4] Watney 1989, p.220.

Longton Hall

The factory run by William Littler at Longton Hall in Staffordshire (1751–60) seems to have been doomed by the choice of a glassy porcelain body, which was impractical for making tewares.

205

Undecorated

*c.*1755
PLATE 68
195mm (B526)
Prov: J. Hawkins coll.
Ref: Bemrose 1926, p.11; Watney 1955

This massive pot was probably intended for punch in view of its size and its moulded vine decoration. It has a strainer. Probably the modeller of the grapes and free-standing stems was used to doing the similar 'vineing' on Staffordshire earthenware (see no.39). There is no footrim, but the base is slightly dished and mostly unglazed. It shows seven stilt marks caused by the supports in the kiln. The pot was so heavy that the stilts of fireclay pushed into the porcelain, and after firing they evidently had to be broken off, leaving their tips embedded in the porcelain. Wares with vegetable moulding were something of a speciality at Longton Hall,[1] and an advertisement Littler placed in *Aris's Birmingham Gazette* on 20 June 1757 mentions '. . . variety of curious useful Ornaments for Deserts, with Figures and Flowers of all Sorts, made exactly to Nature, allowed by the best Judges to be the finest in England . . .'.

[1] Watney 1957, pl.33. A pot apparently matching the present example was in the Sharp coll., sold at Sotheby's on 10 March 1964, lot 102.

206

Painted in enamel colours

*c.*1755–60
PLATE 68
130mm (B560)
Ref: Watney February 1955, fig.14b

Under the footrim are four spur marks caused by the kiln supports. Glaze ran down over the tips of the fireclay spurs in firing, sticking them to the pot. When the spurs were broken away, parts of the tips were left attached. These scars make the pot stand unevenly, but nothing was done to grind them level.

This barrel shape, derived from Meissen, was a standard one at Longton Hall during the middle and later part of the factory's existence.[1] The acorn knob harks back to Limehouse (see no.203 above) and also to the wasters excavated on the site of Steers' unsuccessful venture at Newcastle-under-Lyme not far from Longton Hall (see p.32).[2] The rather perfunctory 'famille rose' enamelling, in pink and green with black outlining, was often used in the factory's last years, probably in a desperate attempt to reach a wider market with a cheaper product. A pot of the same shape painted in underglaze blue is M131.

[1] Watney 1957, pl.72A.
[2] Bemrose 1973, pl.10a.

West Pans

After the failure of Longton Hall, Littler moved to Scotland and set up a factory at West Pans near Musselburgh (*c.*1764–77). Here the problems with his glassy body were compounded by problems with inexperienced local staff and with the preparation of materials.

207

Painted in underglaze blue and gilding

1764–77
PLATE 68
172mm (B651)
Prov: Cotton family, Madingley; Sir George Humphrey, Cambridge; Spearing coll.; Sotheby's, 13 July 1928
Ref: Watney, February 1955, fig.2

The shape with moulded reserves is derived from Longton Hall[1] but the very dirty paste and badly run underglaze blue proclaim it as a product of West Pans. The lightly fired gilding has rubbed away except in the hollows. Most of Littler's advertisements for West Pans, including the one for the opening of his warehouse in Edinburgh in 1766, mention 'fine Mazarine blue and gold china'.[2] The blue was used as a ground colour because it usually ran too much in the glost kiln to be used for painting designs.

[1] Watney 1957, pl.15.
[2] Bimson, Ainslie and Watney 1966, p.171.

'Caddy Class'

Simeon Shaw recorded in his *History of the Staffordshire Potteries* in 1829 that William Littler was manager of a porcelain manufactory in Shelton, for Messrs Baddeley and Fletcher. Ralph Baddeley's partnership with Thomas Fletcher ended in 1775, when Littler was still at West Pans, but Shaw's statement is likely to have a kernel of truth, for a tea canister in Stoke-on-Trent Museum has an ancient label and once had an accompanying note by Enoch Wood which relate a distinctive class of porcelain of about 1780 to Littler. The legible portions of the label read: '1758 . . . William Littler of Longton in the Parish of Stoke-upon-Trent, I well remember his living at Stoke. There once more tried to make china but did not succeed better. This was before Cornish Clay and Stone was used . . . potters . . . E.W.' The note, recorded by Jewitt in 1878, read: 'This was given to E. Wood by William Fletcher in January 1809. He informs me he remembers it being made by Mr Littler at Longton near Stoke, about 55 years ago – say in the year 1754. It has never been out of his possession during that time and is highly valued . . .'. Despite the confusion with Longton Hall, including the dates, there is a definite link between Longton Hall porcelain and wares like the Stoke tea canister, the 'caddy class' as they have been called. The two groups have pastes which are chemically very similar, including an unusually high lead content.

208

Painted in enamel colours

*c.*1777–84
COLOUR PLATE 15
141mm (B unnumbered)

The glaze is extensively pitted and has pooled thickly on parts of the base while leaving the rest uncovered. The so-called 'scum line', where the glaze stops just above the foot is a familiar feature of this group. The Chinese figures waving strings are similar to those on the Stoke tea canister (see above). The tall figure bent over to fit into the shape is distinctive of this class.

209

Painted in enamel colours

*c.*1777–84
PLATE 67
156mm (M324)
Ref: Godden 1983, p.41 pl.54

The glaze characteristics are very similar to the previous pot. The upper part of the body has vertical alternating ribs and flutes which die away as the body swells outwards. Another globular pot of this class, B465, has a kicked handle matching a mug in the Godden reference collection,[1] and decoration including a pinkish-white enamel noted on other pieces of this class.[2]

[1] Godden 1983, p.41 pl.53.
[2] *Op.cit.* p.39 pl.49.

Plymouth

For Cookworthy's ventures into the production of hard-paste porcelain at Plymouth and Bristol see p.33.

210

Painted in enamel colours and gilding

1768–70
PLATE 69
167mm (M311)
Painted mark in red enamel: alchemical sign for tin[1]

The body shows some spiral wreathing, caused by the lack of plasticity in the porcelain paste, which made it difficult to throw. The pattern is the 'Dragon in Compartments', as it was called at Chamberlain's Worcester factory, one of the many which employed it.

[1] Godden 1964, no.3071.

Bristol

211

Painted in enamel colours and gilding

1770–80
PLATE 69
163mm (B141)
Painted mark in blue enamel: cross
Prov: Trapnell coll. no.128; Christie's 22 May 1913
Ref: Oxford 1912, p.15 and pl.3; Hodgson 1923, p.29 pl.IV

The base has warped in the kiln and the pot does not stand evenly. As with many Bristol teapots, the spout and handle seem to have been attached to the pot without any thought of their relationship with each other. They were clearly designed to match, however, because they both have similar crabstock moulding.

212

Painted in enamel colours

1770–80
PLATE 69
138mm (B230)
Painted mark in blue enamel: 10 over cross
Prov: Trapnell coll. no.110; Christie's, 22 May 1913
Ref: Oxford 1912, p.13

The moulded form of spout is also found on two other pots (M313 and M363) accompanying an elaborate handle which was copied at New Hall.[1]

[1] Miller and Berthoud 1985, pl.362.

213

Painted in underglaze blue

1770–80
PLATE 69
109mm (B429)
Prov: Broderip coll.

The body shows spiral wreathing. The cover is not original to the pot, but is a contemporary Bristol example, painted with a Chinese garden scene and a lattice border. Not much underglaze blue seems to have been done at Bristol, no doubt because it would not easily stand the high temperature at which the glaze was fired. The smoky greyish colour of the blue on this pot is typical.

6

Pottery Goes Classical

By about 1765 the fashion for interior decoration in the neoclassical taste was firmly established. 'Athenian' Stuart, the Adam brothers and William Chambers were replacing rococo scrollwork with copied – or more often cleverly adapted – Greek and Roman ornament. As the bands of chaste classical bas-reliefs in fashionable matt, or 'dead', colours spread themselves over cornices and furniture, it became evident that unglazed or 'dry-bodied' stoneware pottery, with its crisp relief decoration, offered an ideal vehicle for the style. The unglazed stonewares currently in production were the redwares, with their chinoiserie or rococo reliefs (see p.57). It is an appropriate irony that to Josiah Wedgwood in later life these 'red teapots' came to represent everything common and 'pot-like' which he wanted his own products to avoid.

The invention of Sheffield Plate had far-reaching effects on the design of teapots in pottery and porcelain. For the first time it was possible by 1760 to buy durable vessels which looked like silver but were only plated with a thin layer of the metal and were very much cheaper than their solid silver equivalents. The silver trade had to compete by cutting the costs of its most expensive item, the amount of precious metal in an object of given size. Sheffield plate consisted of silver fused on to copper. It could only be manufactured in sheets, and this required the use of powerful rollers. The silversmiths adopted this technology to roll their own metal thinner and make it go further. The spherical or globular shape of a traditional teapot is much more awkward to make out of sheet metal than various box shapes with angles at the corners. By the 1780s these were the shapes in which silver teapots were made.

It is one of those coincidences of history that this was just the time when the neoclassical taste was making the traditional globular shape for teapots look unfashionable. It must have seemed not at all classical and rather dumpy. The technically convenient box shapes of the silversmiths were treated as classical plinths and decorated with architectural details. Just because the Greeks and Romans had not had teapots did not prevent designers from coming up with modern classical ones. The potters copied the silver shapes as they usually did.

The preponderance of the Wedgwood archives among surviving documentary evidence has led to an assumption that Wedgwood, and no other manufacturer, invented each new type of dry-bodied stoneware: black basalt, caneware, jasper. Attempts to credit other manufacturers with being first in the field – Humphrey Palmer with basalt, for example – are doomed from the outset by the lack of documentary evidence for other manufacturers. They do, however, draw attention to the length of time required for the development of a new type of ware, the close-knit nature of the Staffordshire industry, the mobility of the workforce, and the rapid spread of information despite the best efforts of some master potters to preserve secrecy. This situation, a melting pot of ceramic ideas, should encourage caution in giving sole credit to any one manufacturer.

Wedgwood gave his new factory the classical name 'Etruria', because it was then thought that the ancient vases being unearthed in Italy were Etruscan, not Greek as we now know them to be. The 'Etruscan' vases which Wedgwood threw on the first working day at Etruria in 1769 are of the black stoneware nowadays commonly called basalt. It was Wedgwood who coined the name 'basaltes' for this ware, suggesting its resemblance to the hard black stone which was valued as a material for sculpture. A reference to 'Etruscan' teapots in 1768 suggests that he was already making them in basalt. In 1770 Wedgwood suggested buying a teapot from James Neale's shop in London as evidence that Humphrey Palmer was infringing his patent for painting in 'encaustic' colours. Like Wedgwood's own encaustic painted wares, this was presumably basalt. Production of basalt teaware was not yet widespread, however, for two years later Wedgwood noted that Palmer was the only other potter making black teapots.[1] From the 1780s onwards, when many potters were making the ware, it was generally known as 'Egyptian black'. Wedgwood prophesied in 1774: 'The Black is sterling, and will last for ever.' His explanation of its success, 'I hope white hands will remain in fashion, and then we may continue to make black teapots',[2] is only half in jest.

Wedgwood apparently had cane-coloured stoneware teapots of an experimental kind on sale as early as 1771.[3] In 1776 he noted: 'I am glad the Bamboo Teapots are likely to sell . . . I thought the light-coloured ones too yellow, and am preparing to make them equally pale colored, but not of such a yellow Calf Turd tint.' His principal problem with the caneware body was that it was easily stained by tea, and he therefore tried to 'make the body closer' to prevent this. He wanted to avoid glazing the interiors of the pots, because of his experience with basalt. As he wrote in 1772: 'All Teapots, or other pots, with a body of a Porcelain Texture and Glazed on the inside only will be very liable to break with hot water. Common red china ones do the same. I believe we had therefore better not to glaze them . . .'. By the time he issued his 1787 catalogue, these problems had been overcome. William Greatbatch was producing caneware of advanced design before his bankruptcy in 1782.[4] Enoch and Ralph Wood were already manufacturing caneware by 1784, and John Turner advertised his own version in January 1785. Humphrey Palmer's successor James Neale, whose factory was run by Robert Wilson, may have been equally well advanced.

Jasper was the ware which Wedgwood regarded as his greatest achievement, and which is still synonymous with his name and his firm in the mind of the general public. His experiments were well advanced in 1774, but it was not until three years later that he was able to report to his partner Bentley: '. . . I am now ABSOLUTE in this precious article and we can make it with as much facility, and certainty as black ware. We have now only to push it forward into the world – keep our secret, &c &c.' By whatever mixture of native wit and industrial espionage, jasper did not remain a secret for long. In the 1780s both Neale & Co. and Turner were making versions of it, to be joined perhaps not long afterwards by Adams.

White feldspathic stoneware appears to have been developed by the Turners in the 1780s, although Simeon Shaw in the early 19th century thought that a version introduced by Chetham and Woolley about 1795 marked an important change. This body was often covered with a light smear of glaze achieved by washing the saggars, in which the pots were fired, with a lead glaze. The heat of the kiln caused the glaze to volatilise and a thin layer to be deposited on the pots. This 'smear-glazing' was soon applied to many other stoneware bodies, varying in thickness from an obtrusively glittery coat to the merest hint of a sheen, sometimes spread quite unevenly over the pot.

The same shapes tended to be made in stoneware of different colours and, sometimes a little simplified, in the 'china glaze' earthenware known nowadays as pearlware. The same basic body design was often made with different sorts of cover, one of the usual lift-off kinds or a hinged or sliding one. The sliding ones must have been very tricky to make and fit, but any inclination of the pot backwards to prevent tea dribbling from the spout would send the cover

pl.70

217	216
214	215

sliding off to smash on the floor. Some handles on pots with this type of cover have a right-angled thumb-rest which looks as though it was designed to stop such an accident. It cannot have been very effective, and sliding covers were short-lived. The Staffordshire potters' minimum price agreement of 1796 stated that for a large 'Egyptian black' pot costing two shillings with a normal cover, a sliding cover would cost an extra threepence.

[1] Reilly 1989, I, p.444.
[2] Farrer 1906, II, p.123.
[3] Reilly 1989, I, p.495.
[4] Barker 1991, p.269.

214

Basalt stoneware, Wedgwood

1780–1800
PLATE 70
166mm (1637)
Impressed mark: 'WEDGWOOD'

The cover is held in place by a projecting lug at the rear. The applied relief is the 'Dancing Hours'. This design was derived from a Hellenistic sculptured relief formerly in the Villa Borghese, and now in the Louvre,[1] perhaps via an engraving in Montfaucon's *L'Antiquité Expliquée*, of which Wedgwood is known to have owned a copy as early as 1770.[2] Wedgwood's patron Sir Lawrence Dundas had a chimney piece of marble and lapis lazuli from the Borghese collection, incorporating a copy of the relief, installed in his house at Moor Park, Hertfordshire. This is now at the Lady Lever Art Gallery, Port Sunlight.

Wedgwood's version is thought to have been modelled by John Flaxman junior, being mentioned in a letter of 1778 along with the Apotheosis of Homer and the Marriage of Cupid and Psyche, both known to have been designed by him.[3] The same letter records a visit to Etruria by Sir Lawrence Dundas and that Wedgwood intends to use the Dancing Hours for a chimney piece. It seems likely that this is not mere coincidence, and that Dundas' Borghese chimney piece had suggested this use for the design. The design was, however, already in existence in September 1776 when Wedgwood wrote to Bentley about a drawing 'you sent for plain Vases to paint, which we find likewise very suitable for Bass reliefs particularly for the Dancing Hours.'[4] It was evidently Bentley's decision to employ Flaxman: Wedgwood wrote to him on 14 January 1775: 'I am glad you have met with a Modeler and that Flaxman is so valuable an Artist. It is but a few years since he was a most supreme Coxcomb, but a little more experience may have cured him of that foible.'[5] It has been noted that Flaxman's version of the Dancing Hours is more elegant than the original.[6]

Wedgwood had considered a design for an oval teapot as early as 1771, but decided that 'round ones suit us better'.[7] The sibyl knob is the first of the three classified Wedgwood forms of sibyl.[8] Teapots with sibyl knobs were evidently already being made in 1774 when, complaining about his depleted stock, he noted he had 'no Sybil Teapots and only a few of the Parapets . . .'.[9] A pot with a similar spout and a copy of the Dancing Hours relief was made by Neale & Co.[10]

[1] Haskell and Penny 1981, p.195.
[2] Montfaucon 1719–24, III, part 2, pl.173; Chellis 1962, pp.60–4; Finer and Savage 1965, p.7.
[3] Farrer 1906, II, p.419; Reilly 1989, I, p.585.
[4] Dawson 1984, p.59.
[5] Farrer II, p.216.
[6] Irwin 1979, pp. 21–2.
[7] Finer and Savage 1965, p.115.
[8] Rakow 1983, p.166.
[9] Finer and Savage 1965, p.158.
[10] Miller and Berthoud 1985, pl.499; Edwards 1987, p.81 pl.54.

215

Basalt stoneware, Wedgwood

*c.*1780–1800
PLATE 70
137mm (M1161)
Impressed mark: 'WEDGWOOD'

For similar classical scroll designs by Turner and Wood see nos.241 and 238.

216

Basalt stoneware, Birch, Shelton, Staffs.

*c.*1800
PLATE 70
130mm (M623)

Metal reinforce to spout tip. The applied reliefs are, on the obverse, standing woman with chalice and dagger (Tragedy?), boy with lion (the Power of Love), seated woman holding branch, and dancing woman holding wand and mask (Comedy?); on the reverse, dancing boy with tambourine, Plenty supplying Hope, and dancing girl child with triangle. The dancing children seem to be distinctive of Birch's wares.[1] The knob is the widow of Zarephath in the form classified as made by Neale & Co. as well as by Birch.[2] The partnership of Birch and Whitehead is recorded in 1796, and was succeeded by Edmund John Birch potting in his name alone. His works were advertised for sale in 1814.

[1] Rakow 1978, p.178.
[2] Rakow 1983, p.168.

217

Basalt stoneware, Elijah Mayer, Hanley, Staffs.

c.1800
PLATE 70
120mm (M622)
Impressed mark: 'E. Mayer'

The applied reliefs are, on the obverse, 'The Power of Love' and a putto with a hind; on the reverse, figures from 'Domestic Employment', and a standing and a kneeling putto with torches. The widow knob is of the type recorded for this maker, and has bare feet and the legs not crossed.[1] Elijah Mayer was potting at the Cobden Works, Hanley, from about 1790 and died in 1813. The firm traded as E. Mayer & Son after 1804.

[1] Rakow 1983, pp.167–8.

218

Basalt stoneware, Wedgwood

c.1780–90
PLATE 71
98mm (B695)
Impressed mark: 'Wedgwood'
Ref: Reilly I, p.435 pl.621

The knob is the second of the classified Wedgwood forms of sibyl knob.[1] The turning of the body imitates the staves and hoops of a barrel.

[1] Rakow 1983, p.166.

219

Basalt stoneware, Leeds Pottery

c.1800
PLATE 71
97mm (B638)
Impressed mark: 'LEEDS.POTTERY'

The widow knob is very similar to the versions made by Neale & Co. and by Birch (see no.216)[1] but is distinguished by the zig-zag fall of the mantle behind the left arm.

[1] Rakow 1983, p.168.

220

Basalt stoneware, Chetham and Woolley, Longton, Staffs.

c.1800
PLATE 71
117mm (M564)

The firm of Chetham and Woolley was active in 1796. On the death of James Chetham in 1807, the partnership was continued by his widow Ann until its dissolution in 1809. Ann Chetham continued the business, which in 1818 was styled Chetham & Son. The Venus and Cupid knob appears to match that on the pot incised 'Chetham & Woolley, Lane End' in the Stoke-on-Trent Museum.[1] The scalloped gallery and simple dot beading at the shoulder on the present pot are found on sherds excavated on the Chetham site in Commerce Street.[2]

The knob (fig.17a) differs from the version (fig.17b and c) on another basalt pot (M574) used by S. Hollins and possibly by other potters:[3] the latter has incisions indicating toes on what would otherwise be taken for drapery-covered feet, while the

Figure 17a

Figure 17b

Figure 17c

Chetham version has no such incisions. It has been suggested that the edge of the dress round the front of the neck seems to square off on the Chetham version, descending more diagonally on the other version, but this distinction does not seem to hold true of the museum's examples. The difference noted in the hair falling down on to Venus' back[4] is, however, confirmed by these examples: the Chetham version has a single lock which just touches the edge of the dress (fig.17a), while the lock on the other version is forked, and one fork overlaps the edge of the dress (fig.17c). It is also noticeable that the diagonal fold on the back of the non-Chetham version hangs down below the waist. The non-Chetham Venus (fig.17b) also wears her hair with a central parting, while the Chetham one has a curly fringe. Another Chetham and Woolley pot with this knob (M577) has the same scalloped gallery, and a band of oak-leaves at the shoulder like the marked pot at Stoke.

[1] Hollens 1983, pl.112.
[2] *Op.cit.* pl.113a.
[3] Rakow 1983, p.169 and pl.92a and b.
[4] Robertshaw 1984, pp.13–18.

221

Whiteware painted in enamel colours, Wilson, Hanley, Staffs.

*c.*1800–10
PLATE 73
155mm (1628)
Impressed mark: 'WILSON'

Robert Wilson, who had managed the Church Works at Hanley for Humphrey Palmer and James Neale in turn, ran it in his own name from 1790 or 1792 until his death in 1801. His son David succeeded him.[1] The white body of this piece, covered with a blue-tinted glaze, resembles Wedgwood's whiteware (see following entry) and is

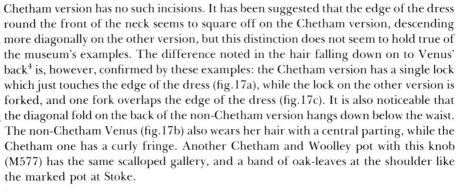

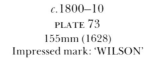

possibly the 'chalk body' referred to by Simeon Shaw.[2] The form of handle is found on the wares Wilson made previously under Neale, for example the jasper pot no.223.

[1] Edwards 1987, p.156.
[2] Shaw 1829, pp.224–5; Edwards 1987, p.169.

222

Whiteware, Wedgwood

*c.*1805–10
PLATE 72
82mm (B131)
Impressed mark: 'WEDGWOOD'
Ref: Reilly 1989, II, p.352 pl.503

On 1 January 1802 Thomas Byerley suggested developing a new white earthenware with a 'body made much finer by finer Lawns', that is, with the ingredients refined by sieving with a finer mesh, and 'glazed with a white glaze ... perhaps adding a small addition of Cornwall clay.' In 1805 it was reported that 'the new white ware' was crazing, and that to prevent this it should be fired not with the creamware but by itself, as it required a higher temperature for both biscuit and glost firing. The recipe for the body, given in 1824, was 'dry weight 24 flint 31 china clay 31 blue clay 1½ stone' making it higher in china clay and lower in flint and stone than creamware or pearlware. The ware was in competition with the cheaper sort of bone china, and Bateman, the firm's traveller, reported in 1810: 'Our white ware patterns stick on hand, the dealers say they can never dispose of them, it is admitted it surpasses anything of the kind, but when the customer holds it up to the light to find a transparency they exclaim it is not china, and feel disappointed, of course, they give the preference to a daubed thing bearing the name of china' [see Ref.]. The glaze has a blue tinge like that of pearlware.

223

Blue jasperware body with white applied reliefs, Neale & Co., Hanley

*c.*1778–92
COLOUR PLATE 17
122mm (1629)
Impressed mark: 'NEALE & Co.'

The applied reliefs are the Choice of Hercules on the obverse, on the reverse an urn flanked by trees. James Neale was in partnership with Humphrey Palmer, running the London end of the business. When Palmer failed, Neale took the business over. The form of handle is found also on wares made after Neale's departure, when Wilson potted in his own name (see no.221 above). A matching Neale tea service of this type is in the Rakow collection.[1]

[1] Edwards 1987, p.92 pl.71.

224

Jasperware, blue body with white applied reliefs, William Adams, Tunstall, Staffs.

*c.*1800
COLOUR PLATE 17
131mm (M602)
Impressed mark: 'ADAMS'

The applied reliefs are, on the obverse, Sacrifice to Pomona, and on the reverse another sacrifice scene.[1] William Adams was potting at Burslem in 1769 and is said to have started a potworks at Greengates, Tunstall, in 1779. He died in 1805, and his son Benjamin took over after he came of age in about 1808. Adams' jasperware has a relatively livid, violet tint when compared with that of his contemporaries.

[1] As Reilly 1989, I, p.652 pl.995 right.

pl.73

227 225

221 231

225

Caneware painted with blue, brown and green enamels and gilding

*c.*1790

PLATE 73

128mm (1697)

Five-sided. The shape matches a marked Spode example[1] and a basalt example lacking its cover (M536). A closely related but different type, also with seven 'sticks' to each side, is a basalt pot M542. The Wedgwood and Turner versions of this shape have five sticks to each side.[2] The idea of a teapot shape imitating bamboo originated in the Chinese red stoneware of Yixing.[3] An example of this is M540.

[1] Spode 1966, no.4.
[2] Reilly 1989, I, p.428 pl.608, p.496 pl.714; Hillier 1965, pl.20a.
[3] Lo 1986, p.59 pl.XXIII.

226

Yellow-glazed earthenware decorated with green bat-prints

*c.*1810–20

PLATE 72

105mm (B545)

Despite the existence of several pieces inscribed with dates in the 1790s, this type of ware with a bright yellow glaze does not seem to have been widely produced before 1800. The colouring agent seems to have been antimony rather than chrome, to judge from surviving recipes.[1] Only a faint colour has been achieved in the green prints, as is normal before the 1820s. The subjects are in the widely imitated manner of Adam Buck. Another yellow-glazed pot (M464) is printed with a design in the same style showing a woman at a fortepiano, flanked by two children, which is found on an engraved copper plate from the Maling family of potters at Newcastle-on-Tyne (now in the Laing Art Gallery there) and on a Staffordshire pot marked 'WOOD'.[2]

[1] Miller 1974, pp.119–20.
[2] *Op.cit.* p.84 fig.51, p.64 fig.37, and *cf.* p.36, fig.20.

227

Pearlware printed in underglaze blue, probably Thomas Wolfe, Stoke

*c.*1800–1810
PLATE 73
151mm (M725)

The pot has a domed strainer and a pouring guard with a central notch. The form of handle with its vertical thumb-rest looks as though it was designed for a pot with a sliding cover. The print is a version of the pattern known variously as 'the Two Temples',[1] 'Broseley-Willow' or 'Pagoda'.[2] It differs both from the Wolfe-Mason version made at Liverpool (see no.383) and from that made subsequently by Mason in Staffordshire (see no.421). It is, however, known on porcelain shapes very similar to the Wolfe-Mason Liverpool ones,[3] and it has thus been attributed to Thomas Wolfe's factory at Stoke.[4]

[1] Copeland 1980, p.62. [3] *Op.cit.* pl.22; Miller and Berthoud 1985, pl.686.
[2] Godden 1980, p.35. [4] Markin 1989, p.9.

228

Pearlware printed in brown and painted in enamel colours

*c.*1800
PLATE 123
125mm (M635)

Only the decoration in the ovals is printed.

229

Basalt stoneware, probably Birch

*c.*1800
PLATE 74
165mm (1631)
Impressed mark at base of handle: 'R? B'

The applied reliefs are, on the obverse, a woman with challice and dagger (Tragedy?), Liberty and Peace at an altar, and a woman holding a wand and a mask (Comedy?); on the reverse, a dancing boy with a tambourine, the Power of Love, a seated woman holding a branch and an inverted cornucopia, and a small girl dancing and holding a triangle. The distinctive reliefs of dancing children match no.216 above.

230

Basalt stoneware

*c.*1800
PLATE 74
120mm (B unnumbered)

Modelled in the form of a house, with the vent in the chimney so that a wisp of steam would rise from it as the pot sat brewing.

231

Pearlware painted with enamel colours and gilding by William Absolon,
Great Yarmouth, Norfolk

*c.*1800
PLATE 73
159mm (1.927)
Prov: presented by the Friends of the Norwich Museums, 1927
Ref: Howell 1980, pl.139a

The obverse bears a view of St Nicholas' church, Yarmouth, in brown monochrome
with gilt lettering. The reverse has flower sprays in red, brown, purple and green.
There are traces of a gilt inscription on the top and cover. The body shape is a slightly
simplified version of a basalt pot (M922) and has the same handle. William Absolon
decorated pottery, porcelain and glass, beginning probably after his move to 25
Market Row in 1789, and continuing probably until his death in 1815 (see Ref.). This is
probably the 'teapot, with St Nicholas' church' exhibited in the Art Loan Exhibition of
1889 at Yarmouth Town Hall as no.96, lent by Mr Marsh.

232

Caneware painted in green enamel, Neale & Co.

1778–92
PLATE 75
135mm (B466)
Impressed mark: 'NEALE & CO.'
Prov: Caldwell

The moulded shape is identical to the Spode pot in the following entry. An unmarked
pearlware pot of identical shape, painted in enamel colours, is B276.

233

Caneware painted in blue and green enamels, Spode

*c.*1790
PLATE 75
137mm (B691)
Impressed mark: 'SPODE'

The moulded shape is identical to the Neale & Co. pot in the previous entry. While it is
not unusual to find matching mouldings for body shapes in use by different
manufacturers, there is often a difference in the shape of spout, handle or knob (see
nos.277 and 278; and no.266). It is less usual to find an exact match for a whole pot, as
here and in the following two entries. See no.236 below for an instance of matching
pots marked Spode and Wood. Correspondences between moulded bodies or other
individual features may indicate that the potteries concerned were being supplied by
the same freelance block-maker, but one would not necessarily expect to find the same
spout, handle, knob and body teamed up together. The present example raises the
possibility of one firm directly copying another.

234

Caneware painted in blue, green and white enamel, Spode

*c.*1790
PLATE 76
146mm (M1131)
Impressed mark: 'SPODE'
Ref: Edwards 1987, p.95 pl.73

The moulded shape is identical to the following pot, but the strainer is flat. See also the
previous entry.

235

Caneware, painted in blue enamel with gilding, Neale & Co.

c.1778–92
PLATE 76
144mm (M1132)
Impressed mark: 'NEALE & Co.'
Ref: Edwards 1987, p.95 pl.73

The moulded shape is identical to the previous pot, but the strainer is domed.

236

Basalt stoneware painted in blue, white and pink enamels,
John or Enoch Wood, Burslem, Staffs.

1780–1800
PLATE 71
133mm (B404)
Impressed mark: 'WOOD'

Apart from the pose of the lion knob, this pot is identical in shape to a pearlware one (see next entry). John Wood has been overshadowed by his cousin Enoch, but worked the Brownhills Pottery in his own name from 1780 until his death in 1797, and is known to have been making 'Egyptian black' during the period 1783–7. He was shot by the family doctor after refusing him permission to court his eldest daughter. His son John continued the business.[1] Enoch Wood potted in his own name at Fountain Place from 1784 or earlier, and in that year was also making 'Egyptian black', but by 1792 was in partnership as Wood and Caldwell. A caneware pot of apparently identical shape apart from the knob is impressed 'SPODE'.[2]

[1] Halfpenny 1986, p.122.
[2] Spode 1966, no.5.

237

Pearlware painted in underglaze blue, probably John or Enoch Wood
or Spode

1780–1800
PLATE 77
144mm (B403)

This pot is identical in shape to the previous one, apart from the pose of the lion knob.

238

Pearlware painted in blue, green, red and yellow enamels,
John or Enoch Wood, Burslem, Staffs.

1780–1800
PLATE 77
125mm (B114)
Impressed mark: 'WOOD'
Prov: Solon coll.; his sale, Butters & Sons, Hanley, 26 November 1912, lot 190

The design of classical foliage scrolls is related to that of the Wedgwood basalt no.215 above and the Turner caneware no.241. The spout matches nos.236 and 237 above.

239

Earthenware with beige-yellow glaze, painted in black enamel.
T. Phillips, Lane End, Staffs.

*c.*1780
PLATE 77
157mm (1915)
Impressed mark: 'T. PHILLIPS'
Ref: Hampson 1986, p.31

A creamware pot of matching shape but lacking its cover, and painted in underglaze blue, is M397. Another such pot of this shape, inscribed 'Miss Starres Emsworth 1777' is in the British Museum.[1] Thomas Phillips took over the lease of a cottage at Green Dock, Longton, from George Bolton Phillips in 1769, is recorded as an earthenware manufacturer of Lane End in 1783 and died in 1791.

[1] *NCSN* 62, 1986, p.17.

240

Pearlware decorated with green glaze at the shoulder, and painted in
underglaze blue

1780–1800
PLATE 77
153mm (B401)

241

Caneware painted in green enamel, with stand, Turner, Longton, Staffs.

*c.*1785–1800
PLATE 78
104mm (B678)
Impressed mark (on pot and stand): 'TURNER'

The design of classical foliage scrolls is related to those of the Wedgwood basalt no.215 and the Wood pearlware no.238. John Turner's works at Lane End were taken over at his death in 1787 by his sons John and William, who were bankrupt in 1806. On 6 June 1807 the *Staffordshire Advertiser* announced the sale of:

> a large and elegant assortment of Earthenware and China; comprising the different articles usually manufactured both useful and ornamental; and consisting of Cream Colour, China-glazed blue edge, china glaze printed and painted, Egyptian Black, Cane, Stone, Jasper, Pearl and Patent China Goods; being the well known and highly reputed manufacture of Messrs TURNER and Co. of Lane-end aforesaid; . . . The purchasers will have the opportunity of matching, and continuing the patterns at Mr WILLIAM TURNER'S present Manufactory, in Lane-end, and Merchants, Tradesmen, Commission packers, and others, will find their account in attending the above sale, which offers advantages of rare occurrence.

William Turner's business at Fenton Culvert failed in 1813. It is likely that until then he continued to use earlier Turner moulds and marks, and he may even have done so during a subsequent return to running his own business.[1]

[1] Hollens 1983, p.226; Leese 1984, pp.61–78.

242

Caneware painted in blue, white and green enamels, Spode

1780–1800
PLATE 78
121mm (B620)
Impressed mark: 'SPODE'

Of hexagonal shape, with a shallow foot at each point of the hexagon. A handle of similar shape was used by Neale & Co. (see no.245 below). The knob is in the form of a boy riding on a dolphin. The boy's head is missing.

243

Basalt stoneware, Turner, Longton, Staffs.

1780–1800
PLATE 80
159mm (M514)
Impressed mark: 'TURNER'
Ref: Edwards 1987, p.84 pl.60

The cover is double-walled, the outer wall being pierced. The distinctive lion knob, with head and mane rather large in proportion to the body, matches that on a marked Turner caneware pot (M484). A marked Turner example with the same body shape in white feldspathic stoneware (M513, cover missing) has neoclassical applied reliefs on brown slip in place of the chinoiserie moulded design on the side panels. On the panels at both spout and handle ends, however, the chinoiseries were allowed to remain, presumably being less noticeable there. For the Spode version of this body moulding, which is somewhat different, see the next item. A related shape (1526, cover missing) lacks the figures but has a diapered ground of four-petalled flowers behind the tree in the reserves, similar but not identical to a pot in a private collection.[1]

[1] Miller and Berthoud 1985, pl.512.

pl.79
244

pl.80
245
243

244

Caneware painted in blue enamel, Spode

1780–1800
PLATE 79
143mm (M516)
Impressed mark: 'SPODE'

245

Basalt, Neale & Co.

1778–92
PLATE 80
121mm (M518)
Impressed mark: 'NEALE & Co.'
Ref: Edwards 1987, p.84 pl.60

The body moulding is a rather dispirited version of nos.243 and 244 above. A similar handle was used by Spode (see no.242 above).

246

Pearlware painted in high-temperature underglaze colours,
Rawmarsh Top Pottery or Kilnhurst Pottery, Yorkshire

*c.*1800–10
COLOUR PLATE 16
130mm (B712)
Impressed mark: 'HAWLEY'
Ref: Lewis 1984, p.76 pl.16

The strong tone of the underglaze blue and green is typical of marked Hawley pieces. Another marked example in the Royal Scottish Museum, Edinburgh (1973.129), differs in having a widow knob. William Hawley founded the Rawmarsh Top Pottery in 1790, and died in 1818. His brother Thomas was already working the Kilnhurst Old Pottery in 1783, and died in about 1808. Both potteries were continued by their descendants. A pot with very similar but not identical moulding is impressed 'ASTBURY',[1] and was therefore made in Staffordshire at the Foley Pottery, Lane Delph. A note by Colonel Bulwer on a scrap of paper inside the present pot states: 'Hawley worked at the Foley, Fenton, Lane Delph, Staffordshire to about 1840.' This is at present unsubstantiated, and a confusion is possible with the John Hawley who is known to have been working at the Foley Pottery from 1842 to 1887. A William Astbury is also said to have worked for the Hawleys as a model maker and mould cutter for over 63 years.[2]

Another pot with very similar but not identical moulding, and lacking its cover, is 1643, painted in enamel colours. Another is a marked Bradley & Co. Coalport basalt in the Victoria and Albert Museum (3392.1901).

[1] Lewis 1984, p.36.
[2] *Op.cit.* p.72.

247

Pearlware painted with blue, pink, green and yellow enamels and gilding

*c.*1790
PLATE 81
120mm (B302)
Ref: Hodgson 1921, p.149 pl.II

The body is different in plan from the previous pot, but its moulded decoration is very similar. The body matches a design in a Teapot Drawing Book from the Leeds Pottery.[1] The spaniel knob is slightly different from the version found on two Spode basalt pots (M613 and M615), and a Neale & Co. tea-kettle (M549). The spaniel on B302 wears a collar and does not have his front left paw tucked underneath.

[1] Leeds Central Library SF.738.30942 (L517), illus.; Lewis 1984, p.63.

248

Pearlware painted with underglaze blue and gilding

*c.*1790
PLATE 81
99mm (B282)

The strainer is domed. The lion knob matches no.237 above.

249

White jasper body with blue dip and white applied reliefs, Spode

*c.*1810–20
PLATE 100
110mm (B647)
Impressed mark: 'Spode'
Prov: Sotheby's, 22 June 1928

The applied reliefs are, on the obverse, Charlotte at the tomb of Werther, and on the reverse 'Sportive Love'. A pot matching the present example is in the Spode Museum, Stoke-on-Trent.[1]

[1] Whiter 1970, pl.153.

250

Dark red stoneware, Neale & Co.

1778–92
PLATE 82
118mm (M770)
Impressed mark: 'NEALE & Co.'
Ref: Edwards 1987, p.99 pl.79

The applied reliefs are, on the obverse, a triton blowing a conch, a cupid on a dolphin with a lion's foreparts, and a dolphin; on reverse, a mermaid holding a shell to her head, Venus reclining in a shell, and a dolphin. The handle matches the Neale porcelain pot no.345.

251

White feldspathic stoneware with brown slip, Turner

*c.*1790–1800
PLATE 83
162mm (M826)

The cover is sliding. The spout is of a type found on Turner porcelain (no.367). The applied reliefs are from the 'Domestic Employment' series.

pl.83

255 253
254 251

252

Pearlware painted in enamel colours, probably Lakin & Poole,
Burslem, Staffs.

*c.*1792–6
COLOUR PLATE 16
145mm (1598)

The shape matches an example in the Victoria and Albert Museum with the impressed
mark 'LAKIN & POOLE'. The thumb-rest on the handle appears to have been
designed to prevent the sliding cover from slipping backwards off the pot. Thomas
Lakin was in partnership with William Ellison Poole at the Hadderidge Pottery,
Burslem, probably from late 1791. He withdrew in 1796, and a year later the other
partners were bankrupt. In 1797 he was working a pottery at Bourne's Bank, Burslem,
but by September 1799 he had vacated the works. Shortly thereafter he became a
manager for Davenport, and did not have his own business again until 1810 when he
moved to Stoke-on-Trent.[1] For his later career see no.324 below.

[1] Blakey 1984.

253

Pearlware painted in brown enamel

*c.*1795
PLATE 83
120mm (1599)

The shape is different from the previous example.

254

Pearlware painted in high-temperature underglaze colours

c.1800
PLATE 83
157mm (B296)

The strainer is domed. The shape is very similar to a pot marked 'G. TAYLOR' in the Stoke-on-Trent Museum[1] which, however, has four moulded feet, unlike the present example. George Taylor potted at Hanley *c*.1784–1811. A pot of very similar shape in the Yorkshire Museum is marked 'WEDGWOOD & CO.'[2] For Ralph Wedgwood see no.113.

[1] Miller and Berthoud 1985, pls.867 and 869; *cf.* Stoke 1986, no.210.
[2] *Op.cit.* pl.866.

255

Pearlware, undecorated, probably George Taylor

c.1800
PLATE 83
158mm (1580)

The body and handle match the previous pot. The applied relief on both sides is Cybele with paired lions. An undecorated sugar-box of this design bears the mark 'G. TAYLOR'[1] (see previous entry).

[1] *NCSN* 71, 1988, p.46.

256

Pearlware transfer-printed in underglaze blue

c.1800
PLATE 84
139mm (1583)

The cover has no flange. The shape is similar to a basalt pot with the impressed mark 'BARKER'.[1] For the Barker family see p.183. The handle 'dies' into the body at the lower end, unlike a basalt pot (M895) and two pearlware pots of very similar shape (M896 and 1582, the latter printed in underglaze blue) which have a clearly defined lower terminal. A simpler version of the body shape, lacking the horizontal and vertical mouldings, is found on a pot with a distinctive type of small knob (as M906) in a private collection.

[1] Stoke 1982, no.118; Miller and Berthoud 1985, pl.897.

257

Pearlware painted in enamel colours

c.1800
PLATE 84
137mm (1607)

The strainer is domed. The shape matches another pot (M913) bearing an underglaze blue print with a curling palm tree. The spout and knob are found on another pot (M915) whose handle occurs on a different shape (M917) of which another example (1606) bears the 'bungalow' pattern[1] and the impressed mark 'ROGERS'. This chain of inference makes it uncertain whether these forms could be limited to one manufacturer. John and George Rogers potted at Dale Hall, Longport, between *c*.1784 and 1814. The curling palm tree print has previously been noted on the wares of Job Ridgway.[2]

[1] Coysh and Henrywood 1989, p.199.   [2] Coysh and Henrywood 1982, p.100.

pl.84

258   259

257   256

258

White feldspathic stoneware outlined in blue, David Dunderdale & Co.,
Castleford Pottery, Yorkshire

c.1800
PLATE 84 and fig.18
110mm to rim (1564)
Cover missing
Impressed mark: 'DD & Co./CASTLEFORD'. Incised mark: '2'

The applied reliefs on both sides are a seated woman holding a bunch of flowers (Flora?). The handle is distinguished from other manufacturers' similar versions (see no.266, fig.30) by the moulded 'tie', which is double not single. The Castleford Pottery was bought by Dunderdale & Co. in 1790 and the partnership was dissolved in 1820.[1] Castleford's obliging habit of marking their wares of this type has led to the misleading habit of describing all white feldspathic stonewares with blue outlining as Castleford.

[1] Edwards Roussel 1982.

  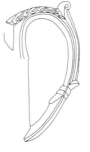

Figure 18

Figure 19

259

White feldspathic stoneware, possibly Sowter & Co., Mexborough, Yorkshire

*c.*1800–10
PLATE 84 and fig.19
154mm (B568)
Impressed marks in individual characters: 's & oC', 'no 6'
Ref: Godden 1966, p.297 pl.529

Figure 20

The applied reliefs are, on the obverse, the Power of Love, and, on the reverse, Cybele with two lions. Three other pots in the collection have matching body mouldings, spouts and handles, and all have '22' impressed (M843, M845 and 1565). Instead of the trefoil knob of the present pot, these three all have a flower knob, that on M843 (fig.20) having a longer leaf at either end than the others (fig.21). This form with the longer leaves was excavated on the Chetham and Woolley site.[1] For Sowter and Co. see no.289 below. Related moulded forms, probably the product of another factory, are found on two basalt pots, 1578 (fig.22, knob missing) and M904 (fig.23) whose moulded bodies match each other.

Figure 21

[1] Edwards Roussel 1982, pl.73; Hollens 1983, pls.113c, 116a.

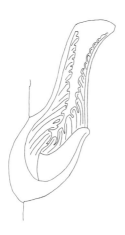

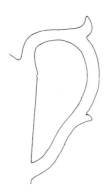

Figure 23

Figure 22

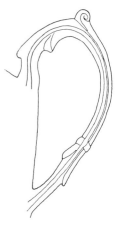

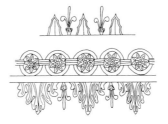

pl.85

264	262
260	261

260

White feldspathic stoneware, possibly Sowter & Co.

*c.*1800–10
PLATE 85 and fig.24
146mm (M844)
Impressed mark: 'M' at base of handle

The applied reliefs are, on the obverse, Plenty supplying Hope; on reverse, a reclining Cupid. The handle matches that on the marked '3 & Co.' pot no.261 below. The knob matches that on the '22' marked pot M845 (fig.21). Another pot with matching body and spout moulding (M842) has a handle matching the marked 'S & oC' pot no.259 (pl.84).

Figure 24

261

White feldspathic stoneware, possibly Sowter & Co.

*c.*1800–10
PLATE 85
155mm (M946)
Impressed marks '3 & Co.', 'No 1'

The knob matches that on the marked 'S & oC' pot no.259 (fig.19). The handle matches no.260 above (fig.24). The mark was made by separately impressing type characters, and a '3' was probably used by mistake for an 'S'. An almost identical pot is marked 'S & Co.' 'No.1'.[1]

[1] Edwards Roussel 1982, pl.88.

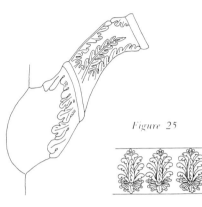

Figure 25

262

White feldspathic stoneware

*c.*1800
PLATE 85 and fig.25
145mm (M846)
Impressed mark: '36'

The applied reliefs are, on the obverse, a standing woman weeping at an urn and obelisk and, on the reverse, a woman with a palm branch (probably Peace). The floral knob matches the 'S & Co.' type (fig.21) but the moulded details are otherwise quite different.

262A

Basalt stoneware, Warburton, Cobridge, Staffs.

*c.*1800
PLATE 88 and fig.26
160mm (M830)
Impressed mark: 'WARBURTON'

The applied reliefs are, on the obverse, Peace seated and Liberty standing at an altar; on the reverse, Plenty supplying Hope. It is not known to which member of the Warburton dynasty of potters at Cobridge this mark refers. Jacob Warburton is probably less likely than his sons Peter and Francis, who were in partnership from *c.*1795. After the dissolution of the partnership in 1802, Peter continued the works until 1812. Francis emigrated to France and made creamware at La Charité sur Loire. The other likely candidate is John Warburton, active *c.*1802–1825.

Figure 26

pl.86

265	263
267	266

263

White feldspathic stoneware, possibly Warburton

*c.*1800
PLATE 86 and fig.27
107mm to rim (1567)
Impressed mark: '21' (large 2 and small 1)
Cover not original

The applied reliefs are, on the obverse, Jupiter with an eagle and, on the reverse, Mercury with a dog. The body moulding matches a marked sugar-box.[1] The spout matches no.264 below (fig.28). The handle matches no.266 below (fig.30).

[1] Godden 1966, pl.593.

264

White feldspathic stoneware, possibly Warburton

*c.*1800
PLATE 85 and fig.28
136mm (1566)
Impressed mark: '12' (small 1 and large 2)

Figure 27

The applied reliefs are, on the obverse, a standing woman pouring a libation at an altar and, on the reverse, a standing woman garlanding a bust. The spout matches no.263 above. The handle matches M831, a pot with identical body moulding to no.263 (fig.27).

Figure 28

265

White feldspathic stoneware, possibly Warburton

c.1800
PLATE 86 and fig.29
148mm (B215)
Raised moulded mark: '8'

The applied reliefs are, on the obverse, Hebe giving the eagle a drink and, on the reverse, two young girls from 'Domestic Employment'. The spout, knob and handle all match no.264 (fig.28). The handle matches M831, a pot with identical body moulding to no.263 (fig.27). An almost identical pot to the present example is M856, which is marked with an incised '8', but has a different form of tied-leaf spout matching no.266 below (fig.30). It is therefore quite possible that both forms of leaf-spout were made by the same pottery.

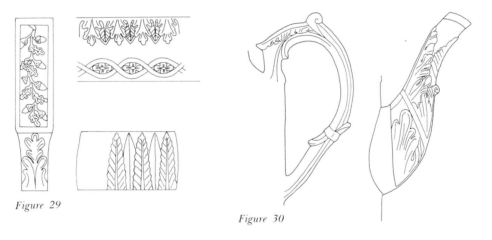

Figure 29

Figure 30

266

White feldspathic stoneware

c.1800
PLATE 86 and fig.30
164mm (M840)
Impressed mark: '22'

The single tie on the handle distinguishes it from the double tie used at Castleford (no.258, see fig.18). The body moulding matches the marked 'S & Co' pot no.259 above and its fellows impressed '22' (fig.19). The spout, however, matches M856 which is otherwise identical to no.265 above. It is evident that the same moulded spouts or bodies, or perhaps both, were used by more than one factory. Another pot, M837, has a similar mixture of elements: it also has the same spout and body moulding as the marked 'S & Co' pot no.259 and is also impressed '22', but has the same type of knob and handle as no.264 above (fig.28).

pl.87

273   268

270   274

267

White feldspathic stoneware

*c.*1800
PLATE 86 and fig.31
167mm (1568)
Impressed mark: '23'

The applied reliefs are, on the obverse, a standing woman garlanding a bust, and a standing and a seated woman each with a book; on reverse, a seated woman holding a cornucopia and a small tree. The knob matches no.264 (fig.28) but the tied-leaf spout matches no.266 (fig.30) rather than no.264. The form of handle is found on a pot in the Stoke-on-Trent Museum,[1] whose spout and body moulding match no.263 (fig.27) and whose knob matches no.264 (fig.28).

[1] Miller and Berthoud 1985, pl.827.

Figure 31

268

Pearlware painted in high-temperature underglaze colours

*c.*1800
PLATE 87
154mm (B107)
Prov: General Bulwer

The body moulding matches no.265 above, but the other moulded details are different. There is no flange to the cover. A pot with a different body, (B263, cover missing) has a related handle.[1] Another pot decorated in this technique (B108) matches in shape and colouring an example in the V&A.[2]

[1] Lewis 1984, p.228 lower.
[2] *Op.cit.* p.227 upper.

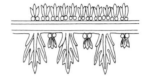
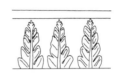

Figure 32

269

Basalt stoneware, Barker, Staffordshire or Yorkshire

*c.*1810
PLATE 88 and fig.32
146mm (M893)
Impressed mark: 'A'

The applied reliefs are, on the obverse, a horseman and waves and, on the reverse, Venus standing in a shell pulled by dolphins. The body moulding matches an earthenware pot marked 'BARKER' in the V&A.[1] The spout matches stoneware pots with the same mark.[2] Another pot (1608) has a matching body and spout, with a different handle (fig.33). Another with a matching body (1572) has a straight spout and another handle (fig.34).

Peter Barker worked at the Low Pottery, Rawmarsh, Yorkshire until 1812 when he joined his brother Jesse at the Mexborough Pottery not far away, where the latter had been since 1809. At the same period, however, there were four separate businesses in Lane End and Lane Delph run by Joseph, Samuel, Thomas and William Barker, any of whom is equally likely to have made this pot.[3]

[1] Godden 1966, pl.34.
[2] *Op.cit.* pl.33; Miller and Berthoud 1985, pl.858.
[3] Stoke 1986, no.179.

Figure 33   *Figure 34*

pl.88

269   262A

276   275   270

White feldspathic stoneware, Barker, Staffordshire or Yorkshire

*c.*1810

PLATE 87 and fig.35

162mm (1610)

The applied reliefs are, on the obverse, a standing woman holding a large garland and, on the reverse, Fame inscribing a shield before a column. An apparently identical pot in the Yorkshire Museum is impressed 'BARKER'.[1]

[1] Miller and Berthoud 1985, pl.858.

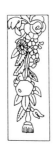  

Figure 35

271

Pearlware, decorated in enamel colours, Barker, Staffordshire or Yorkshire

*c.*1810
COLOUR PLATE 17
155mm (1622)

Apart from the handle, this pot matches the shape of another marked example in the Yorkshire Museum.[1]

[1] Miller and Berthoud 1985, pl.848.

272

Pearlware, painted in high-temperature underglaze colours, Barker, Staffordshire or Yorkshire

*c.*1810
COLOUR PLATE 16
148mm (B106)

A pot with apparently identical moulding is impressed 'BARKER'.[1] A cruder version was made at the Herculaneum factory, Liverpool.[2]

[1] Lewis 1984, p.38.
[2] *Op.cit.* p.97.

273

White feldspathic stoneware, possibly Barker, Staffordshire or Yorkshire

*c.*1810
PLATE 87
146mm (1609)

The applied reliefs are, on the obverse, Liberty encouraging Peace, Art and Labour,[1] and two small girls from 'Domestic Employment'; on the reverse, more figures from 'Domestic Employment'. The handle matches no.270 (fig.35).

[1] Reilly I, 1989, p.613 pl.905.

274

White feldspathic stoneware, possibly Barker, Staffordshire or Yorkshire

*c.*1810
PLATE 87
175mm (1625)

The applied reliefs are, on the obverse, Ganymede on the eagle and a woman holding a veil in a billowing loop by both ends. The handle matches no.272 above, and the relief on the neck of the pot matches that on no.270 (fig.35).

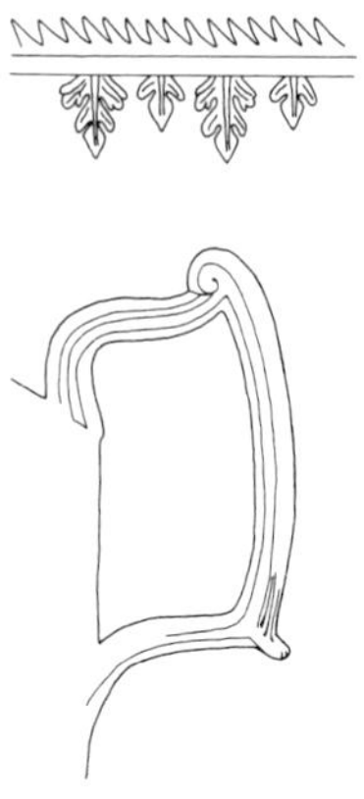

275

Basalt stoneware, William Baddeley, Eastwood, Hanley, Staffs.

*c.*1810
PLATE 88 and fig.36
159mm (B409)
Impressed mark on outer edge of footrim below spout: 'EASTWOOD'

The applied reliefs are, on the obverse, Nelson (named) and on the reverse, Britannia. William Baddeley was active from 1802 to 1822. Another pot with the same mark (M883) has matching details apart from its triangular spout.

Figure 36

276

Basalt stoneware, William Baddeley, Eastwood

*c.*1810
PLATE 88 and fig.37
169mm (M889)
Impressed mark on outer edge of footrim below spout: 'EASTWOOD'

The applied reliefs match those on no.275 above. Another pot (1563) has the same
mark, is identical apart from the applied reliefs and lacks its cover. Two further
examples lacking their covers (M892 and 1633) have handles matching no.275 (fig.36).
The handle of the present pot is found again on a pot with the same mark but a
different shape (M887): it has a distinctive bulging midriff, accentuated by the
moulded design of two bulging columns on either side of the pot.

Figure 37

277

Basalt stoneware, Leeds Pottery

*c.*1810
PLATE 89 and fig.38
171mm (M875)
Impressed mark: 'LEEDS POTTERY'

The applied reliefs are, on the obverse, Liberty standing and Peace sitting at an altar, and on the reverse, Plenty supplying Hope. Another pot with the same mark (M876) is identical but for its cover, which is probably not the original. Plaster moulds from the Leeds Pottery match the applied decoration, and a sherd almost identical to the rim and neck design was found on the Leeds Pottery (Jack Lane) site. An almost identical pot is illustrated as no.29 in the Leeds Blackware Drawing Book.[1] An apparently identical moulded body was, however, also made by John Glass with different spout, knob and handle forms (see next entry).

[1] Walton 1976, p.261 no.1113.

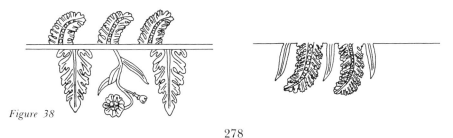

Figure 38

278

Basalt stoneware, John Glass, Hanley, Staffs.

*c.*1810
PLATE 89 and fig.39
177mm (M873)
Impressed mark: 'J. GLASS/HANLEY'

The applied reliefs are, on the obverse, a dancing woman holding a wand and a mask (Comedy?) and, on the reverse, a standing woman holding a cup and a dagger (Tragedy?). A pot at Temple Newsam, identical apart from the applied reliefs, has been attributed to the Leeds Pottery (see previous entry), but is evidently also by John Glass. Two white stoneware pots (1576 and B476) are of identical form apart from the applied reliefs. 1576 has painted panels instead of reliefs. B476 has, on the obverse, a half length figure of Flora and, on reverse, the arms of the United States of America with thirteen stars, one for each state. Another pot (1573) is identical to B476 but for the handle (fig.40).

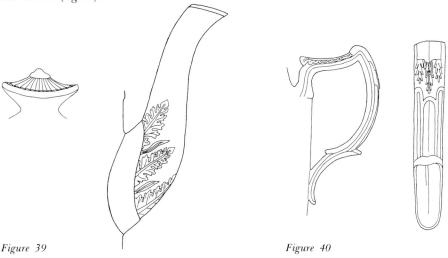

Figure 39   *Figure 40*

pl.90
286
285

pl.91
287

279

Basalt stoneware

c.1810
PLATE 89 and fig.41
162mm (M872)

The applied reliefs are, on the obverse, two putti and a tree and, on the reverse, Endymion resting on a rock. This and another pot (M874) which is identical apart from a knob similar to no.278 above, may be evidence of a third manufacturer making the same moulded body as Leeds and John Glass. Two pots with another design of body moulding, M871 (fig.42) and 1575, may be connected, because the latter's handle matches the present pot.

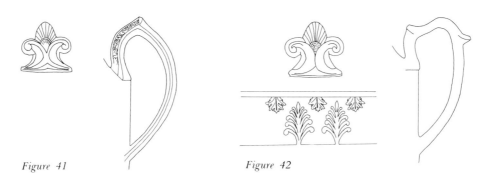

Figure 41   *Figure 42*

280

Basalt stoneware, probably John Moseley, Cobridge or Burslem, Staffs.

c.1810
PLATE 89
159mm (1571)

The applied reliefs are, on the obverse, Britannia, and on the reverse, two figures from 'Domestic Employment'. The body and knob appear to match an example impressed 'MOSELEY' in a private collection.[1] John Moseley was in partnership with William Dale at Cobridge before November 1801. In 1818 John Moseley is recorded as a maker of Egyptian Black at the Churchyard Works, Burslem. It is uncertain whether these are two different men or the same man running two potteries.

[1] Stoke 1982, no.129.

281

Pearlware with painted lines in underglaze blue

c.1800
PLATE 92
171mm (B418)

The applied reliefs are seated figures playing the lyre, a man on the obverse and a woman on the reverse. This pot imitates the fashionable white feldspathic stoneware in a cheaper material. A pearlware example of a different shape (M1168) closely follows a white stoneware pot (M1166). Another pearlware example (B111, knob modern) is heart-shaped in plan and moulded with acanthus scrolls.

282

Pearlware painted in enamel colours

*c.*1800
COLOUR PLATE 16
167mm (B587)

The knob is missing and the handle is modern. The muzzles of cannon appear along the battlements of the castle. The spout is moulded with the Royal Arms. A pot of apparently matching shape in the Stoke-on-Trent Museum, the only other recorded example, has a knob in the form of a dog seated on its haunches.[1]

[1] Lewis 1984, p.229.

283

Brown-glazed earthenware transfer-printed in yellow

*c.*1810
COLOUR PLATE 17
163mm (1585)

The shape matches a porcelain example (M1117). The old attribution of yellow-printed brownware to Portobello in Scotland is now thought to be mistaken. The ware was evidently made by a number of potteries.[1] See also no.312.

[1] Williams-Wood 1986.

pl.92
289
281

284

Pearlware painted in high-temperature underglaze colours, with on the obverse the inscription 'Love and Live Happay', and on the reverse a landscape

c.1800
PLATE 93
171mm (B371)
Ref: Hodgson 1921, p.151 pl.IV; Lewis 1984, p.227

285

Basalt stoneware

c.1800
PLATE 90
156mm (B537)

The applied reliefs are, on the obverse, figures from 'Sportive Love' designed by Lady Templeton for Wedgwood, and a standing and a kneeling Cupid with torches; on the reverse a woman holding a snake and a branch at an altar, a woman dancing with a large garland, and Charlotte at the tomb of Werther. The body and spout match a jasper pot attributed to William Adams[1] and thought to be the one now in the City Museum, Stoke-on-Trent.[2]

[1] Turner 1904, pl.XXIV no.164.
[2] Miller and Berthoud 1985, pl.957.

286

Dark red stoneware with silvered bands, Samuel Hollins, Shelton, Staffs.

c.1800
PLATE 90
143mm (B573)

The applied reliefs are, on the obverse, figures from 'Domestic Employment' and a seated Cupid with a harp, and on the reverse a kneeling girl with a book, a standing woman pouring a libation at an altar, and two Cupids with a tree. The silver bands, now tarnished to dark grey, were also used by other makers. The almost plum-coloured shade of deep red stoneware is distinctive of Hollins, who worked at Vale Pleasant, Shelton, from about 1781 to 1813. The thumb-rest on the handle, picked out in silver, is a moulded oval with three pendant drops, a feature distinctive of Hollins' ware. The leaves on the gallery are broader than those on no.285 above: each fills the recessed width of its panel.

287

Fawn stoneware with silvered bands, Samuel Hollins

c.1800
PLATE 91
139mm (B646)
Impressed mark: 'S. HOLLINS'
Prov: Sotheby's, 22 June 1928

The applied reliefs are, on the obverse, putti representing music, and cupids, and on the reverse figures from 'Domestic Employment', a putto, and the Death of General Wolfe. The deep fawn body is another distinctive Hollins colour. The handle with its moulded oval thumb-rest matches no.286 above. A pot of the same shape in dark red stoneware is M582.

288

Grey-green stoneware with silvered bands, with stand, possibly Samuel Hollins, Shelton, Staffs.

*c.*1800
PLATE 82
140mm (B598)

The ribbed handle is quite different from those of nos.286 and 287 above.

289

Pearlware painted in high-temperature underglaze colours with the inscription 'I[oh]n and Elizebeth Francis 1806, Gainsboro', probably Don or Mexborough Pottery, Yorkshire

dated 1806
PLATE 92
153mm (B105)
Prov: R. Levine, Norwich
Ref: Hodgson 1921, p.151 pl.IV

The shape matches a pot in the Yorkshire Museum marked 'SOWTER & CO. MEXBOROUGH' apart from a difference of knob, which is a swan on the latter.[1] Both pots have no flange on the cover. The Mexborough Pottery was established by Robert Sowter in 1800, let to Jesse Barker in 1809, and bought by him and his brother Peter in 1811. In 1801 the Don Pottery was established less than a mile away by John Green of the Leeds Pottery and John and William Brameld from the Swinton Pottery. The Don Pottery's 1807 printed catalogue, recorded by Jewitt in 1878, was thought lost but has been rediscovered and reprinted. Item 48 in the teaware section of that catalogue[2] is a pot which matches the present pot and the marked Mexborough one, with a swan knob like the latter. The tall proportions of the body distinguish these from other versions of the shanked lozenge shape. Gainsborough in Lincolnshire is due east of the South Yorkshire pottery district, and for John and Elizabeth Francis this was a convenient source for a specially decorated pot. See however no.34.

[1] Miller and Berthoud 1985, pl.961.
[2] Don 1983; Lewis 1984, p.71 (upper).

290

Pearlware transfer-printed in underglaze blue

1805–10
PLATE 94
153mm (118.977)
Prov: presented by Florence E. Evans, 1977

The trophy inscribed 'TRAFALGAR' is also found as an applied relief on dry-bodied stonewares (see no.294 below). Another pot (M963) is of matching shape, and another (M968) has the same print in brown and the same shape apart from a swan knob. Another pearlware shanked lozenge pot (1617) has a body of unusually long, low proportions, and is evidently from another source. It is impressed '2', is enamelled with a rose spray in an oval cartouche and bears the pattern number '171' in black.

291

Pearlware transfer-printed in underglaze blue

1800–10
PLATE 93
161mm (B607)

Another pot (84.950) is identical but for a painted mark '2' and a domed strainer, unlike the flat strainer of the present example. Unlike the other example, the present pot has had incised lines added to indicate the edges of the wings and the tail-feathers of the swan knob. A pot of identical shape painted in enamel colours (B103) is marked with an impressed circle under the footrim.

292

Pearlware hand-coloured over a brown transfer print, Thomas Harley, Longton, Staffs.

c.1805–10
PLATE 94
156mm (B562)
Impressed mark: 'HARLEY'
Prov: Caldwell

Harley's version of the lozenge shape is distinguished by the low thumb-rest on the handle. The decoration is similar to the 'Boy at the Door' pattern used by Miles Mason (see no.383). A pot of matching shape (B102) is painted in enamel colours. Thomas Harley was at Longton in 1801. Wares are usually attributed to his period of potting up to 1808, but he then moved to the Park Works, Longton, with a solicitor named Seckerson as his partner. They moved again in 1812, and the partnership continued into the 1820s.

293

Pearlware painted in enamel colours

1800–10
PLATE 94
147mm (B104)
Painted mark in puce enamel: 'No 2'

Another pot (B264) has the same body moulding, the same version of the swan knob with a turned-up tail and the same technique of pink borders decorated in sgraffito. It has a taller thumb-rest to the handle. The pink sgraffito is found on another pot (M971) of a different shape which matches another (2.84.950) decorated with a blue-printed pattern of formal scrolls.

294

White feldspathic stoneware with brown slip

c.1805–10
PLATE 94
141mm (B254)
Ref: Hodgson 1921, p.151 pl.IV

The applied reliefs are, on the obverse, a trophy of arms inscribed 'PATRIOTS', flanked by a pyramid with a crocodile, and a castle; on the reverse, Fame inscribing 'HOWE' and 'NELSON' on a shield before an obelisk, and Britannia. Two pots of matching shape are M1007 and M1008. See also no.298 below.

295

Basalt stoneware

c.1805–10
PLATE 95
157mm (1546)
Impressed mark at base of handle: 'W'

Two white stoneware pots (1593 and M853) are of matching shape apart from the knob of the latter. A sugar-box of matching design[1] has applied reliefs matching those on the reverse of no.294 (see previous entry).

[1] Edwards Roussel 1982, pl.85.

296

Basalt stoneware, Keeling Toft & Co., Hanley, Staffs.

c.1800–10
PLATE 95
136mm (M1004)

The applied reliefs are, on the obverse, Peace seated and Liberty standing at an altar; on the reverse, Liberty with Science, Art and Labour. A leaf has been sprigged on to complete the bottom border at either end of the pot, where the two press-moulded halves of the pot were joined together and the border moulding would have suffered. The shape matches a marked pot and fragments excavated in Hanley.[1] Keeling Toft & Co. were in business in 1802, and by 1807 were running three potworks. They continued until 1826.

[1] Hollens 1983, pl.120c & d.

pl.96
299

297

Basalt stoneware, possibly Chetham & Woolley, Longton, Staffs.

*c.*1810
PLATE 95
158mm (M1003)

The applied reliefs are, on the obverse, the Power of Love and, on the reverse, a kneeling and a standing putto with torches. Part of a cover and part of a body showing the spandrel of the arch and the side panel have been excavated on the site of Chetham and Woolley's works in Commerce Street, Longton.[1] They are of white stoneware but match the present example. Another pot (M1014) has a handle of related but different shape and is probably by another manufacturer. For Chetham and Woolley see no.220.

[1] Edwards Roussel 1982, pl.73; Hollens 1983, pls.113c and 116a.

298

Basalt stoneware

*c.*1805–10
PLATE 95
158mm (B641)
Impressed mark at base of handle: 'B'
Ref: Warner 1947, p.127

The applied reliefs are, on the obverse, as the reverse of no.294 above, except that Fame inscribes only Nelson's name; on the reverse, as the obverse of no.294 except that 'TRAFALGAR' is the inscription.

299

Caneware painted with blue enamel trim, Thomas Lakin, Burslem

*c.*1796–9
PLATE 96
146mm (M1141)

A pot matching the present example and impressed 'Lakin' is in Stoke-on-Trent Museum,[1] and another example impressed 'Lakin & Poole' is in the Harris Museum, Preston. A pot of very similar shape, but lacking the moulded foliage on the shoulder, is a marked Davenport one in Dover Museum.[2] A pot in hybrid hard-paste porcelain (M1135) matches the latter and is attributed to Davenport.[3] Like the present Lakin pot, it lacks a flange to the cover. The similarity between these Lakin and Davenport pots is likely to be related to Lakin's move to work for Davenport. For Lakin see no.252 above.

[1] Miller and Berthoud 1985, pl.1143.
[2] *Op.cit.* pl.1136.
[3] *NCSN* 49, 1983, pp.24–5.

300

Basalt stoneware, possibly John Glass, Hanley, Staffs.

*c.*1810
PLATE 97
130mm (B362)
Impressed mark at base of handle: 'S'
Ref: Hodgson 1921, p.152 pl.V

The applied reliefs are, on the obverse, a lion with a fox (from Aesop's Fables), and on the reverse, Diana with a nymph and hound. Apart from the knob, the shape appears to match a pot marked 'J. GLASS, Hanley' in the Rakow collection.[1] Another pot of the same body shape with the same mark has a variant of the handle with an extra projection from the top towards the neck of the pot:[2] this handle is found on two other pots (M734 and M739) which have the same body shape as the present pot. One (M739) has a different spout with at its tip five projecting bobbles graduated in size from the middle. Another pot (M741) matches the latter but has a different handle shape.

[1] Miller and Berthoud 1985, pl.744; and see Godden 1974, p.170 pl.219.
[2] Miller and Berthoud 1985, pl.742.

301

Basalt stoneware

*c.*1830
PLATE 97
153mm (B194)
Impressed mark: '87' or 'L8'
Prov: General Bulwer
Ref: Hodgson 1921, p.152 pl.V

The body moulding is of the same design as an earthenware pot in the Yorkshire Museum incised 'Made by Enoch Barker at the Don Pottery',[1] and another in a private collection incised 'Made by Enoch Barker, May 1876'[2] but the handle, spout and knob on the present pot are all different. Another example in basalt (1601) has a replacement knob but otherwise matches the present pot and bears the roughly incised mark '26'.

[1] Miller and Berthoud 1985, pl.1375.
[2] Doncaster 1983, no.98.

302

Pearlware painted in high-temperature underglaze colours

c.1810
COLOUR PLATE 17
167mm (1623)

The body moulding apparently matches a basalt pot marked 'LEEDS POTTERY' at Temple Newsam.[1]

[1] Walton 1976, p.261 no.1114.

303

Basalt stoneware, probably Keeling Toft & Co., Hanley, Staffs.

c.1810
PLATE 98
141mm (1611)
Impressed mark: '17'

The applied reliefs are, on the obverse, Diana and Endymion, and on the reverse a winged female carrying a torch and emptying a pot of water. The moulding apparently matches a fragment comprising the handle and the rear portion of the body, in a batch of excavated material which has been identified as coming from the partnership of Keeling Toft & Co.[1] (see also no.296 above).

[1] Hollens 1983, p.228 and pl.122a.

304

White feldspathic stoneware

c.1810
PLATE 99
152mm (B109)
Impressed mark: 'I' at base of handle

The applied reliefs are, on the obverse, a seated Mercury, and on the reverse Venus in her shell boat pulled by dolphins. The knob matches the marked 's & Oc' pot no.259, and the spout matches 1578 (p.177, fig.22). One pot with matching moulded details (1621) has the same mark, while another (48.21, cover missing) is impressed 'R' in the same position.

305

White feldspathic stoneware

c.1810
PLATE 99
157mm (B110)

The applied reliefs are, on the obverse, a group of cupids with sheep, and on the reverse 'Sportive Love'. A pot with matching body and spout (M757) has a handle matching the previous pot, and also has the impressed mark 'I'. Another example (M759) has a handle found also with another body shape (M881). Two pots with another body shape (M947 and 1594) have the same lower border of fleur-de-lys as no.306 and also have the impressed mark 'I'. The former example also has the same handle as the present pot.

306

White feldspathic stoneware, possibly Cyples

*c.*1810
PLATE 99
151mm (M864)
Impressed mark: 'R'

The applied reliefs are, on the obverse a standing woman garlanding an urn, and on the reverse a standing woman weeping at an urn, behind which stands an obelisk. All three of the horizontal border mouldings, the two on the body and the one on the cover, are found on two oval pots (M859 and M861). The former of these also has the same knob and spout, and its handle matches a pot in a private collection[1] whose body and spout match M947 (see previous entry). M861 has the same handle as the present pot, and is impressed 'I' at the base of the handle, but lacks its cover. The attribution of the present pot to Cyples was made by the late David Hollens. For the Cyples family see no.329 below.

[1] Miller and Berthoud 1985, pl.945.

307

White feldspathic stoneware, possibly Heath & Son, Burslem, Staffs.

*c.*1810
PLATE 99
141mm (1605)

The applied reliefs are paired cupids emblematic of (obverse) Painting and (reverse) Music. A pot impressed 'Heath & Son' in the Victoria and Albert Museum has the same body shape but a loop handle with thumb-rest. A pot lacking its cover (M1009) is of this shape. A very similar shape with slightly taller proportions is found on two other pots (M1012 and 1604). These two have a loop handle with acanthus foliage but no thumb-rest, and 1604 has a bail knob like the present pot. Turner made a version of this body shape, lacking the horizontal bands of ornament: a marked sugar-box is in the Rakow collection.[1]

[1] Edwards Roussel 1982, pl.103.

308

White feldspathic stoneware, Heath & Son, Staffs.

*c.*1800
PLATE 100
123mm (1624)
Impressed mark: 'HEATH & SON'

Pointed oval in plan. The knob is missing. The applied reliefs are of Pomona and Hygeia. The moulded border around the neck of the pot is a slightly simpler version of that on the marked Warburton pot no.262A. A matching example complete with its knob is in the Stoke-on-Trent Museum.[1] The existence of similar examples marked by the short-lived firm of Bradley & Co., Coalport, *c.*1796–1800, suggests a similar date for the present pot.

[1] Miller and Berthoud 1985, pl.925.

309

Pearlware painted in enamel colours

*c.*1800
COLOUR PLATE 16
178mm (M926)

Pointed oval in plan. The cover has no flange. The applied reliefs are, on the obverse, a figure with a bow and, apparently, a key; on the reverse, a figure with a lyre. The border on the neck of the pot is quite different, and very much simpler, than that on the previous pot.

310

Pearlware, painted in enamel colours

*c.*1800
COLOUR PLATE 16
123mm (B392)

Pointed oval in plan. The applied reliefs are, on the obverse, a standing Venus with a dolphin, and on the reverse, a profile bust over a shell. Other pots with very similar moulded bodies (M927 and M928 in pearlware and M930 in basalt) have heads of Mercury with a winged helmet in the spandrels flanking the upper part of the central cartouche.

311

Pearlware printed in underglaze blue, possibly Herculaneum Pottery,
Liverpool

*c.*1800
PLATE 101
148mm (1640)

Pointed oval in plan. The cover is hinged. The print is a version of one known on marked Turner pottery and porcelain,[1] but in the present version the man has a white collar. The lower part of the print, showing a two-legged bird, was cut off and stuck on the handle. In the Turner version the bird appears to have only one leg. I am grateful to Minnie Holdaway for suggesting the tentative attribution for this piece.

[1] Godden 1983, p.93 fig.144A.

312

Pearlware transfer-printed in underglaze blue, Thomas Harley,
Longton, Staffs.

*c.*1810–15
PLATE 101
159mm (B216)

The print on the reverse differs only in having a unicorn in place of the lion.[1] The shape matches an example (B615) with a blue print of formal flowers and the impressed mark 'HARLEY'. It also matches a brown earthenware example (M724) with a Chinese landscape transfer-printed in yellow. The traditional attribution of yellow-printed brownware to Portobello in Scotland is now thought to be mistaken.[2]

[1] As Coysh and Henrywood 1989, p.236, the 'Vulture Centre'.
[2] Williams-Wood 1986, pp.31–5.

313

White feldspathic stoneware, with stand

*c.*1810–15
PLATE 107
137mm (B111)

The strainer is domed. The body shape, basically the 'New Oval' in porcelain (see p.214), is unusual in dry-bodied stoneware. The handle matches that on no.297, attributed to Chetham & Woolley. Another pot (M1014) has a handle of different, though related, form.

314

Pearlware transfer-printed in purple, Shorthose, Hanley

*c.*1815–20
PLATE 102
128mm (B364)
Impressed mark: 'SHORTHOSE & CO.' Printed mark in purple 'Shortho . . .'
Ref: Hodgson 1921, p.151 pl.IV

The cover is held in place by a two-pronged restraint at the rear of the pot. John Shorthose was in partnership with Thomas Heath at Shelton from 1794 until 1815, and was working until bankruptcy in 1823. The form Shorthose & Co. occurs in the Rate Books only in 1817 and 1822.

pl.102
315
314

pl.103
316
317

315

White earthenware, transfer-printed in underglaze blue, Spode

c.1815–20
PLATE 102
110mm (B155)
Impressed mark: 'Spode'
Prov: gift of Colonel Waverstein

The print is the 'Milkmaid' pattern, thought to have been introduced about 1814–15.[1]

[1] Drakard and Holdway 1983, p.136 P702.

316

Basalt stoneware, Davenport

c.1820
PLATE 103
127mm (M567)
Impressed mark: 'DAVENPORT' with the letters arranged in an arc above an anchor

The applied reliefs are, on the obverse, 'Sportive Love', Liberty addressing Science, Art and Labour, and Poor Maria; on the reverse, the Bourbonnais Shepherd, a standing woman weeping at an urn before an obelisk, and another garlanding an urn. The knob is a sibyl of the type recognised as Davenport's, a copy of the Wedgwood type classified as no.1.[1] The mark with capital letters is thought not to have been used before about 1815.

[1] Rakow 1983, p.166.

317

Basalt stoneware lined in pale blue enamel, possibly Spode

c.1810
PLATE 103
151mm (1666)

The knob is in the form of a sibyl seated with a book, her right elbow leaning on a broken column.[1] This rare type has been reported on a Spode pot,[2] and the distinctive handle and notched parapet also match marked Spode examples.[3]

[1] Rakow 1983, p.167.
[2] Gunson and Robertshaw 1980, p.18.
[3] Miller and Berthoud 1985, pl.571.

318

White earthenware transfer-printed in underglaze blue

c.1820
PLATE 104
302mm (B182)
Prov: General Bulwer

A pot of this size is impossible to lift when full unless it has an additional handle near the junction of spout and body. The absence of a handle suggests that this pot may have been made for advertising purposes, perhaps for a shop display, like the famous pot made in 1773 at the Swinton Pottery for Richard Patrick's shop.[1]

[1] Bennett 1978–9, p.149; Cox and Cox 1983, pl.7.

pl.104

318
319   320

pl.105
324
321

319

Pearlware transfer-printed in orange and painted in underglaze blue, red enamel and gold, Wedgwood

*c.*1810–20
PLATE 104
131mm (B130)
Impressed mark: 'WEDGWOOD'
Prov: General Bulwer

A piece is missing from the rear of the parapet. The decoration is Wedgwood's Japan pattern no.2. Another pot with this pattern (M439) is marked 'N2' in red enamel, and differs in having a plain loop handle. A pot of the same shape as the latter (1642) is transfer-printed in underglaze blue with the 'Basket' pattern.[1]

[1] des Fontaines 1983, pl.105b.

320

White earthenware painted in red, green and brown enamels with purple lustre, John Wedg Wood, Burslem, Staffs.

*c.*1840
PLATE 104
89mm (M449)
Impressed mark: 'WEDG WOOD'

The knob is modern: the original was probably globular. John Wood II (1778–1848), the son of John Wood I (see no.236), christened one of his sons John Wedg. In a potting family, this represented a shrewd investment for the boy's future! John Wedg Wood (1813–1857) was in partnership with Edward Challinor before 1837. Not long after this date he was renting the Hadderidge Potbank in Burslem. In 1841 John Wood II gave his share in the Woodlands Pottery to his three sons, and from 1845 John Wedg Wood became sole owner. It has been suggested that he used the above form of mark between 1837 and 1840 or 1844.[1] Wedg Wood was not making serious efforts to deceive, since his mark is often, as in this example, so badly impressed as to be scarcely legible.

[1] des Fontaines 1987, pp.143–66.

321

Pearlware with silver resist lustre decoration

*c.*1810–20
PLATE 105
140mm (B135)
Ref: Warner 1947, p.126

The resist is the waxy substance used to paint the design, so that when the pot was coated in the platinum mixture, the latter would not adhere to the design. For the dating of the introduction of platinum (including 'silver') lustres, see no.426.

pl.106
322

322

Caneware, Elijah Mayer, Hanley, Staffs.

*c.*1800–10
PLATE 106
98mm (1558)
Impressed mark: 'E. Mayer'

Projections at either side of the opening engage with notches on the cover to prevent it from slipping forwards when the pot is tilted. The cover has no flange. The strainer is domed. The same shape was made in basalt (B363). For Elijah Mayer see no.217. A pearlware pot of similar shape impressed 'MEIGH' (M1272) lacks the applied relief of anthemions around the body, and has a plain strainer, a pouring guard with a central notch and a flange on the rear part of the cover.

323

Calcedony earthenware painted in red and black enamel

*c.*1810
COLOUR PLATE 17
113mm (1557)

The Davenport factory referred to their orange-brown ware as 'calcedony', and both their former manager Thomas Lakin and William Brameld of the Swinton Pottery give recipes for 'chalcedony'.[1] The shape is not a known Davenport one. The handle has a cover restraint attached, and three moulded acanthus leaves in the position of a thumb-rest. The strainer is, however, of the cylindrical form used by the factory (see fig.54, p.235). The pot has no pouring guard and the cover engages in the normal way, unlike the pot in the previous entry. A black basalt pot (1556) has a handle similar to one used by Davenport (see no.425) but apart from its knob matches exactly the shape of an earthenware pot marked 'TH & Co.' (M1169) attributed to Thomas Harley.

[1] Lockett and Godden 1989, p.92.

324

Drab earthenware painted in blue and white slip, brown enamel and gilding, Thomas Lakin, Stoke-on-Trent, Staffs.

1812–17
PLATE 105
127mm (M2245)
Impressed mark: 'Drab Porcelain'

For Lakin's earlier career see no.252 above. He potted at Stoke from 1810 until about 1817, when his business appears to have failed. After working briefly as a freelance enameller, he moved to Leeds, becoming a manager at the Leeds Pottery, and died there in 1821. His widow saw to the publication by Edward Baines of Leeds in 1824 of 'The Valuable Receipts of the Late Mr Thomas Lakin'. The ingredients for his 'drab body' are given as '24 parts of Argillaceous Marl/48 parts of Cornish Stone/24 parts of Blue Clay/10 parts of Bones/1 part of Nickle (calcined)'.[1] The 'London' shape is thought to have been introduced by porcelain manufacturers about 1812. Undecorated drab earthenware pots of this shape were made by Wedgwood (M1467) and Ridgway (M1469). Lakin's attempt to raise the status of these wares in the market by ambitious decoration was apparently unsuccessful. His term 'Drab porcelain' was strictly inaccurate, but no more so than the 'Opaque China' of other manufacturers.

[1] Blakey 1984, pp.79–114.

325

Basalt stoneware, Riley, Staffs.

*c.*1820
PLATE 108
134mm to top of cover, without knob (1520)
Impressed marks: 'RILEY' and '6'
Ref: Pomfret 1988, p.21 pl.19

The surface has a distinctive grey appearance rather like cast iron. The present knob is a metal replacement. A marked sugar-box of matching design in Warrington Museum suggests that the knob was an open flower. (See Ref.) The piece is noticeably heavy in weight. The outer edge of the cover is angled downwards and the flange is angled inwards. The strainer is domed, with oversized holes. Two other pots of different shapes which share these features of cover and strainer are M1405, impressed '30', and M1407, impressed '24'.

326

Basalt stoneware, Leeds Pottery

*c.*1820
PLATE 108
129mm (M1396)
Impressed mark: 'HARTLEY GREENS & CO.'

The shape corresponds to a design in the Leeds Pottery's Blackware Drawing Book.[1] On this example the strawberry pattern on the body extends around the ends of the pot, but on another marked example the pattern does not.[2] Unmarked examples in which the pattern does not extend around the ends are a basalt (M1395),[3] a silver lustred earthenware (M1394), and a white feldspathic stoneware (B274), which has a different knob matching no.294. Since other factories made this shape (see next entry), these are of uncertain origin. A copper lustre earthenware pot (1537) has panels not moulded but painted with the strawberry and vine patterns in enamel colours, but its shape otherwise matches the present pot. Another marked Leeds oblong basalt is of a different shape (M1402).

[1] Print Room, Leeds City Libraries.
[2] Walton 1976, p.262 no.1115.
[3] Miller and Berthoud 1985, pls.1395 and 1396 were interchanged in error.

327

Basalt stoneware, probably Riley, Staffs.

*c.*1820
PLATE 108
149mm (1542)

The shape is extremely close to the pot in the previous entry, but the body is of the grey 'cast-iron' type like no.325 above. The cover has the same curious arrangement of down-bent outer edge and in-bent flange. The strainer is flat but has the same oversized holes.

328

White feldspathic stoneware

*c.*1820
PLATE 107
142mm (1521)

The handle and knob match no.326 above.

329

Basalt stoneware, Cyples, Longton, Staffs.

*c.*1820
PLATE 108
140mm (M1384)
Impressed mark: 'CYPLES'

The Cyples family were active at Lane End from *c.*1784. After the death of Jesse Cyples in 1810, the works were continued by his widow Lydia until their sons Richard and William were old enough to take over.

pl.109

333	331
330	332

330

Basalt stoneware, probably Swinton Pottery (known as Rockingham from 1826), Yorkshire

*c.*1825
PLATE 109
159mm (B191)
Prov: General Bulwer
Ref: Hodgson 1921, p.152 pl.V

The moulded decoration of roses, thistles and shamrock includes the inscription 'IUNCTA IN UNO TRIA' (three joined in one), referring to the union of England, Scotland and Ireland. These were popular decorative motifs at the time of George IV's accession in 1820, even before his visits to Ireland and Scotland in the following two years. Sherds matching this pot were excavated on the Swinton site.[1]

[1] Eaglestone and Lockett 1973, pl.X.

331

Basalt stoneware

*c.*1825
PLATE 109
143mm (1527)
Impressed mark: '23' in cursive script

The moulded decoration takes the form of roses, thistles and shamrock, and the knob is a thistle. These three plants were popular decoration for basalt pots in the 1820s (M918, and see previous entry). For the style of mark see the following entry.

332

Basalt stoneware

*c.*1820
PLATE 109
161mm (1529)
Impressed mark: '35' or '65' in cursive script

The unusual cursive style of the impressed numbers suggests that this may be from the same factory as the previous pot.

333

Basalt stoneware, Yates, Shelton, Staffs.

*c.*1820
PLATE 109
146mm (1528)

The shape matches an example impressed 'YATES' in the V&A.[1] A very similar handle is found on Yates porcelain (no.499 below). Another pot (M1400) has the same knob and spout and the same anthemion design on a different body shape, and is impressed '21'.

[1] Miller and Berthoud 1985, pl.1383.

Porcelain Goes Classical

This chapter covers the years from about 1780 to the period of the 'London' shape around 1820. The neoclassical taste was the most important fresh influence upon the design of teapots, but the oriental associations of porcelain and the vigorous development of watercolour painting, whether of land-scapes or flowers, ensured that the classical influence on form would be tempered by picturesque exoticism or naturalism in the decoration.

pl.110

335	338
339	336

Round and Barrel Shape

334

Worcester. Painted with an underglaze blue border, enamel colours and gilding

*c.*1780
COLOUR PLATE 14
137mm (M334)
Painted mark in underglaze blue: open crescent

Compare the Caughley barrel shape (next entry). The decoration[1] is related to, but different from, the 'Lord Henry Thynne' pattern.[2] An unusual Worcester pot of bulging square shape with indented corners (1935, knob missing) has the same spout and handle as the present pot.

[1] *Cf.* Spero 1984, no.141.
[2] *Op.cit.* no.140.

335

Caughley, Shropshire. Painted with enamel colours and gilding

*c.*1780
PLATE 110
136mm (B322)
Ref: Hodgson 1923, p.33 pl.VI

Thomas Turner left the Worcester factory about 1772 to set up a rival factory at Caughley. The porcelain produced there is often very similar to Worcester. The Caughley version of this barrel shape is most readily distinguished from its Worcester counterpart (see previous pot) by the larger upper lobe to the ear-shaped handle.

336

Caughley. Printed in underglaze blue

*c.*1780–90
PLATE 110
147mm (B329)
Printed mark in underglaze blue: 'S'

The distinctive spout and handle are a close copy of an imported Chinese shape (M326). The same shape is also found in creamware. The 'Pagoda' pattern with which it is printed is also similar to Chinese painted originals.

337

Caughley. Painted with enamel colours and gilding, probably by Fidelle Duvivier at Chamberlain's Worcester establishment. Cover missing

*c.*1792
COLOUR PLATE 18
121mm to rim (M342)
Ref: Godden 1982, p.194 and pl.238

Robert Chamberlain left the Worcester porcelain factory about 1786 to set up his own porcelain decorating studio in the town. Thomas Turner at Caughley was regularly sending glazed porcelain to him for decoration by 1788 (see also no.358). A single one of Chamberlain's fortnightly wage lists in October 1792 records a payment of three guineas to 'M. Deviea'. A guinea and a half a week would be the wages of a top enameller. It has been suggested (see Ref.) that Fidelle Duvivier was intended. The service to which the present pot belongs is the only porcelain which has yet been connected with his presence at Chamberlain's. Some pieces of the service, for example the sugar dish, appear to be decorated by another hand, apparently an imitator. As the wages records suggest, he was evidently not at Chamberlain's for long.

Duvivier was born in Belgium in 1740 and learnt his art at the Tournai porcelain factory. By 1792 he had worked in London, at Derby, perhaps for the 'Dr Wall' Worcester factory and, after an interval in France, for New Hall and for Turner in Staffordshire.

338

New Hall, Shelton, Staffs. Painted in pink enamel

1782–5
PLATE 110
128mm (B293)
Ref: Holgate 1987, p.141 pl.126

The beginnings of the firm which was to be commonly known as New Hall date from 1781, when Richard Champion of the ailing Bristol factory sold his patent for the production of hard-paste porcelain to a consortium of ten Staffordshire potters. Two of these potters, John Turner and Anthony Keeling, withdrew and by 1784 the firm was styled Heath, Warburton & Co. By 1787 it was known as Hollins, Warburton & Co. The type of hard-paste made at New Hall has been called 'hybrid' because it was fired in the manner of British soft-paste rather than oriental hard-paste, the unglazed or 'biscuit' porcelain being fired at high temperature and re-fired at lower temperature after glazing. The more demanding oriental method, which had caused insuperable problems at Plymouth and Bristol, required the high temperature firing after glazing.

pl.111

341	340
343	342

The 'clip' handle on the present pot is so-called because it looks as though the two parts have been clipped together. The pattern is New Hall's no.12. The open flower knob is also found on a covered sugar dish with corrugated ribbing in the museum's collections.[1]

[1] Stoke 1981, no.3.

339

Unknown factory. Painted in enamel colours

c.1790–1800
PLATE 110
148mm (1930)

The body appers to be of hybrid hard-paste porcelain. The shape of the spout is very reminiscent of 'Factory Z' (see no.375). Spirally fluted shapes such as this were referred to at the time as 'shanked' or 'shankered'.

340

New Hall. Painted in enamel colours

c.1790
PLATE 111
167mm (B246)

The pattern is New Hall's no.20. This body shape is distinguished from that of no.342 below by the angle above the footrim.[1] The knob is pierced with a steam vent. The spout is moulded with ten flutes rising to a wreath of husks around it. The handle has a projecting thumb-rest. The various ribbed or fluted versions of this shape have a plain strap handle without the thumb-rest, and may have a knob moulded in the form of a pine cone (see no.348 below) instead of the simple onion shape seen on the plain body shape here. It became normal for the factory to differentiate its plain from its fancy versions of a body shape in this way.[2] An example of this body shape with broad flutes (B317) has a spout without the encircling wreath, but with ten longitudinal flutes instead.

[1] *Cf.* Holgate 1987, pl.15 left.
[2] *Op.cit.* p.51.

341

Factory X. Painted in enamel colours

c.1790
PLATE 111
171mm (1929)

The unidentified group known as 'Factory X'[1] employed a hybrid hard-paste porcelain resembling New Hall. The present shape is distinguished from New Hall particularly by the more conical knob with no steam vent, and the stubby thumb-rest projecting upwards on the handle. Sometimes a knob more like the onion shape of New Hall is used, as on a pot in the Harris Museum and Art Gallery, Preston.[2] The tip of the spout may also have a raised moulding on the upper edge (see no.343 below).[3] The lower terminal of the handle separates from the body of the pot, unlike New Hall.

[1] Holgate 1971, pp.96–103.
[2] *Op.cit.* pl.215.
[3] *Ibid.*; Miller and Berthoud 1985, pls.385–6.

pl.112
344   347
348   349

342

New Hall. Printed in underglaze blue

*c.*1790
PLATE 111
152mm (1939)

The tip of the onion knob is missing. The plain version of this shape, like the present pot, has the 'clip' handle (see no.338 above),[1] while the ribbed or fluted versions have a plain strap handle. The printed pattern[2] is also found in a slightly different version.[3]

[1] Holgate 1987, pl.12.
[2] *Op.cit.* pl.100.
[3] de Saye Hutton 1990, pl.287 no.U176.

343

Factory X. Painted in enamel colours

*c.*1790
PLATE 111
159mm (M1111)

The handle has a 'clip' similar to New Hall (see previous entry). The spout tip has a raised ridge on the upper edge.

344

Neale & Co., Hanley, Staffs. Painted with pink and green enamels and gilding

*c.*1790
PLATE 112
162mm (M374)
Ref: Godden 1983, p.54 pl.80; Edwards 1987, pl.173

James Neale was the principal partner in Humphrey Palmer's former business from 1778 to 1792. It is uncertain when during this period the rare porcelains of the firm were made. Their body contains some 25 per cent bone ash and, despite claims for them as the earliest bone china, the body does not appear to be like that employed by Spode in the late 1790s. The cover of the present pot has a bayonet fitting, derived, like the shape, from Paris porcelain (M375).

345

Neale & Co. Painted with pink and blue enamels and gilding

*c.*1790
COLOUR PLATE 18
171mm (M376)
Painted mark in pink enamel: 'B'
Ref: Godden 1983, p.52 pl.77; Edwards 1987, pl.169

The spiral fluting (shanking or shankering as it was known in the late 18th century) travels up the pot in an anti-clockwise direction and has a moulded leaf in the lower part of each hollow flute. Only Derby porcelain shares these features (see next entry).

346

Derby. Painted with salmon-pink enamel and gilding

*c.*1790
PLATE 118
132mm (1441)
Painted mark in puce enamel: crown over crossed batons and D, and pattern no. '94'
Ref: V&A 1948, no.320 pl.120

The shape is also found with a pine cone moulded knob and a different handle having a projecting thumb-rest (M349). On the spirally fluted version (M353) the flutes are moulded with acanthus leaves in the hollows and travel anti-clockwise upwards just like the Neale version (see previous entry). Contrast the direction of earlier Derby spiral fluting (no.188 above).

347

Pinxton, Derbyshire. Painted with mauve, blue and green enamels and gilding

*c.*1796–1800
PLATE 112
172mm (B405)
Painted pattern no. in purple enamel: 'P/44'

The short-lived factory started at Pinxton in 1796 by the local landowner John Coke with William Billingsley, a leading painter from the Derby factory, produced soft-paste porcelain of high quality. After Billingsley withdrew in 1799, it is not certain whether production continued or whether the firm only decorated porcelain.

pl.113

350	353
352	351

Commode Shape

Known as 'silver shape' by the older generation of collectors, but so many shapes were copied from silver that it seems better to use the term 'commode shape' employed by silversmiths. This name was presumably suggested by analogy with serpentine-fronted furniture. The pots in this section are of hybrid hard-paste porcelain.

348

New Hall. Painted with pink and black enamels and gilding

*c.*1785–90
PLATE 112
144mm (1944)

The earliest version of the shape, with four applied feet moulded as flower heads. The acanthus moulding under the spout is picked out in gilding, and the handle has pronounced herringbone moulding. The present pot, as usual with ribbed or fluted versions of these New Hall shapes, has a pine cone knob. The plain shape has the onion knob pierced with a steam vent (M775).

220

349

New Hall. Painted in enamel colours including the inscription 'Thomas & Betty Hanson 1798'

PLATE 112
146mm (B288)
Painted pattern no. in purple enamel: 'N195'

The standard later form of the shape, in its plain version. In the spirally fluted version (M786) the two projecting vertical 'pillars' on either side of the pot remain vertical, rather than following the curve of the fluting as on the 'Factory X', 'Y' and 'Z' versions. The New Hall spout has two broad facets on either side joined by a curve at top and bottom. The lower curve is much longer than the upper (fig.44b. The drawings do not show the seams at the top and bottom caused by the joins between the two halves of the press-mould).

350

Chamberlain's, Worcester. Painted with enamel colours and gilding

c.1791–5
PLATE 113
127mm (M809)
Ref: Godden 1982, pl.52

About 1791 Robert Chamberlain and his son Humphrey expanded their business from decorating other people's porcelain and began manufacturing their own in a hybrid hard-paste body. The thumb-rest on the handle is a distinctive Chamberlain feature. It has been suggested that this pot is the form referred to in the factory's records as 'organ shape', and that the pattern may be no.1, 'Plain, enamelled sprigs with gold edge'.[1]

[1] Godden 1982, p.72.

351

Factory X. Painted in enamel colours

c.1790–1800
PLATE 113
141mm (1753)
Painted pattern no. in purple enamel: '136'

The 'Factory X' shape has the two pillars on the side noticeably closer together than on New Hall or 'Factory Y' examples. On standard New Hall pots (base about 150mm long) the distance between the mid-points of the pillars (as measured in a straight line across the base) is about 98mm, but on 'Factory X' it is only about 85mm. The 'X' spout (fig.44c) has only one broad facet on either side, flanked by concave curves. The knobs (fig.43b and c) are more exaggerated in form than New Hall's gently curved one (fig.43a). 'X' handles generally have a shorter upper terminal than New Hall or 'Y', and above the terminal the inner surface of the handle usually curves slightly towards the body of the pot. The terminals are usually pointed like an arrow, as New Hall examples before about 1790 also often are. Other example: (1760) pattern 145 (like New Hall pattern 195).

Figure 44
Spout sections:

a Factory Y,

b New Hall,

c Factory X,

d Factory Z

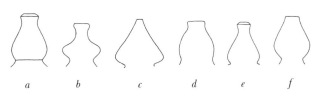

Figure 43 Knobs:
a New Hall,
b & c Factory X,
d & e factory Y,
f Factory Z

a *b* *c* *d* *e* *f*

352

Factory Y. Printed in black and painted over with other enamel colours

*c.*1800
PLATE 113
146mm (B618)

The 'Factory Y' shape has a spout (fig.44a) with two facets at either side like New Hall, but joined at top and bottom by curves of more even size: the spout has fatter proportions than New Hall's. The knob (fig.43d and e) is rather shapeless compared to New Hall. Covers often have flanges much deeper than the 4mm or so of New Hall examples. Handle terminals are semicircular. The pattern on the present pot is similar to New Hall's no.425. Other example: (1757) pattern 119, coloured flower spray and smaller sprigs, scalloped pink border with separate small flower-heads made of blue and pink dots.

353

Factory Z, probably Wolfe, Stoke-on-Trent. Painted with enamel colours

*c.*1800
PLATE 113
141mm (1761)

The 'Factory Z' shape has a spout (fig.44d) with one very broad facet on either side. The pillars on the body of the pot have a concave face or groove running down them. The usual knob is shown in fig.43f. The handle generally has a thumb-rest.

pl.114

357	370
355	356

354

Factory Z, probably Wolfe. Painted with enamel colours and gilding

c.1800
COLOUR PLATE 18
162mm (M801)
Ref: Godden 1983, p.503 pl.654

Other pieces of the service bore the pattern number 109. The opening of the pot is partly covered at the front by a pouring guard (to prevent spillage when the pot is tipped forwards), whose edge curves in, out into a bulge and then in again. The cover, humped at the ends, has no flange.

355

Factory Z, probably Wolfe. Painted with enamel colours

c.1800
PLATE 114
145mm (1947)
Painted pattern no. in red enamel: '127'

The pattern number is near the edge of the base, with the edge below the number as one reads it. This is the usual way round for 'Factory Z' pattern numbers but the opposite to most factories. Elsewhere it was usual to write the number with the edge of the piece just above rather than below it, presumably because it was easier to steady one's hand on the pot. The pouring guard matches the previous pot, as does the form of the cover.

356

Herculaneum, Liverpool. Painted with enamel colours

c.1800
PLATE 114
162mm (M810)
Painted pattern no. in puce enamel: '77'

The Herculaneum pottery was established at Toxteth in Liverpool at the end of 1796, with a skilled workforce largely imported from Staffordshire. In about 1800 the production of porcelain was begun. The present shape is apparently derived from 'Factory Z' porcelain or from Wolfe-Mason Liverpool porcelain.[1] The cover, humped at the ends, has no flange. The knob, much longer than it is wide, is distinctive to Herculaneum. The pouring guard has a central notch.

[1] Godden 1980, p.49 pls.33 and 34.

357

Unknown factory. Painted in enamel colours

c.1800
PLATE 114
135mm (B600)
Painted pattern no. in red enamel: 'No 95'

An apparently identical pot bearing the same pattern number is in the Godden Reference Collection, and belongs to a group of hybrid hard-paste porcelain which often has a small 'x' next to the pattern number.[1]

[1] Godden 1983, p.60 and pl.84.

Oval

358

Caughley. Painted in enamel colours and gilding, probably at Chamberlain's factory, Worcester

1795–99
PLATE 115
152mm to top of cover (M1039)

Thomas Turner appears for a brief period to have made hard-paste porcelain to compete with his new neighbour John Rose, shortly before Turner sold out to him in 1799.[1] This pot is made of a very dirty paste full of black specks, and has a heavily blue-tinted glaze. It is clumsily potted, the base being thin but the cover extremely thick and heavy. The pronounced mould seams, with slight fissures resulting from the casting process, have been noted as typical of this group.[2] The shape is similar to Chamberlain's Worcester (see no.369 below), but the handle is slightly different, and the spout, with its fourteen ribs running half-way up, resembles that usually found on the plain rather than the shanked shape at Chamberlain's (see p.229 fig.48b). The double-line shanking on the body and cover is also frequently found on Chamberlain's porcelain. The knob is missing.

There is evidence from Chamberlain's sales records that his decorating establishment in Worcester was painting this pattern of two doves with the inscription 'L'Amitié' on Caughley porcelain. The abbreviation 'Brosy' stands for 'Broseley', a term often used at Chamberlain's to refer to Caughley porcelain as it was the nearest town to the factory:

> 1 complete set. Brosy. New Amitie £7.7.0. [10 January 1792]

> 2 complete setts, 2nd [size] Nf'd [new fluted] Doves L'Amitie £12.12.0. [6 August 1792].[3]

A coffee cup of the standard Caughley soft-paste porcelain painted with this design is also in the museum's collections.

[1] Edmundson 1989, p.82; Godden 1982, p.80 pl.76.
[2] Edmundson *loc.cit.*
[3] Godden 1969, p.77; Godden 1982, p.51.

359

John Rose, Coalport, Shropshire. Painted with underglaze blue borders and gilding

c.1800
PLATE 115 and fig.45
168mm (1781)

Rose briefly ran the Calcut factory at Jackfield, before moving to Coalport nearby in 1796. Both he and his brother Thomas (see next entry) made hybrid hard-paste porcelain.

The present pot is of the John Rose shanked shape with twenty-eight flutes to the body and cover, twelve to the knob and ten to the spout. The flutes on the knob are straight. The knob and spout are the same on the standard plain body shape. The standard version with straight flutes (M1054) has twenty-eight of them to the body and twenty-four to the cover. The standard ribbed version (B277) has thirty-two ribs to the body and cover, and fourteen to the spout, though an early version (M1052) has ten. One example with a plain body (1942) was given, perhaps accidentally, the spout for the standard ribbed version.

Figure 45

360

John Rose, Coalport. With stand. Painted with enamel colours and gilding

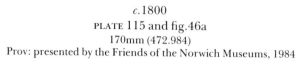

*c.*1800
PLATE 115 and fig.46a
170mm (472.984)
Prov: presented by the Friends of the Norwich Museums, 1984

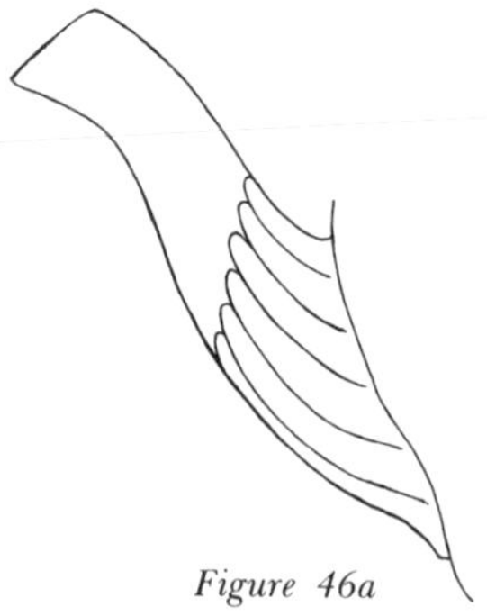

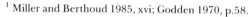

Figure 46a

Figure 46b

An alternative shanked shape made by John Rose. There are twenty-four flutes to the body, cover and stand, and twelve to the knob and spout. The spout is different from the previous pot, with the fluting ending on a slant. It was previously thought that this feature could be used to distinguish the products of John Rose from those of the second, independent factory run by his brother Thomas only a few yards away on the other side of the canal.[1] Thomas also used both the spout whose fluting ends on a slant (1780) and that whose fluting does not (M1047). The most distinctive feature of Thomas' pots is the knob (fig.46b), whose proportions are both taller and less elongated than the John Rose version (fig.45), and which lacks a defined nipple on top. A pot with a vertically fluted body by Thomas Rose (1780) has twenty-eight flutes to both the body and the cover.

[1] Miller and Berthoud 1985, xvi; Godden 1970, p.58.

361

John Rose, Coalport. Painted with blue and mauve enamels and gilding

*c.*1815–20
PLATE 120
121mm (M2247)

This small pot, probably from a 'déjeuner' or 'cabaret' service for one or two people, imitates French porcelain in the solid and sculptural version of the neoclassical taste known generally nowadays as the Empire Style.

362

Derby. Painted with underglaze blue and gilding

*c.*1805–10
PLATE 116
184mm (1931)
Painted mark in red enamel: crown, crossed batons and D over pattern no. '726'

The factory sometimes combined this body shape with a heavy beak-like spout resembling a ship's prow (1936).[1] The latter was presumably an attempt to attain neoclassical dignity.

[1] Miller and Berthoud 1985, pl.1106.

363

New Hall, Staffs. Painted in red enamel

*c.*1800
PLATE 115
187mm (1938)
Painted pattern no. in red enamel: '295'

The knob has no fluting even on this shanked version of the New Hall oval shape. The plain version (1941) also has a waisted body. The strainer is distinctive (see no.386

below). A different New Hall shape, half-way between Oval and Old Oval, is distinguished by its sides which taper gradually inwards in a convex curve towards the base (M670).

Other example: plain shape: 1941, pattern 408.

364

'Pattern Book' factory. Painted in light red enamel and gilding

*c.*1800
PLATE 116
178mm (M1105)
Painted pattern no. in light red enamel: '163'

A version of a shape produced at Pinxton (see no.366 below) and by Flight and Barr at Worcester (see no.372 below). The group to which this piece belongs has been connected by its numbered patterns to a pattern-book of unknown origin in the Victoria and Albert Museum.[1] Grainger's Worcester factory has been suggested as a possible source, but the book's description of the present shape as 'Worcs' might suggest a factory elsewhere. Self-esteem would surely have prevented Grainger's from writing 'Worcs' when they meant the rival factory of Flight and Barr.

[1] Miller and Berthoud 1985, xvi; Berthoud 1987, pp.46–9; Godden 1988, pp.579–85.

365

Pinxton, Derbyshire. Painted in enamel colours and gilding

*c.*1796–1800
COLOUR PLATE 18
159mm (M1103)
Impressed mark: 'C'. Painted pattern no. in gold inside cover: 'P272'

A version of this strange knob is found on Mason porcelain (see no.392). Pinxton also used a simpler knob and handle (fig.47) on the present body shape (1932).

366

Pinxton, Derbyshire. Painted in enamel colours and gilding

*c.*1796–1800
COLOUR PLATE 18
172mm (B649)

Figure 47

A similar shape was made by Flight and Barr at Worcester (see no.372 above) and by the 'Pattern Book' factory (see no.364 above). The vignettes of Peak District scenery were executed by a painter who came, like Billingsley, from the Derby factory.

367

Turner, Lane End, Staffs. Painted in enamel colours

*c.*1800
PLATE 117
178mm (M1082)
Painted pattern no. in pink enamel: '19'
Ref: Godden 1983, p.95 pl.148

In 1800 the Turners took out a patent for earthenware and porcelain made with 'Tabberner's Mine Rock'. Both earthenware and porcelain is known bearing the mark 'TURNER'S PATENT'. Other potters were concerned that they would be prohibited from using this ingredient. A letter in the Wedgwood archives, written by Thomas Byerley at Etruria in 1800, mentions that '. . . W. & J. Turner made china 12 months ago from Cornwall clay but I am told the discovery of this new material is not above two months old . . .'.[1] The Turners were therefore making porcelain before they began using the patent material, and the type with the patent mark does indeed appear different from the present pieces (see also next entry).[2]

Distinctive Turner features on this pot are the moulded spout, whose leaves grow down on to the body (see also no.251 above), the pine cone knob and the form of handle.

[1] Godden 1988, p.733.
[2] *Ibid.*

368

Possibly Turner, Lane End, Staffs. Painted in enamel colours

*c.*1800
PLATE 119
186mm (1940)
Painted mark in red enamel: three parallel straight lines, the middle one longer
than the other two

This shape (M1085 matches) is also found (on M1081) with the same handle as the previous pot, and links the marked Turner porcelains with part of the large group attributed to 'Factory X'. The shape is also linked with porcelain bearing the painted mark 'A.E. Keeling'.[1] Pl.119 shows the cover of M1085 in error.

[1] Godden 1988, p.450.

369

Chamberlain's, Worcester. Painted with yellow borders and sepia enamel and gilding

c.1795–1800
COLOUR PLATE 18
181mm (M1027)

The standard Chamberlain's shanked oval shape. The spout has twelve straight flutes, and the twenty-four shanked flutes on the body and cover are double. The sixteen flutes on the knob are also shanked (fig.48a). The handle is the standard one on Chamberlain's oval shape, having both an inner cusp and an outer one with foliage moulding running down to it. The standard spout for non-shanked pots has fourteen ribs running half-way up (fig.48b). As with most factories' oval shapes, the shanked pot has a waisted body while the fluted, ribbed and plain ones do not. A ribbed example (M1031) has a variant knob (fig.48c). A small, early, plain example (M1036) has a simple knob (fig.48d) and a loop handle unadorned but for some slight moulding best seen from end-on (fig.48e). No Chamberlain Old Oval pot has yet been identified, and it seems that the factory went straight from the Oval to the New Oval: one shanked Oval example (M1033) has the spout and handle of the New Oval shape (see no.416). A plain example (1805) has an open ring knob (fig.48f); this knob also occurs with an angular handle (fig.48g) on a slightly later version of the Oval body (M1030, 1806) having an inward step two-thirds of the way down. This latter shape is apparently referred to as 'Dejeune' in the factory records.[1]

[1] Godden 1982, p.112.

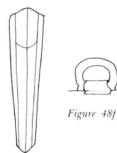

Figure 48a   Figure 48b   Figure 48c   Figure 48d   Figure 48e   Figure 48f   Figure 48g

370

Chamberlain's, Worcester. Painted with a salmon-pink ground, enamel colours and gilding

c.1795–1800
PLATE 114
140mm (M1037)

The handle is a double intertwined one which has leaf terminals like the matching open ring knob. A similar pot, but with the regular form of spout, is in the Godden Reference Collection.[1]

[1] Godden 1982, p.74 pl.61.

pl.118
346   373

371

Flight and Barr, Worcester. Painted with purple enamel and gilding

*c.*1795–1800
PLATE 116
149mm (653.974)
Incised mark: 'B' on base and inside cover. Painted mark in purple enamel: '12'
Prov: bequeathed by Trude Robitschek, 1974

From 1792 the proprietors of the old Worcester factory were Joseph Flight and Martin Barr. The handle on their Oval shape curves in towards the body at the top (M1022 is another example). Sometimes (M1026) it has the extra kink shown in fig.49, a version found also on a tapered round shape (M345).

372

Figure 49

Flight and Barr, Worcester. Painted with red and brown enamels and gilding

*c.*1800
PLATE 116
184mm (M1099)
Incised mark: 'B'

The shape (M1100 matches) differs from most Ovals in that the cover does not overlap the neck of the pot, but sits inside a parapet as on the New Oval (see p.247). A similar shape was made at Pinxton (see no.366 above) and by the 'Pattern Book' factory (see no.364 above).

373

Factory X. Earthenware, printed in underglaze blue

c.1800
PLATE 118
305mm (B279)
Ref: Miller and Berthoud 1985, pl.1068

This shape is found in both porcelain and earthenware. There are thirty shanked flutes to the body and cover, and twelve to the knob. This is an exceptionally large pot, and the more normal size (M1071) has twenty-six to the body, twenty-four to the cover, and ten to the knob (fig.50a). The spout (fig.50b) is distinctive, and some examples (M1073, 1740) have single rather than double lines of fluting, as well as a different form of knob (fig.50c). One example (M1073) has twenty-six rather than twenty-four flutes to the cover.

The related plain body shape (M1079) is waisted and rather broad in the beam, like that of New Hall. It may have a kicked handle like that on the New Oval (see no.418).

374

Factory X. Painted in enamel colours

c.1800
PLATE 117
179mm (1784)

This shape (M1077 matches), narrower in the beam than the previous one, has twenty-eight shanked flutes to the body and cover, twenty-eight straight flutes to the knob and twelve to the spout.

375

Factory Z, probably Wolfe. Painted in enamel colours

c.1800
PLATE 119
180mm (1943)
Painted pattern no. in red enamel: '136'

The standard 'Factory Z' oval shape (M1087 etc. match) is of neoclassical purity. The opening into which the cover fits is humped fore and aft, and the edges of the cover are curved accordingly (see end view, fig.51). The strainer may be either flat or domed.

Other examples: (1786) pattern 24, black bat-printed vase entwined with string of gilt leaves; (1787) pattern 125 (like New Hall pattern 195); (1789) pattern 38, border of gilt triple leaf shapes, joined by grey feather scroll and intertwined with dotted wavy gilt line.

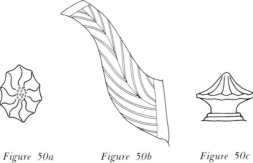

Figure 50a   *Figure 50b*   *Figure 50c*   *Figure 51*

Old Oval

The shape was given this name in the book made for the throwers and turners at the Spode factory in about 1820.[1] By then it was indeed an old shape, and this is a salutary reminder that older shapes and patterns often continued in production, or were re-introduced, alongside newer ones. This shape was accompanied at some factories by the introduction of two practical features: a pouring guard across part of the opening, to prevent tea spilling from it when the full pot was tilted; and a strainer that was domed, to reduce clogging by tea-leaves. Unless stated otherwise, the pots in the following entries have a flat strainer and no pouring guard.

[1] Whiter 1970, p.111.

Figure 52a

376

Caughley, Shropshire. Painted with underglaze blue, green enamel and gilding

1795–9
PLATE 122
127mm (M691)

The body is a distinctive soft-paste which, it has been suggested, reflects Thomas Turner's new source of soapstone about 1795.[1] Another shanked example (1752) and a ribbed one (M692) have a different handle (fig.52a), and the latter has a different spout (fig.52b) and knob (fig.52c).

[1] Edmundson 1989, p.80.

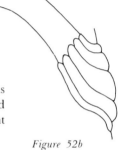

Figure 52b

377

John Rose, Coalport, Shropshire. Painted in green enamel with black outlining

c.1805
PLATE 121
147mm (1957)

Figure 52c

The knob (fig.53) is very similar to the Thomas Rose version of the shape, but the base of the spout joins the body lower down than on his version (see next entry). John Rose used the same handle on a tapered version (M694) resembling Caughley's. A variant with vertical sides (M695) has a flat-topped handle and a high cover with a bayonet fixing.

378

Thomas Rose, Coalport, Shropshire. Painted with enamel colours and gilding

Figure 53

c.1805
PLATE 121
149mm (1774)
Painted pattern no. in puce enamel: '63'

The base of the spout joins the body higher up than on the John Rose version (see previous entry). The numbered patterns on this shape tie up with those of Thomas Rose.[1] The version of the Old Oval formerly thought to be Thomas Rose's[2] is now known to be from the mysterious 'Pattern Book' factory (see no.387 below).

[1] Miller and Berthoud 1985, xvi.
[2] Godden 1970, p.59.

379

Davenport, Staffs. Knob missing. Earthenware, printed in underglaze blue

*c.*1800
PLATE 123
140mm (M716)
Impressed mark: 'Davenport' over an anchor

Figure 54

The shape is found in earthenware and porcelain, with or without the parapet. Note the delicate inner cusp on the handle: another form has its upper part divided into two.[1] The strainer is domed; some examples (M718) have a neatly made little cylindrical one (fig.54).

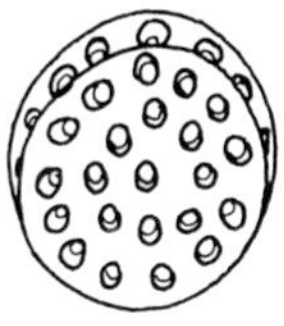

[1] Miller and Berthoud 1985, pl.719.

380

Derby. Painted with underglaze blue and gold

*c.*1800
PLATE 122
162mm (M647)
Painted mark and pattern no. in puce: crown over crossed batons over 'D110', also '2'

The opening in the neck of the Derby Old Oval is sometimes octagonal, as with this pot (compare Pinxton below). The cover has no flange. Two handle variants are shown in fig.55a (M643) and fig.55b (M644).

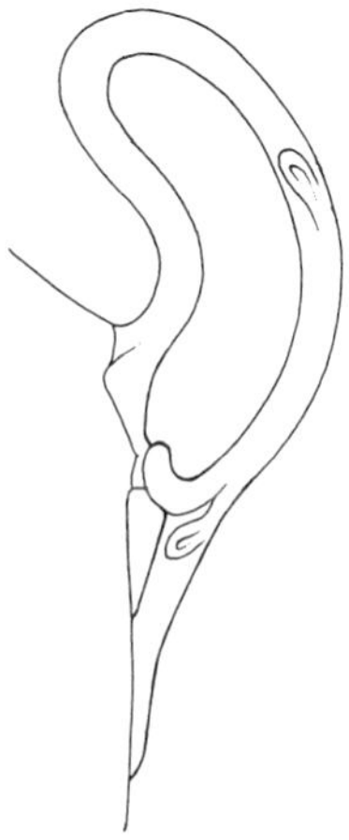

Figure 55a

381

Wolfe and Mason, Liverpool. Printed in underglaze blue

*c.*1796–1800
PLATE 122
171mm (1777)

Figure 55a

Miles Mason, the London dealer in Chinese porcelain, changed direction after the East India Company ceased importing porcelain on its own account (see p.22). In 1795 he went into partnership with Thomas Luckock and the Stoke potter Thomas Wolfe, who made hybrid hard-paste porcelain for him at the Islington factory in Liverpool until 1800. Fragments printed with this version of the pattern known variously as the 'Pagoda', 'Two Temples' or 'Broseley-Willow' have been found on the factory site.[1]

The body has vertical grooves on either side in the pattern 2–1–2. Unusually for an Old Oval shape, the cover overlaps, rather than fitting inside, the edge of the neck, but this is quite normal on Wolfe-Mason pots. Another example (9.159.985) is of matching shape (and pattern) apart from a three-lobed knob (fig.56).

[1] Smith 1972, pls.152b, p.153a; Godden 1980, p.32 pl.11.

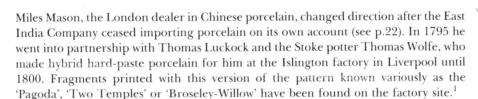

Figure 55b

382

Wolfe and Mason, Liverpool. Printed in underglaze blue

*c.*1796–1800
PLATE 122
155mm (1950)

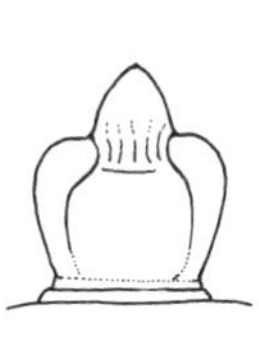

Figure 56

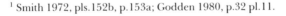

The same pattern as the previous pot, on the version of the shape without vertical grooves, with a different handle and an unusual knob.

pl.123
228
379

pl.124
388   385
386   389

383

Mason, Lane Delph, Staffs. Painted with enamel colours and gilding over black outline print

*c.*1805
PLATE 120
141mm (1959)

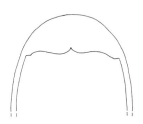

Figure 57a

Mason's partnership with Thomas Wolfe was dissolved in 1800, and in 1804 porcelain of hybrid hard-paste type made at his new factory, the Victoria Works at Lane Delph, was on sale. In 1807 he moved to the Minerva Works in Fenton. The rather globular knob is reminiscent of the wares made during the Wolfe partnership (see no.381 above), and the same vertical grooves on the body are often found. The present pot has a pouring-guard of distinctive Mason type, having angled or notched corners (fig.57a); another version (M706, M714) is a simple curve at both ends of the pot, leaving a circular opening. The more usual handle has a kick, either small or large (M714), as in fig.57b. A knob with four horizontal lobes (fig.57c, M712) reminds one of the roof of a pagoda. The pattern on the present pot is the so-called 'Boy at the Door', which it is suggested might have been Pattern 1 at Mason's Victoria Works.[1]

[1] Godden 1980, p.71.

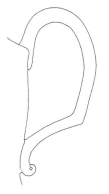

Figure 57b

384

Mason. Bat-printed in black enamel and painted with salmon-pink borders and gilding

*c.*1805
COLOUR PLATE 19
152mm (M710)

Figure 57c

The body has on both sides the vertical grooves in the pattern 2–1–2, derived from Wolfe's Liverpool wares (see no.381 above). The pouring guard resembles the previous pot (fig.57a). Some handles (M706) omit the linking bar to the neck of the pot, but retain the thumbpiece.

Other example: (1776) pattern 22, orange vase of pink flowers, single sprigs of red flowers, pink border with flowers.

385

Minton, Stoke-on-Trent. Painted in enamel colours. Knob missing

*c.*1800
PLATE 124
139mm to top of cover (1948)
Painted pattern no. in puce enamel: 'N7'

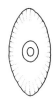

Figure 58a

Thomas Minton's works became operational in 1796. References to 'china' in the factory records for the following year may refer to wares bought in for resale. It was apparently not until 1798 that Minton visited Cornwall to secure his source of china clay for porcelain production.[1] His body is bone china, which he must have begun to make within a very few years of Spode.

The present pot is illustrated, despite its condition, because it is the rare shanked version of the shape. It has the standard Minton handle. The pouring guard (fig.58a) is usually a little larger than Spode's (fig.61b), and the strainer is domed. The usual knob (fig.58b and c) has a taller nipple on top than Spode's, and is covered in fine ribbing.

[1] Cumming 1988, p.1; Godden 1988, p.541.

Figure 58b

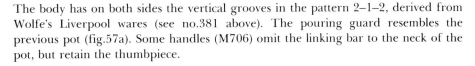

386

New Hall. Painted with underglaze blue and gilding

c.1805
PLATE 124
163mm (473.984)
Painted pattern no. in purple enamel: '575'
Prov: presented by the Friends of the Norwich Museums, 1984

The Old Oval has the same strainer as New Hall's Oval (fig.59a). The pouring guard is a simple curve at both ends of the pot (fig.59b), but may also be at one end only and with a central notch (M669, see fig.59c). The underside of the base is dished and covered with glaze. As on the present pot, covers frequently have no flange (but M669 does). The knob is relatively broad in the beam and has a thick neck.

Other example: 1958 pattern 538.

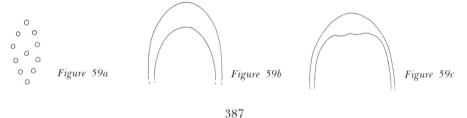

Figure 59a   *Figure 59b*   *Figure 59c*

387

Pattern Book factory. Painted with underglaze blue and gilding

c.1800
PLATE 121
151mm (1949)

Figure 60

This shape was previously[1] thought to be Thomas Rose's, but has now been tied up with the pattern book of unknown origin in the Victoria and Albert Museum (see no.364). This is the vertically fluted version, which includes a fluted knob. A plain knob (M680) is shown in fig.60. Both knob and handle are quite different from those of John and Thomas Rose. The base of the 'Pattern Book' factory's version is also distinguished by its stepped recess on the underside of the base.

[1] Godden 1970, p.59.

388

Pinxton, Derbyshire. Painted with enamel colours and gilding

c.1796–1800
PLATE 124
152mm (M649)

Like Derby, Pinxton favoured an octagonal opening to the pot, no flange to the cover, a rather tall flat strainer, and an open ring knob. The present pot exhibits all these features. The handle is unmistakeably Pinxton's own.

389

Spode, Stoke-on-Trent. Printed in underglaze blue

c.1800
PLATE 124
155mm (M657)
Impressed mark: '28' on base and inside cover

The factory probably began producing bone china about the time that Josiah Spode II became head of the firm in 1797. The pouring guard of this pot (fig.61a) is unusual in being a simple curve and at both ends of the pot. The standard Spode pouring guard (on 1770) is shown in fig.61b and is only at the front end. An earthenware example (1641), however, has the standard guard at both ends. An early bone china pot (M655) has no pouring guard at all. The Spode strainer is domed. The knob is shown in fig.61c and d.

Other example: (1770) pattern 685, alternating panels of solid underglaze blue with gilding, and red stylised plants with gilding.

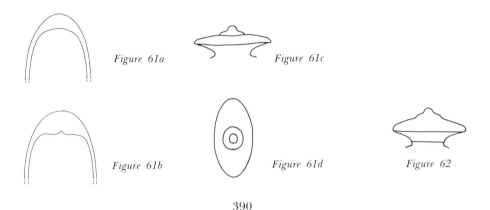

Figure 61a

Figure 61c

Figure 61b

Figure 61d

Figure 62

390

Factory Z, probably Wolfe. Painted in enamel colours

*c.*1805
PLATE 121
144mm (1960)

A shape extremely close to Coalport, but distinguished by the knob, which has a faint ridge around the lower part (fig.62). Another example is M701.

Narrow Oval

Figure 63a

391

Mason. Decorated with gilding

*c.*1805
PLATE 125
152mm (M1188)
Impressed mark under footrim: 'M. MASON', and incised cross

The version of the shape with straight flutes. The knob from the plain version (M1184) is shown in fig.63a. The pouring guard has a central notch but can (M1184) be more elaborate (fig.63b). The cover has no flange.

Figure 63b

392

Mason. Decorated with black bat-prints and gilding

*c.*1805
PLATE 125
158mm (1962)

A rarer shape than the previous pot. The pinnacle knob resembles a Pinxton form (see no.365). A rounder form of knob and a squarish handle are also found with this body shape (M1187). The pouring guard has a central notch and, as with Mason's Old Oval shape, is angled rather than curved at the corners.

pl.125
392
391

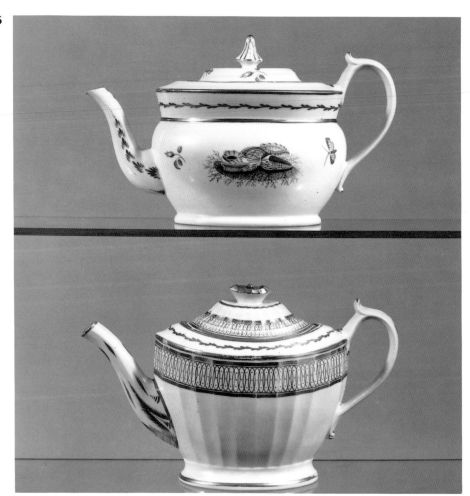

pl.126
394 396
393 395

Octagonal

393

Probably Herculaneum, Liverpool. Painted in enamel colours

*c.*1805
PLATE 126
155mm (M unnumbered)
Painted pattern no. in purple enamel: '37'

On this example the neck of the swan knob is missing. The shape matches a pot formerly in the Miller collection.[1] Another pot, formerly in the possession of Geoffrey Godden, bore the same pattern and pattern number. A related shape with a different handle was made by Miles Mason.[2]

[1] Miller and Berthoud 1985, pl.980.
[2] Godden 1980, pls.53 and 52.

394

Factory X. Painted in blue, pink, red and green enamels

*c.*1805
PLATE 126
159mm (M986)

The spout is fluted both above and below the horizontal division. Another version (M988) is fluted only on the lower part. The shape is also found with a more oblong handle (M988).

395

Unknown factory. Painted in red and purple enamels with brown trim

*c.*1805
PLATE 126
173mm (1750)
Painted pattern no. in red enamel: '12'

A pot of matching shape is M987. M985 has a matching body but a knob with a 'stepped roof' and a loop handle with a thumb-rest curving towards the body.

396

Unknown factory. Painted in enamel colours with blue trim

*c.*1810
PLATE 126
147mm (1749)
Painted pattern no. in red enamel: '90'

The strainer is domed. The spout tip has seven poorly moulded beads on the upper edge. A pot of matching shape is M978.

pl.127
398
397

pl.128
401   402
399   400

397

Spode 'stone china'. Printed in underglaze blue and painted over in pink, yellow and green enamels

*c.*1815–20
PLATE 127
159mm (M974)
Printed mark in underglaze blue on base and inside cover: 'SPODE', imitation of part of Chinese seal mark, and 'Stone China'. Painted pattern no. in red enamel: '2886'

The strainer is domed. Spode introduced their 'stone china' by 1814. Three years later Josiah Bateman, Wedgwood's chief travelling salesman, wrote: 'Since the Queen went to Mr Spode's the Stone China is much inquired for and is got more into repute – indeed, a dealer cannot be without it, and a great deal is sold'.[1] This type of body is earthenware rather than porcelain, but this pot is included here because of its similarity to porcelain shapes.

[1] des Fontaines 1969, p.130.

398

Machin, Burslem, Staffs. Painted in red, blue, green and turquoise enamels

*c.*1805–10
PLATE 127
169mm (1221)
Painted pattern no. in red enamel: '222'

Joseph Machin and Jacob Baggerley are recorded as china manufacturers in 1809. Some examples of this Machin shape (M1002) have a more simplified version of this handle, without the stubby little thumb-rest or the scroll moulding at the outer end of the top bar. The cover is a variant of the usual form (M997), and differs in having a flat platform below the knob and a stepped moulding one-third of the way up. Covers usually have no flange, but an unusually tall specimen (1967) does have one.

Other examples: 1748, pattern 1, flower trail in red, blue and green enamels, with puce line border; 1967, pattern 108, line borders enclosing band of leaves and berries, in red enamel and silver lustre.

Prow, Bridge Spout and Oval Footed Shapes

399

John Rose, Coalport. Prow shape. Painted with dark grey and pink enamel colours and gilding

*c.*1805
PLATE 128
165mm (M1195)

Figure 64

The thumb-rest on the handle is not angled as far towards the body as on the Thomas Rose version (see next entry). The differences between their knobs are even more obvious when seen end-on (fig.64 is John Rose, fig.65 Thomas Rose): the upper surface of the John Rose one is also divided by ridges into eight sections.

Figure 65

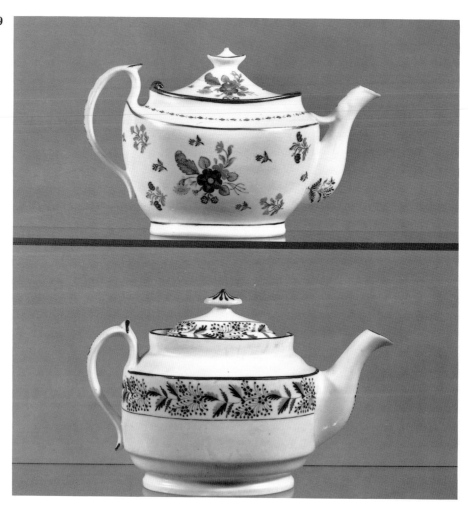

400

*Thomas Rose, Coalport. Prow shape. Painted with underglaze blue,
red enamel and gilding*

c.1805
PLATE 128
165mm (M1205)
Painted pattern no. in gold: '372'

The thumb-rest is angled further towards the body than on the John Rose version (see previous entry). The end-on view shows the difference between the knob of Thomas (fig.65) and that of John (fig.64). The cover has a slight horizontal ridge half-way up; on the shanked version (m1201) this is exchanged for a flat platform immediately below the knob. Neither ridge nor platform are present on the equivalent John Rose shapes. An unidentified factory made a very similar shape (M1206) whose knob resembles that of Thomas Rose while its handle resembles that of John.

401

John Rose, Coalport. Bridge Spout shape. Decorated with gilding

c.1810
PLATE 128
168mm (M1220)
Impressed mark: '5'

The thumb-rest on the handle does not point as much towards the body as on the Thomas Rose version (see next entry). The strainer is a shallow dome. The cover restraint, projecting from the neck of the pot at the back, has a smaller central lobe (fig.66a) than on the Thomas Rose version (fig.67a). The ends of the knob do not project upwards as on the Thomas Rose version. The upper face of the knob has twelve ridges (fig.66b) in contrast to Thomas Rose's (fig.67b). A rare variant (1731) has no cover restraint, and a knob more like that of John Rose's Prow Shape (no.399 above).

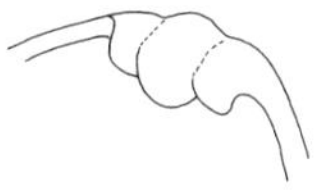

Figure 66a

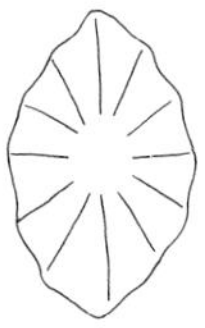

Figure 66b

402

Thomas Rose, Coalport. Bridge Spout shape. Decorated with pink enamel and gilding

*c.*1810
PLATE 128
171mm (M1225)
Painted pattern no. in brown enamel: '164'

The thumb-rest on the handle points further towards the body than on the John Rose version (see previous entry). The strainer is flat, in other words the holes are pierced directly into the wall of the pot rather than into an additional piece of clay as on the John Rose version. The cover restraint (fig.67a) has a bigger central lobe than on the John Rose version (fig.66a). The ends of the knob project upwards, and the upper face has nine asymmetrical ridges (fig.67b) in contrast to John Rose's (fig.66b).

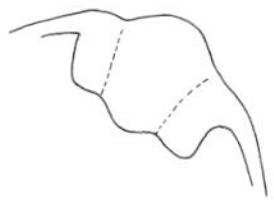

Figure 67a

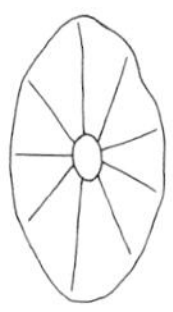

Figure 67b

403

Factory Z, probably Wolfe. Bridge Spout shape. Decorated with enamel colours and silver lustre

*c.*1810
PLATE 129
160mm (1853)

The spout is moulded with two lobes on either side above the bridge, as opposed to the three lobes of the John and Thomas Rose versions. The cover restraint has shallower moulding (fig.68a). The strainer is cylindrical (see no.419, fig.79b), although a domed one is occasionally found (M1217). The ends of the knob are kinked (fig.68b). At least two other unknown factories made the shape: one (M1219, M1221) used a handle like that of John Rose's Prow Shape (M1195 above), a flat lozenge-shaped strainer, a knob moulded with eight ribs on the upper face, and no cover retrait; the other (M1214, M1216) has a cover restraint rather like John Rose's (fig.66a), a domed strainer, and a knob moulded with twelve ridges on the upper face. Both these mystery groups have two lobes on the spout at either side like 'Factory Z'.

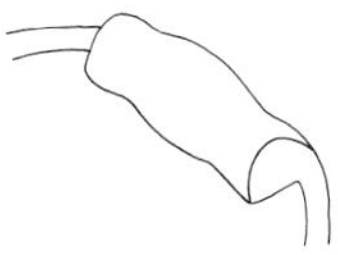

Figure 68a

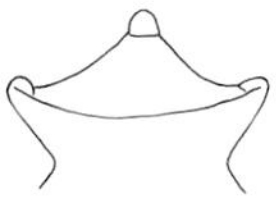

Figure 68b

404

Oval Footed shape. John Rose, Coalport. Painted with pink enamel and gilding

*c.*1810
PLATE 130
171mm (M1189)
Painted pattern no. in black enamel: '148'

The John Rose version has an extra kink in the top bar of the handle which the Thomas Rose version does not (see next entry). There is an imitation rivet-head moulded on both handle terminals. The strainer is domed.

405

Oval Footed shape. Thomas Rose, Coalport. Painted with red enamel and gilding

*c.*1810
PLATE 130
171mm (M1193)
Painted pattern no. in gold: 'N185'

The Thomas Rose handle has an imitation rivet-head moulded only on the lower handle terminal. The cover is lower than the John Rose version. The strainer is flat, but may be domed (M1191). An unknown factory made a version (1966) with a similar handle, but lacking the rivet-heads, and having three moulded lobes on either side of the spout rather than two as John and Thomas Rose.

406

Oval Footed shape. Machin. Painted with blue, green and red enamel colours

*c.*1810
PLATE 129
175mm (M752)
Painted pattern no. in puce enamel: '19'

This shape is also found with the handle of Machin's Octagonal shape (see no.398 above). The strainer is flat. The cover has a step half-way up and lacks a flange. Other examples (M751, M753) may have a flange and no step.

New Oval

This shape has been named in contradistinction to the Old Oval, following the book made for the throwers and turners at Spode's factory about 1820. Some manufacturers referred to 'boat' or 'canoe' shapes, but it is not always clear whether this shape or the Low Oval was intended. Strainers are flat unless the entry specifies that they are domed.

407

Thomas Rose, Coalport. Painted with red enamel and gilding

*c.*1805–10
PLATE 131
152mm (M1309)
Painted pattern no. in gold: '505'

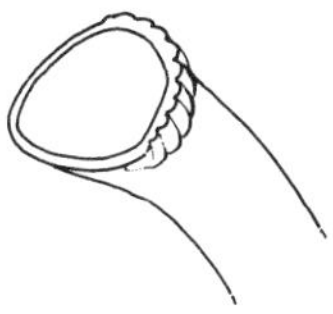

The slight pouring guard is a simple curve. The spout tip is moulded with nine beads along the upper edge (fig.69). This feature is shared with an unknown factory (M1314) but the handle on the latter has a much more generous loop.

Figure 69

408

*Davenport. Painted with enamel colours, salmon-pink borders,
and gilding*

*c.*1810–15
COLOUR PLATE 19
156mm (1974)
Painted pattern no. in purple enamel: '141'

It has been suggested that Davenport's first porcelain was bone china, that he changed to hybrid hard-paste about 1807, and that he changed to bone china again in about 1812.[1] The present pot is of bone china. The slight pouring guard has a central notch. The spout tip has three beads along the upper edge (fig.70a). The strainer is domed. The knob has pointed ends as seen from above (fig.70b). The flange of the cover has ends which are undercut (fig.70c), presumably designed to engage with the pouring guard, although they actually do not. These undercut ends are a distinctive Davenport feature. A variant shape (M1304) has a spout moulded with stylised leaves and a handle with a divided upper terminal.

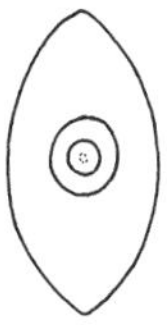

Figure 70a

Figure 70b

[1] Lockett and Godden 1989, p.205.

409

Herculaneum, Liverpool. Printed in underglaze blue

*c.*1810
PLATE 132
176mm (1813)

Figure 70c

The neck has a projecting cover restraint at the rear of the opening. Most examples of this shape are impressed 'L' on the footrim. Some (M1355) are reinforced at the upper edge of the spout tip. The strainer is sometimes domed (M1361).

Other example: (1812) pattern 599, pink flower spray and smaller multi-coloured sprigs, pink border interrupted by pink flowers.

410

Machin. Printed in underglaze blue

c.1810
PLATE 131
171mm (M1363)

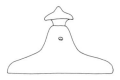

Figure 71

Like Ridgway, Machin used a forward-pointing thumb-rest and a cover which is broad in the beam (fig.71). Seen in this end-on view, the upper part looks almost as though it had been pinched in. The cover has no flange, although one is occasionally found (M1364).

411

Mason. Decorated with a black bat-print and gilding

c.1810
PLATE 131
152mm (M1348)

The most striking feature of Mason's shape is the huge domed strainer up to 70mm tall (fig.72a), which seems to occupy the whole front of the pot. The pouring guard is only slightly curved (fig.72b), and may be virtually straight. From end-on, the cover looks humped (fig.72c). Its knob is bulky and rounded (fig.72d), even when seen from above (fig.72e). The tip of the spout sometimes has a step at either side (1980).

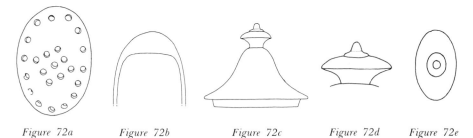

Figure 72a   *Figure 72b*   *Figure 72c*   *Figure 72d*   *Figure 72e*

Other examples: (1831) pattern 246, narrow orange border with running black scroll pattern, blue trim; (1832) pattern 349, black bat-print of goddess attended by putti and pulled in chariot by leopards/lions, gold borders; (1834) pattern 473, broad underglaze blue band with reserved white flowers and gilding; (1835) pattern 328, black bat-print, landscapes with ruins; (1980) pattern 770, underglaze blue and gilt border of oak leaves and acorns.

412

Minton. Decorated with a black bat-print, red enamel and silver lustre

c.1805–10
PLATE 132
156mm (1844)

The pouring-guard (fig.73a) is larger than Spode's (see p.251 fig.76e): some examples (M1286) lack the central notch. The strainer is domed, and the spout of triangular section, with five beads at the tip (fig.73b). The knob (fig.73c) is shorter than Spode's. The cover is shallower than Spode's, as is apparent when it is viewed from end-on (fig.73d). A variant (M1286, 1843) has an extremely tall cover. The position of the

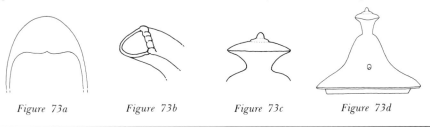

Figure 73a   *Figure 73b*   *Figure 73c*   *Figure 73d*

thumb-rest on the handle varies a good deal. An unknown factory made a pot of very similar shape, which has a projection at the front of the opening to stop the cover from slipping forwards (M1290).

The service from which the present pot comes is the only lustre-decorated porcelain so far recorded from Minton's first period, before 1816. Other pieces from the same service were said to bear the pattern no.534.[1]

Other examples: (1843) pattern 238, arcade containing alternately a vase and a stylised leaf, in gold; (1973) pattern 539, Chinese boys in landscape, in enamel colours and gilding.

[1] Cumming 1990, p.16.

413

New Hall. Decorated with a black bat-print and gilding

*c.*1810
PLATE 132
184mm (M1339)
Painted pattern no. in red enamel: '462'

The pouring guard, a small one, is a simple curve (fig.74a). The upper edge of the spout tip has a moulded ridge (fig.74b). The cover has almost straight sides when seen from end-on (fig.74c), and like Machin's, it has no flange. The knob is relatively long and broad in the beam. One example (M1342) has a variant handle (fig.74d).

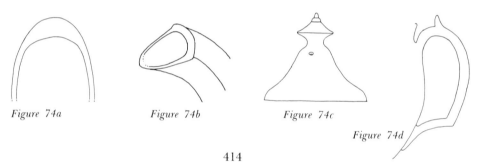

Figure 74a   Figure 74b   Figure 74c

Figure 74d

414

Ridgway, Shelton, Staffs. Painted in underglaze blue, red and green enamels and gilding

*c.*1810
PLATE 131
165mm (M1291)
Painted pattern no. in red enamel: '334'

The autobiographical *Memoir of Mr Job Ridgway* states he gave his sons John and William an equal share in his business in 1808, and that they began to make porcelain in the same year. Like Machin, Ridgway's thumb-rest points well forwards, and the cover looks broad when seen end-on (fig.75a). The Ridgway strainer, however, is domed, the knob is particularly long and 'streamlined' (fig.75b and c), and the cover has a flange.

Other examples: (1828) pattern 455 or N55, floral spray and border in black and grey enamel; (1830) pattern 323, floral spray and simple trim in orange-red enamel.

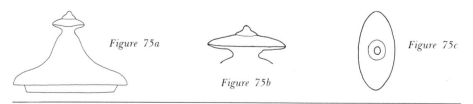

Figure 75a   Figure 75c

Figure 75b

415

Spode. Bat-printed in gold over an underglaze blue ground

1810–15
COLOUR PLATE 19
165mm (M1279)

Spode's pouring guard is of medium size (fig.76e), the strainer domed. The upper part of the handle, including the thumb-rest, is broad. The spout tip has five beads on the top edge (fig.76d). The spout is usually round, but a triangular section is also found (M1282). The cover is steeper than Minton's when seen end-on (fig.76a), and the knob is slightly longer (fig.76b and c). The gold bat-print is a technique patented by Peter Warburton of the New Hall factory in 1810. It was difficult to powder the gold finely enough for it to adhere to the detailed design printed in sticky oil on the pot, and the process seems to have been short-lived.

Other examples of the shape: (1840) pattern 341, simple gilt borders; (1972) pattern 892, underglaze blue ground with reserved white flowers and gilt foliage scrolls; (1979) pattern 312, deep border of gold cornucopias containing pink and blue flowers.

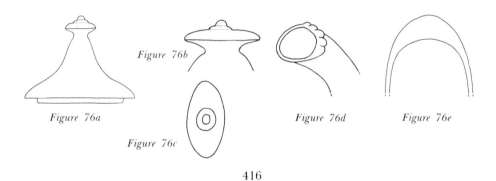

Figure 76b

Figure 76a

Figure 76c

Figure 76d

Figure 76e

416

Chamberlain's, Worcester. Painted with sepia and gilding

*c.*1810
COLOUR PLATE 19
157mm (1798)

The pouring guard is large (fig.77a), the strainer domed. The long knob on the present pot is less usual than a distinctive short one (fig.77b). The spout is round in section with four light grooves running its length. One example (M1175) has a triangular spout with a fluted base.

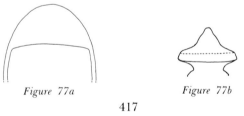

Figure 77a

Figure 77b

417

Grainger's, Worcester. Painted with light and dark red and gilding

*c.*1810
PLATE 132
157mm (1924)

Thomas Grainger was producing porcelain by 1807, and seems to have recovered rapidly from a severe fire which devastated his works in 1809. His porcelain at this period was a hybrid hard-paste.

The pouring guard of the present pot is very similar to Chamberlain's, but another form (fig.78a) is also found (1969). The strainer is flat and elongated (fig.78b). The form of short knob is distinctive (fig.78c). The collection includes a vertically fluted variant of the shape (1799).

Figure 78a

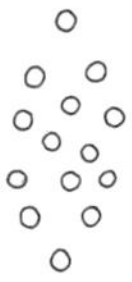

418

Factory X. Knob missing. Painted in enamel colours

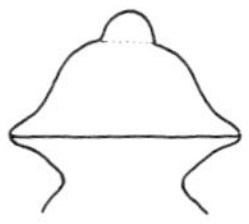

*c.*1810
PLATE 133
140mm (1841)

Figure 78b

The handle is a shape found on Oval pots from the same factory (M1079). The pouring guard is smallish, with a central notch.

419

Factory Z, probably Wolfe. Decorated with a puce bat-print and silver lustre

*c.*1810
PLATE 133
165mm (M1333)
Impressed mark on footrim: 'K'

Figure 78c

The knob (fig.79a) and strainer (fig.79b) are distinctive of this group. A flat triangular strainer (fig.79c) and variant knobs and handles (M1335, M1336) are found. The usual spout tip has a raised ridge (fig.79d).

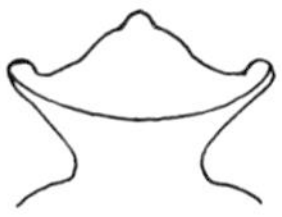

Figure 79a

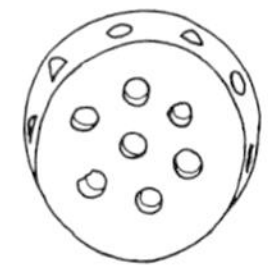

❦ Low and Parapet Ovals ❦

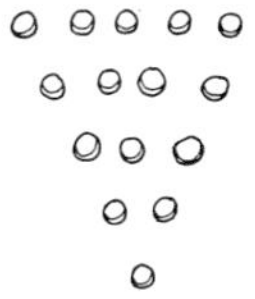

420

Barr, Flight and Barr, Worcester. Painted with brownish-purple enamel and gilding

*c.*1810
PLATE 136
162mm (M1233)
Impressed mark on cover and inside base: crown

Figure 79b

The original Worcester factory did not make a normal New Oval, producing instead this shape with a prominent parapet and a distinctively wide, bulging body. Some examples have the more usual New Oval type of handle (M1231) and a knob in the form of six drooping petals (M1232).

Figure 79c

421

Mason. Printed in underglaze blue and painted with gilding

*c.*1810
PLATE 134
146mm (M1251)

Figure 79d

The taller of the firm's two parapet oval shapes (see no.428 below for the other) may have a larger flaring parapet than the present pot. The present example has vertical grooves on either side of the body in the pattern 2–1–2, a favourite form of moulding with Mason. The knob matches that of the New Oval shape (see no.411). The pouring guard is small, a single shallow curve, and the strainer is triangular. On other examples (M1249) there is no pouring guard. The neck of the present pot is moulded with a projecting restraint for the cover at both front and rear. Other examples (M1249) have the cover restraint only at the front. The tip of the spout has along its upper edge five moulded beads, of which the middle one is the largest.

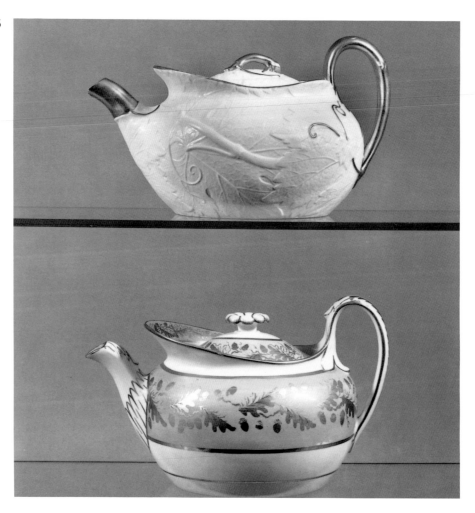

422

New Hall. Painted in enamel colours

*c.*1810
PLATE 134
147mm (B71)
Painted pattern no. in purple enamel: '603'

The strainer is lozenge-shaped. The cover has no flange. The knob matches that of the New Oval shape (no.413).

423

Wedgwood. Painted with underglaze blue and gilding

*c.*1815
PLATE 135
171mm (M1260)
Printed mark in red enamel: 'WEDGWOOD' and painted pattern no. '647'

The tip of the spout has extensive leaf moulding on the upper part. The domed strainer is typical in being wider than it is tall. Wedgwood did not produce porcelain in the generally accepted sense of the term until 1812, when their bone china reached the London showroom. The venture was short-lived, for by the middle of 1819 orders were so few that they were no longer recorded separately but together with the earthenware, and in 1823 the London showroom was instructed to clear 'all the articles not of current sale, *viz.* all the china . . .' at reduced prices. Although the occasional order for bone china was apparently still being carried out even as late as 1830, the firm's tradition of neoclassical restraint was out of touch with gaudy Regency taste. As Josiah Byerley, who had succeeded his father as the London manager, wrote in 1813, 'The public taste has been led to expect such a dazzling mixture of color with gold in broad shades covering the whole ware, that their eyes are spoilt, for delicate and elegant borders, which are not dazzling and do not produce a striking effect.'[1]

The first Josiah Wedgwood had regarded his jasper ware as a form of porcelain, but however one defines porcelain, jasper was not designed to serve as a glazed white body.

[1] des Fontaines 1979, p.90.

424

Wedgwood. Decorated with gilding

c.1815
PLATE 135
146mm (M1258)
Printed mark in red enamel: 'WEDGWOOD'

The pattern is Wedgwood's 730, 'Vine leaf embossed, gold tendrils, gold edge, solid handles'.[1]

[1] des Fontaines 1979, p.102.

425

Davenport. Painted in enamel colours and gilding

c.1815
COLOUR PLATE 19
109mm (1989)

There is a small pouring guard with a central notch, and the ends of the flange are undercut in typical Davenport manner (see no.408, fig.70c). The strainer is cylindrical, again a shape typical of the factory (see no.379 fig.54). The tip of the spout has five beads on the upper edge.

426

Spode. Decorated with steel lustre and gilding

c.1806
COLOUR PLATE 19
115mm (1990)

The strainer is domed. The spout tip has a raised ridge along the upper edge. The leaden grey colour of this lustre, referred to as 'steel' at the Spode factory, was evidently the first of the English lustres to be invented. The more commonly seen bright silver-coloured lustre was apparently applied over a first coat of 'steel' lustre. Both varieties were in fact made with platinum, which in the case of steel lustre was dissolved in a mixture of hyrochloric and nitric acids and then combined with a resin. John Hancock, in a letter published in the Staffordshire Mercury in 1846, claimed to be 'the original inventor of lustre', a claim which was not challenged.[1] Hancock was employed by Henry Daniel in 1805, and the earliest documented British use of platinum for ceramic decoration is a record in Daniel's colour book in November 1805.[2] Daniel was now in charge of the enamelling works, a 'factory within a factory', for Spode. Spode steel lustres, like the present example (pattern 839), are therefore probably among the earliest metallic lustres.

[1] des Fontaines 1988, p.41.
[2] Whiter 1970, pp.42–3.

pl.136

427	428
420	429

427

Derby. Painted with underglaze blue and gilding

*c.*1815
PLATE 136
136mm (M1256)
Painted mark in red enamel: crown over crossed batons and pattern no. '726' and '24';
also '4' in blue

The pouring guard is a simple curve at both ends of the pot. The flat strainer is roughly triangular. The tip of the spout has a notch in the centre of the upper edge.

428

Mason. Painted in enamel colours

*c.*1815
PLATE 136
133mm (1993)

This lower Mason parapet shape generally has a projecting cover restraint at the neck at front and rear (M1244 has one only at the rear). The pouring guard is usually of modest size and may have a central notch (1794), but is large on the present example. The flat strainer is triangular. The upper face of the spout has a moulded channel running down it on either side, a feature which is sometimes found on the taller Mason shape (M1250).

429

John Rose, Coalport. Painted with enamel colours and gilding

*c.*1815
PLATE 136
139mm (1793)

The pouring guard is of modest size, its edge curved into two projecting cusps. The flat strainer is roughly triangular, and the spout tip has five moulded beads on the upper edge.

Oblong Shapes

430

Swansea. Decorated with gilding

*c.*1815
PLATE 137
136mm (M1466)
Painted mark in red enamel: 'Swansea'

L.W. Dillwyn of the Cambrian Pottery, Swansea, attracted William Billingsley and Samuel Walker from their unsuccessful venture at Nantgarw in 1814. By 1817, however, the Swansea works had changed hands and Billingsley was back in Nantgarw. Swansea lingered on, probably with a much reduced production, into the early 1820s.

The present pot is of the creamy soft-paste porcelain for which the factory is famous. The spout tip has a raised semicircular moulding on the upper edge. Swansea and Coalport (see next entry) often produced very similar versions of a shape. In this instance the similarity extends to the knob, which is moulded with fourteen radiating ribs.

431

John Rose, Coalport. Decorated with underglaze blue prints and with gilt borders

*c.*1812
PLATE 137
146mm (M1455)
Printed mark in underglaze blue: imitation Chinese seal-mark and 'C.B. DALE'

This pot has a domed strainer, but a flat one is more usual on this shape (M1453, M1454, 1817). The projecting thumb-rest on the handle points away from the body of the pot, in contrast to the Thomas Rose version (next entry).

432

Thomas Rose, Coalport. Painted with green and black enamels and gilding

*c.*1812
PLATE 137
148mm (1816)
Painted pattern no. in gold: '1356'

Thomas Rose's factory used a knob which is shorter from end to end, but not so short in height, compared with the proportions of John Rose's (see previous entry). The thumb-rest on the handle projects upwards and towards the body, in contrast to the John Rose version. The strainer is usually domed, again in contrast to John Rose.

pl.137

431 432
433 430

pl.138

435
436

433

New Hall. Decorated with gilding

*c.*1815
PLATE 137
149mm (M1447)
Painted pattern no. in red enamel: '1052'

The handle is of a form found also on some New Oval pots from the factory (see fig.74d). The strainer is lozenge-shaped. The spout tip has a raised ridge along the upper edge.

434

Spode. Decorated with a pale underglaze blue ground and with gilding

*c.*1815
PLATE 139
140mm (M1472)
Painted pattern no. in red enamel: '2010'

A fancy variant of the factory's standard version (M1471), which has a knob like their London shape, oblong with a depression in the top. The 'Flower Embossed' moulding was introduced at Spode about 1813.[1] The strainer is a low dome.

[1] Whiter 1970, p.32 and pl.196.

435

Mason. Painted with enamel colours and gilding

*c.*1820
PLATE 138
152mm (M1459)
Painted pattern no. in gold: '1134'

The strainer is the massive domed one used on the factory's New Oval shape (see no.411).

436

Mason 'ironstone china'. Printed in underglaze blue

*c.*1820
PLATE 138
175mm (1243)
Printed mark: 'PATENT IRONSTONE CHINA WARRANTED'

The strainer is a massive domed one like that of the previous pot. Mason's Ironstone is an earthenware rather than a porcelain body, but the pot is included here because of its similarity to porcelain shapes.

Later Octagonal Shapes

437

Machin. Painted with an underglaze blue ground, pink enamel and gilding

*c.*1815
COLOUR PLATE 20
152mm (M991)
Painted pattern no. in purple enamel: '262'

Machin made two versions of this octagonal shape with a projecting shoulder. In the present version the points of the octagon face the cardinal directions of the pot, so that two of them come in the middle of its long sides. In the other version (see next entry) the sides of the octagon face the cardinal directions of the pot, so that two of them correspond to its long sides. The covers usually have no flange.

Other example: (1746) pattern 20, large formalised flowers in red and blue enamels.

438

Machin. Printed in brown and painted over in yellow, green and puce enamels

*c.*1815
PLATE 139
160mm (1747)
Painted pattern no. in puce enamel: '315' and a wavy stroke

The handle on this version of the shape (as M996) has a thumb-rest further towards the body than on the other version (see previous entry). The tip of the spout has five elongated beads of graded size on the upper edge, while the pot in the previous entry has only three. The cover has no flange.

Other example: (1223) pattern 208, large yellow shell with red and green tendrils.

439

Spode. Painted with a grey enamel ground and gilding

*c.*1817–20
PLATE 140
117mm (1323)
Painted mark in red enamel: 'SPODE' and pattern no. '2561'

The strainer is domed. A plain version of this shape is M1438. The 'New Dresden' moulding on the body of the present pot was introduced at Spode about 1817.[1] It was also used by Daniel and Coalport, both of whom made versions of this shape (see next entry). The Daniel one has a pear knob instead of Spode's apple.[2]

[1] Whiter 1970, p.128.
[2] Miller and Berthoud 1985, pls.2251–2.

pl.141

444	456
443	446

440

Coalport. Painted with blue and purple enamels and gilding

*c.*1820–5
PLATE 140
127mm (M1439)
Printed mark in red enamel: 'Coalport Felt Spar Porcelain' in a wreath, and 'Patronised by the
SOCIETY of ARTS. The GOLD MEDAL Awarded MAY 30th 1820' and 'I. ROSE & CO.'

The medal referred to in the mark was awarded for a lead-free glaze containing
feldspar. The feldspar, discovered on the Welsh borders by Thomas Ryan in 1818, was
also employed in the body of the ware, replacing some china stone. Spode was quick to
follow suit, employing a similar large mark for his feldspar porcelain.

441

Unknown factory. Painted with pink and brown enamels and gilding

*c.*1820
PLATE 140
141mm (1240)
Painted pattern no. in brown enamel: '661' (or possibly '199')

A simplified imitation of the Coalport shape (see previous entry).

Other example: (1324) pattern 606, brown printed basketwork ground with flowers in
reserves, the latter painted over in enamel colours.

London Shape

It is ironic that this popular shape, introduced about 1812, should be named after its designation in the Spode shape book of *c.*1820, since very few Spode examples were apparently made. By the late 1820s when the surviving Minton shape book was made, it was old-fashioned and had gone down the social scale, being referred to as the 'Cottage' shape.[1] The general introduction of bone china in the decade 1810–20 led to a dramatic growth in the number of firms making porcelain. Many of these new firms are still lost in obscurity, and their products remain unidentified. There are at least as many 'factory unknown' versions of the London shape as versions from known factories. A few of these are included at the end of this section.

[1] Godden 1968, pls.17–19.

442

Bailey, Lane End, Staffs. Printed in red and painted over in enamel colours

*c.*1825–30
PLATE 143
157mm (1883)

A pot from the 'cottage' end of the market, towards the end of the shape's life. W. and D. Bailey of Lane End are recorded in 1828 and 1830 as making china as well as earthenware. The mark 'Bailey No 3/Warranted' found on porcelain of this type is perhaps more likely to refer to this firm than to Bailey and Batkin of Lane End.[1] The flat strainer is triangular, the spout tip has a slight ridge on the top edge, and the simple knob is oval in plan.

[1] Godden 1988, p.113.

443

Charles Bourne, Fenton, Staffs. Painted with enamel colours and gilding

*c.*1820
PLATE 141
146mm (M1520)
Painted pattern no. in red enamel: 'CB/341'

Charles Bourne took over the Foley Pottery, Fenton, and was described as a china and earthenware manufacturer in 1818. The moulded body design is the one known as 'Floral Wreath Embossed' at the Spode factory.[1] The flat strainer is lozenge-shaped (fig.80a). The spout has a projecting cusp half-way down the upper face, and at the upper edge of the tip is a ridge with a central point (fig.80b). The knob is of stepped form (fig.80c).

[1] Whiter 1970, p.133.

Figure 80a   *Figure 80b*   *Figure 80c*

444

*Charles Bourne. Painted with underglaze blue, enamel colours
and gilding*

*c.*1820
PLATE 141
159mm (M1525)
Painted pattern no. in red enamel: 'CB/676'

The version of the shape with a corrugated body was made also by Ridgway (see
no.456 below) and by unknown factories. Bourne's version has a curved handle and a
slight ridge across the top edge of the spout tip. The knob and strainer match those on
the plain body shape (see previous entry). The flat lozenge-shaped strainer most
readily distinguishes this from Ridgway's corrugated shape (see no.456 below).

Figure 81

445

John Rose, Coalport. Painted with enamel colours and gilding

*c.*1815–20
PLATE 142
146mm (B463)
Prov: Boynton coll. no.1486

The handle resembles that of Nantgarw[1] and Swansea[2] in joining the shoulder of the
pot without curling under itself. The usual strainer is a shallow dome, although on
early examples (M1484) it is occasionally flat. The knob is a stepped type, the narrow
step just below the apex being moulded with vertical divisions (fig.81). These are
sometimes indistinct on later examples of the shape. About 1815 the factory changed
from its hybrid hard-paste to a bone china body. The present pot is of bone china. On

pl.142
445

some earlier examples of this shape (M1484, 1855) the shoulder has a strongly marked indentation at the four corners, and the inner spur low on the handle joins the body of the pot.

Other examples: (1863) pattern 822, underglaze blue border with reserved panels containing flowers in enamel colours framed with gilding; (1995) pattern 873, deep border of gilt foliage with red and blue flowers; (1855) pattern 585, deep pink border with flowers in reserves, with yellow enamel and gilding.

[1] Godden 1974A, pl.402.
[2] *Op.cit.* pl.503.

446

Thomas Rose, Coalport. Painted with underglaze blue borders, enamel colours and gilding

*c.*1812–14
PLATE 141
145mm (1862)
Painted pattern no. in red enamel: '500'

The factory of Anstice, Horton and (Thomas) Rose was taken over in 1814 by Thomas's brother John, whose factory was literally just across the canal. The present pot appears identical in shape to John Rose examples (see previous entry) but in his pattern book this pattern is listed as 297, with a cross reference to 500 at Thomas Rose's. It is possible that Thomas's numbers were used by John after 1814.

447

Derby. Painted with enamel colours and gilding

*c.*1815
COLOUR PLATE 20
146mm (M1446)
Painted mark in red enamel: crown, crossed batons and 'D', and names of views, 'Near Glasgow' and 'View in Cumberland'

Derby's is not strictly a London shape, but is closer to the origins of the London shape in silver and Sheffield plate. These metal pots have wooden handles attached with a rivet at top and bottom. On the present pot the lower rivet is imitated in the moulding, and on the alternative rounded handle (1319) the upper rivet is imitated as well (fig.82).

Figure 82

448

Hilditch, Lane End, Staffs. Printed in red and painted over in enamel colours

*c.*1820–30
PLATE 143
164mm (1887)
Printed mark in red: crown over 'H & S' in wreath

Figure 83a

Hilditch and Co. were producing porcelain by 1813, and from 1819 until 1834 the partnership was officially William Hilditch and Sons. The subsequent partnership of Hilditch and Hopwood continued until 1859.[1]

Figure 83b

The knob is of stepped form (fig.83a), the flat strainer is triangular, and the spout tip has a raised semicircular moulding on the upper edge (fig.83b). An unknown but prolific factory (M1567, M1569, M1571, M1637) used a more triangular moulding in this position (fig.83c), but their knob is of the more usual kind with a channel around the central pyramid (cf. fig.85b and c).

[1] Godden 1983, pp.260–1; Godden 1988, pp.414–15.

Figure 83c

449

Machin. Painted with pink enamel and gilding

*c.*1820
PLATE 145
158mm (1999)
Painted mark in red enamel: '512'

Figure 84

The top bar of Machin's handle often has an 'S' curve so that the thumb-rest curves in towards the body. The cover, like that of their New Oval, has no flange, and its shape is quite humped when seen end-on (fig.84). The knob has a distinctively tall neck.

450

Mason. Painted with green and blue enamels and pink lustre

*c.*1815–20
PLATE 144
137mm (1858)

The top bar and thumb-rest of Mason's handle resemble Machin (see previous entry). The upper face of the spout has at its tip a single, centrally placed bead (fig.85a) and near the body a projecting cusp. The cover is a broad dome when seen end-on. The strainer is usually flat, but one example (M1503) has the massive domed strainer of Mason's New Oval (see no.411). The knob is the type with a channel around a central pyramid (fig.85b and c). The present pot is unusual for Mason in having extensive decoration in pink lustre.

Other example: (1857) pattern 1215, border of grey-green panels interrupted by multi-coloured lozenges, with gilt swags below.

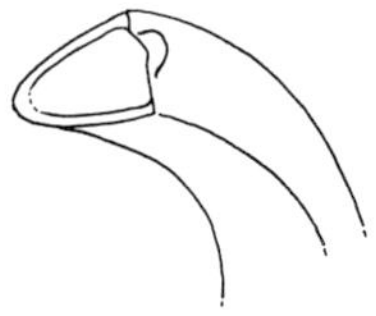

Figure 85a

Figure 85b

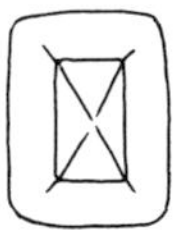

Figure 85c

451

Mason. Printed in underglaze blue

*c.*1815
PLATE 144
163mm (1244)
Printed seal mark in underglaze blue. Painted pattern no. inside cover in brown enamel: '987'

Perhaps an early version of the shape, for it retains the handle, knob and huge domed strainer of the New Oval (see no.411). The spout lacks the bead at the tip which is usual on Mason's London shape. The cover has no flange.

452

Minton. Painted with an underglaze blue ground, enamel colours and gilding

*c.*1812–15
COLOUR PLATE 20
146mm (M1478)
Painted mark in blue enamel: 'M' and crossed 'L's over pattern no. '780'

The Minton handle has a top bar which is almost straight and slopes upwards into the thumb-rest (compare Ridgway and Grainger's Worcester). The strainer is a small dome.

453

New Hall. Painted with enamel colours and gilding

c.1825
PLATE 145
158mm (B147)
Painted pattern no. in red enamel: '2082'
Ref: Holgate 1987, p.66 pl.28

A variant with the basket-weave moulding made by many factories. Earlier London shape handles at New Hall have a top bar which may be horizontal (fig.86a) or may even slope downwards from the body to the thumb-rest (M1533). The flat strainer is triangular in the present example (fig.86b), but other shapes are also found. The tip of the spout has a central notch between two curves on the upper edge (fig.86c). The New Hall knob has a channel around an unusually tall central pyramid (fig.86d).

Other examples: (1237) pattern 434, (1869) pattern 1178, (1870) pattern 1563, (1873) pattern 1063.

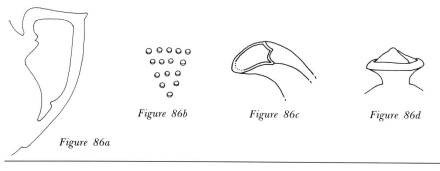

Figure 86b   *Figure 86c*   *Figure 86d*

Figure 86a

454

Rathbone, Tunstall, Staffs. Decorated with an underglaze blue ground, enamel colours and gilding

*c.*1825
COLOUR PLATE 20
149mm (M1561)
Ref: Miller 1983, p.33

Samuel and John Rathbone were in partnership from 1812 to 1818, but are not known to have made porcelain at that period. Pigot's 'Directory General' of 1818–20 lists William, Samuel and John Rathbone as china manufacturers. William died in 1820, but the name of the partnership does not seem to have altered to Samuel and John Rathbone officially until 1823 (see Ref.).[1] The flat strainer is triangular. The top bar of the handle forms an 'S' curve, with the thumb-rest curling in towards the body; a variant (M1555) is less curved, but has a raised keel or spine running its length, including the thumb-rest. The tip of the spout has a raised ridge along the top edge. The knob on the present pot is an open flower, the more usual form (M1555) being shown in fig.87. The form of knob and keeled handle are derived from Swansea porcelain.[2] The stand matching the present pot bore the pattern number 461.

[1] Godden 1983, pp.468–70; Godden 1988, pp.618–25.
[2] Jones and Joseph 1988, p.71.

Figure 87   *Figure 88a*   *Figure 88b*

455

Ridgway. Painted with underglaze blue and gilding

*c.*1815
PLATE 144
140mm (M1513)
Painted pattern no. in red enamel: '445'

On the death of Job Ridgway in 1814, his sons John and William continued the factory he had built at Cauldon Place. From about 1815 they also ran the Bell Works at Shelton, producing porcelain about which little is yet known. The Ridgway porcelain shapes and pattern numbers in the present work are thought to refer only to the Cauldon Place products.

The body has a pronounced indentation on the shoulder at the four corners (compare Coalport, no.445 above). The top bar of the handle is rather straight, slopes upwards away from the body and continues into the thumb-rest. The strainer is a well-rounded dome. The knob is of the type with a channel around a central pyramid (fig.88a, compare fig.88b, no.463 below).

456

Ridgway. Painted with enamel colours and gilding

*c.*1820
PLATE 141
164mm (1334)
Painted pattern no. in purple enamel: '2/437'

A corrugated shape like that produced by Bourne (see above, no.444). The Ridgway version is distinguished by its domed strainer and the absence of Bourne's slight ridge across the top edge of the spout tip. Ridgway's knob matches not that on its plain London shape, but that used by Bourne on both plain and corrugated versions (no.443 and fig.80c above).

pl.146
458
457

pl.147
462
460

457

Spode. Printed in underglaze blue

*c.*1815
PLATE 146
140mm (M2246)
Printed mark in underglaze blue: 'SPODE' and 'D'

Spode's version of the London shape is rare. The strainer is a small dome, and the spout has a raised moulding running along the upper part at either side (fig.89). The knob has a simple depression in the top instead of the pyramid used by most makers, and is the same knob used on the factory's Oblong shape (see no.434).

Figure 89

458

Swansea. Painted with enamel colours and gilding

*c.*1815–20
PLATE 146
152mm (M2241)
Painted mark in red enamel: 'Swansea'

The handle, with its central spine on the top bar, is of a type imitated by Rathbone (see no.454 above). The upper surface of the knob is moulded with radiating straight ribs. The tip of the spout is also delicately moulded (fig.90). An even more distinctive Swansea handle is a pointed one joined to the shoulder of the pot by a loop.[1] The simplest version resembles Coalport's, in that it joins the shoulder of the pot without curling under itself (see no.445 above).

Figure 90

[1] Jones and Joseph 1988, p.72; Miller and Berthoud 1985, pl.1499.

459

Wedgwood. Painted with a gold ground and black enamel

*c.*1815
COLOUR PLATE 20
145mm (1245)

The pattern is Wedgwood's no.785. The rounded handle distinguishes the factory's version of the London shape. The strainer is a shallow dome, and the knob is an open flower.

460

Chamberlain's, Worcester. Painted with enamel colours and gilding

*c.*1815
PLATE 147
136mm (1859)
Printed mark in black enamel inside cover: 'Chamberlain's WORCESTER & 55 New Bond St
London Royal Porcelain Manufacturers' all in wreath under crown
Ref: Godden 1982, p.114 pl.128

The top bar of the handle is almost straight, and slopes upwards away from the body, continuing into the thumb-rest. The strainer is a well-rounded dome except on one example (M1496) which has a flat one, and also a strangely elaborate openwork knob. The usual knob, as here, has a channel surrounding a central pyramid. The upper edge of the spout tip (covered with a metal mount on this example) has a central notch between two curves (fig.91) rather like New Hall.

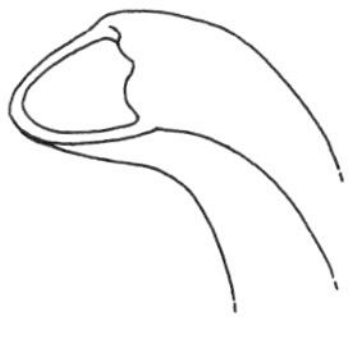

Figure 91

pl.148

464	466
465	467

461

*Grainger's, Worcester. Painted with underglaze blue, red and green
enamels and gilding*

PLATE 144
160mm (1856)
Painted pattern no. in gold on base and inside cover: '1279'

Figure 92

The top bar of the handle is almost straight, and slopes upwards away from the body,
continuing into the thumb-rest. The strainer is flat. The distinctive knob (fig.92) is
sometimes replaced by the one from the factory's New Oval shape (p.253 fig.78c).
Wasters of both types of knob were found on the factory site.[1]

[1] Sandon 1989, pl.12.

462

*Factory Z, probably Wolfe. Decorated with a black bat-print including
the inscription 'TO THE MEMORY OF CHARLOTTE'
and black painted trim*

*c.*1818
PLATE 147
171mm (M1592)

Princess Charlotte died in 1817. The strainer is the factory's distinctive cylindrical one
(p.253 fig.79b), but a flat triangular one is also found (M1593). The upper face of the
spout has a projection near the body and at the tip a central bead (fig.93a). The knob is
stepped (fig.93b). A lower version of the shape (M1596)[1] has different adjuncts: a

knob with a channel surrounding a central pyramid, and a spout tip having a central notch between two curves.

[1] Miller and Berthoud 1985, xviii.

463

Possibly Hicks and Meigh. Painted with pale grey border,
blue and red enamels and gilding

*c.*1815–20
COLOUR PLATE 20
143mm (1820)
Painted pattern no. in red enamel: '719'

This prolific but not yet identified factory was producing London (M1580, M1581, M1583, M1297) and New Oval shapes (M1298, M1300) very similar to Ridgway's (see nos.455 and 414). Seen from above, the knob (fig.88b, p.269) is less elongated than on Ridgway's London shape. The strainer is domed. For Hicks and Meigh see no.484.

Other examples: (1821) pattern 29, yellow shell with red, blue and green enamels; (1867) pattern 30, house and flower spray in blue and red enamel.

464

Unknown factory. Printed in underglaze blue

*c.*1820–30
PLATE 148
148mm (1825)
Painted pattern no. in brown enamel: '904'

One of an interesting group (M1550, M1552) including examples with the printed mark 'Real Nankin China' (M1554). The latter have Chinoiserie outline prints crudely hand-coloured in enamels. If the mark was intended to be taken at face value, it indicates that porcelain was now cheap enough to be afforded by a very unsophisticated market. The rakish angle of the handle is distinctive, the spout tip has a notch in the top edge (fig.94), the flat strainer is roughly triangular and the knob is of stepped form.

465

Unknown factory. Printed in red and painted in pink and green enamels

*c.*1820–30
PLATE 148
151mm (1413)
Printed pattern no. in red enamel: '444'

The printed pattern number is an unusual feature. Like other pots of this group (M1610), this has a handle with no inner spur, a flat triangular strainer, a simple pyramidal knob and a raised ridge on the upper edge of the spout tip.

Figure 93a   *Figure 93b*   *Figure 94*

466

Unknown factory. Printed in grey and painted over in enamel colours

*c.*1820–30
PLATE 148
145mm (1894)
Printed mark in grey enamel: 'D' in oval sunburst. Painted mark in purple enamel: '10' followed
by four dots.

The moulding is that known as 'Floral Wreath Embossed' at Spode's. The printed mark might be that of Thomas Drewery (or Drewry) of Lane End, who is recorded as a china manufacturer in 1818 and 1830.[1] Dimmock & Co. of Shelton and Hanley have also been suggested.[2] Pots of this type (M1607, M1632) lack an inner spur to the handle, have a flat triangular strainer and a knob of the common type with a channel around a central pyramid.

[1] Godden 1983, pl.584; Godden 1988, p.313.
[2] Miller and Berthoud 1985, pl.1607.

467

*Unknown factory. Decorated with a black print coloured over
with enamels*

*c.*1820–30
PLATE 148
159mm (M1608)
Printed mark in black enamel: 'B & S' under a crown

Printed decoration connects this shape with the Bailey group (no.442 above). The handle lacks an inner spur, the flat strainer is lozenge-shaped, and the knob has a channel surrounding a central pyramid. A corrugated shape (M1613) is also found with this mark:[1] on this the handle is curved in towards the body, the knob has a dome and no channel, and there is a projection half-way down the upper face of the spout.

[1] Miller and Berthoud 1985, pl.1614.

8

The Romantic Teapot

By 1820 the elongated shapes of the previous thirty years had begun to pall, and pots of circular plan were once more fashionable. The new shapes were derived from silver, just as their elongated predecessors had been. At first they were low in their proportions, simple in shape and neoclassical in detailing, but they quickly began to break out into forms which were not at all classical in spirit. The term 'Revived Rococo' applied to the style of 1830 is perhaps less helpful than 'Romantic', for this period marks the high watermark of Romanticism in the arts. The amazing variety of shapes being produced, in contrast to the near uniformity of the previous age when the London shape was dominant, suggests that the variety was a response to a public fed on the preconceptions of the Romantic Movement. These ideas laid much emphasis on the personal expression of the gifted individual, but when translated into commercial terms suggested that from a variety of designs an individual consumer might find one to suit their own taste and character.

Low Round Porcelain

468

Coalport. Decorated with an underglaze blue border, pink and red enamels and gilding

*c.*1815
PLATE 149
146mm (M1776)

This shape may have been made in apparently identical versions by John Rose and by Thomas Rose before his works were taken over by John in 1814. The handle is divided into two at the upper part and the upper terminals have foliate ends (fig.95a). The spout moulding is shown in fig.95b. Pieces associated with the present pot are said to bear the pattern number '629'.

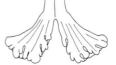

Figure 95a   *Figure 95b*

pl.149

| 473 | 475 |
| 470 | 468 |

469

New Hall. Painted with pink and green enamels and gilding

*c.*1820–5
COLOUR PLATE 21
136mm (M1779)
Painted pattern no. in red enamel: '2901'

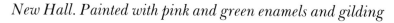

Figure 96a

A slightly simplified version of the Coalport shape (see previous entry). The foliage moulding down the spout is less elaborate (fig.96b), as are the upper terminals of the handle (fig.96a). The strainer is triangular.

470

Unknown factory. Decorated with an underglaze blue border, enamel colours and gilding

PLATE 149
149mm (1994)

Figure 96b

A yet more simplified version of the Coalport shape. The strainer is triangular. The foliage moulding down the spout shows only the edges of large round leaves and no veins at all; that on the knob is quite indistinct. Another unidentified version of the shape (1302) has no flange to the cover, a spout moulded with much shorter leaves than Coalport (see no.468 above) and a knob moulded with four big leaves rather than the three divided leaves of Coalport and New Hall.

471 and 472

Davenport. Painted with pink enamel and gilding

*c.*1820–5
COLOUR PLATE 21
170 and 152mm (M1803, M1849)
Printed mark in reddish brown enamel on bases, and inside cover of larger pot: 'DAVENPORT'
in scroll over anchor. Painted pattern no. in brown enamel: '730' on base of small pot and inside
cover of large one

The larger pot has a domed strainer and a bayonet fitting to the cover. In the early
19th century smart teasets were sometimes supplied with two teapots of different sizes.
The smaller pot is usually explained as a 'cabaret' or 'déjeuner' piece, for use by one or
two people. An additional use is suggested by instruction books for servants, which at
this period begin to specify that two teapots be brought, the second filled with hot
water (see p.25).

473

Ridgway. Painted with red and green enamels and gilding

*c.*1820–5
PLATE 149
171mm (M1798)
Painted pattern no. in red enamel: '2/831'

Figure 97a

A shape made at several factories (see next two entries). The Ridgway strainer is
domed, and the moulded ridge around the shoulder of the pot strikes the upper
handle terminal at the point of a leaf (fig.97a). The cover has a bayonet lock. The spots
on the front and back wings of the butterfly knob are indented (fig.97b). The butterfly
is taller than those on the following pots, and unlike them there is a gap between its
head and the cover of the pot.

Figure 97b

474

Charles Bourne. Decorated in underglaze blue, enamels and gilding

*c.*1820–5
COLOUR PLATE 21
152mm (M1799)
Painted pattern no. in gold: 'CB/742'

Figure 98a

Both the body shape and the butterfly knob are lower than Ridgway or Herculaneum.
The strainer is the usual Bourne flat lozenge (see p.263 fig.80a), and the moulded
ridge around the shoulder of the pot strikes the upper handle terminal at the
indentation between two leaves (fig.98a, contrast fig.97a). Only on the front wings of
the butterfly are the spots indented (fig.98b).

475

Herculaneum, Liverpool. Decorated in green enamel and gilding

*c.*1820–5
PLATE 149
171mm (M1800)
Painted pattern no. in red enamel: '415'
Ref: Warrington 1983, no.94

Figure 98b

The flat strainer is roughly triangular. The moulded ridge around the shoulder strikes
the upper handle terminals at the point of a leaf (see the Ridgway example fig.97a).
The spots on the butterfly's wings are only painted, not indented (fig.99).

Figure 99

476

Derby. Decorated with puce enamel and gilding

c.1820
PLATE 140
127mm (1322)
Printed mark in red: 'BLOOR DERBY' in circle around crown

A small 'cabaret' or 'déjeuner' pot matching a full-sized one of the same shape and decorated with the same pattern (M1768). The second teapot in a service was sometimes used for hot water, see p.25.

477

John Rose, Coalport. Decorated with underglaze blue, enamel colours and gilding

c.1820–5
COLOUR PLATE 21
170mm (1313)
Painted pattern no. in brown enamel: '2/279'

A superficially similar, footed Coalport shape (M1804, M1806), actually has quite different moulded details, including a divided upper handle terminal.

pl.150

482	483
479	481

478

*John Rose, Coalport. Decorated with a red ground, other enamel colours
and gilding*

*c.*1820–5
COLOUR PLATE 21
143mm (M1788)

Davenport employed a similar handle on a body of shouldered shape (M1855).

479

*Grainger's, Worcester. Painted with underglaze blue, red enamel
and gilding*

*c.*1825
PLATE 150
152mm (1303)
Painted pattern no. in red enamel: '1472'
Ref: Sandon 1989, pl.31

The strainer is a small dome. The end of the spout is a metal replacement. The handle is related to a lower Grainger shape (M1782) and no.480. The pattern is 'Blue Ball Japan'.

480

*Grainger's, Worcester. Painted with pink and brown enamels
and gilding*

*c.*1825
COLOUR PLATE 22
162mm (M1868)

The distinctive Grainger shape was known as the 'New Gadroon',[1] and the painted pattern is no.1345. The strainer is domed. A waster from a handle of this shape was found on the factory site.[2]

[1] Sandon 1989, p.56.
[2] *Op.cit.* pl.12.

481

*Yates, Shelton, Staffs. Painted with green, purple and blue enamels
and gilding*

*c.*1825
PLATE 150
162mm (1259)
Painted pattern no. in black enamel inside cover: '1418'

John Yates is described as a china manufacturer from 1822. The particularly hard bone china body of this pot is typical of Yates. Richard Daniel's mention of Yates in a letter to his father Henry between 1823 and 1825 suggests that the quality of his wares led them to consider him a potentially serious rival.[1]

[1] Berthoud 1980, p.146.

482

Samuel Alcock, Cobridge, Staffs. Painted with underglaze blue borders, yellow panels and other enamel colours, and gilding

c.1825
PLATE 150
152mm (M1882)
Painted pattern no. in black enamel: '1952'

The flat strainer is lozenge-shaped. The china manufacturing partnership between Ralph Stevenson, Samuel Alcock and Augustus A.L. Williams was dissolved in 1826. Williams departed but Stevenson remained, with the firm trading as Samuel Alcock & Co. A separate partnership between Stevenson and Williams produced only earthenware. Alcock was not trained as a potter but, with family connections in banking and his own commercial acumen, built up one of the largest firms in the business.[1] During the early years, Stevenson probably supplied the technical knowledge.

[1] P. Halfpenny, 'Samuel Alcock & Co.', *NCSJ* 2, 1975–6, pp.83–90; Godden 1983, pp.307–25.

483

Minton. Painted with red, green and purple enamel colours

c.1825
PLATE 150
152mm (1367)
Painted pattern no. in purple enamel: 23

The Minton factory ceased making porcelain by 1816, and did not resume production until 1824.[1] A new pattern number series was begun from 1.

[1] Cumming 1990A, pp.17–18.

484

Hicks, Meigh and Johnson, Shelton, Staffs. Printed in red and painted over in enamel colours

c.1830
PLATE 151
102mm (M1751)
Painted pattern no. in brown enamel: '270/2'

The strainer is domed. Richard Hicks and Job Meigh were making porcelain by 1813.[1] The firm became Hicks, Meigh and Johnson in 1822. W.M. Binns in 1906 reported seeing a series of the firm's pattern books for tea and dessert wares: 'These patterns are exceedingly rich, beautifully executed and charmingly painted and are quite wonderful in variety and style . . .'.[2] These books have been lost without trace.

[1] Eatwell and Werner 1991, p.105.
[2] Binns 1906, quoted in Godden 1988, p.413.

Shouldered Round Porcelain

485

Hicks, Meigh and Johnson. Painted with underglaze blue borders, enamel colours and gilding

c.1825
COLOUR PLATE 22
146mm (M1790)
Painted pattern no. in gold: '1342'

The flat strainer is triangular. The present pot is a ribbed version of the shape. The distinctive handle is probably derived from French porcelain in the Empire style.[1]

[1] *Cf.* de Plinval de Guillebon 1972, pl.120.

486

Chamberlain's, Worcester. Painted with pale yellow enamel borders and gilding

c.1825
PLATE 153
147mm (1306)

Variants of this shape were made with gadrooning around the shoulder (M1793) or the lower body (M1794); both varieties have a more elaborate handle.

487

Daniel, Stoke-on-Trent. Painted with a blue ground and other enamel colours, with gilding

c.1825–30
COLOUR PLATE 22
129mm (M1792)
Painted pattern no. in black enamel: '4025'

Henry Daniel ran the enamelling works, a 'factory within a factory', at Spode's, until 1822, and thereafter began making his own porcelain with his son Richard as Daniel & Son. By the beginning of 1827 the firm was trading as Henry and Richard Daniel. The

factory's first shapes were derived from Spode, and the potting of these wares was often less expert than the decoration, which was the Daniels' strength. The 'sprung' crack on the cover of the present pot is not untypical. The decoration supplies the reason why smart West End retailers could not get enough of this porcelain. Richard wrote to his father from London on paper watermarked 1823: 'Take no more common painters or gilders, we must have the very best only. You may venture on another ground layer . . . Now is the time or never. Everybody says they never saw such goods before. Poor Ridgway says we cut up his trade and John Rose sends out the goods so bad everybody complains'.[1] The strainer of the present pot is domed.

[1] Berthoud 1980, p.146.

488

Derby. Painted with enamel colours and gilding

*c.*1825–30
PLATE 153
162mm (M1766)
Printed mark in red enamel: 'BLOOR DERBY' in circle around crown. Painted marks '20' in red enamel, '31' in puce, and names of views: 'Near Eggington Derbyshire' (obverse) and 'View in Germany' (reverse)

489

John Rose, Coalport. Painted with enamel colours and gilding

*c.*1820–5
PLATE 154
133mm (M1811)

A very similar shape was made by an unknown factory (see next entry).

490

Unknown factory. Decorated with green borders, other enamel colours and gilding

*c.*1820–5
COLOUR PLATE 22
142mm (1976)

491

John Rose, Coalport. Painted with a yellow ground, purple enamel and gilding

*c.*1820–5
PLATE 151
157mm (1363)
Painted pattern no. in gold: '2/66'

The handle makes this Coalport shape (as M1829) particularly distinctive.

Other example: (1362) pattern 2/218, border in green and blue enamels and gilding with pendant foliage.

492

*Minton. Painted with underglaze blue, pink, red and green enamels
and gilding*

*c.*1825–30
PLATE 152
157mm (1733)
Painted pattern no. in gold: '112'

This shape is also found with a more stylised, horizontally placed flower knob
(M1830).[1] The flat strainer is lozenge-shaped.

[1] Cumming 1990, pp.17–18.

493

New Hall. Painted in red enamel

*c.*1825–30
PLATE 152
145mm (1238)
Painted pattern no. in red enamel: '2959'

A relief-moulded version of a standard and distinctive late New Hall shape (M1778).[1]
The flat strainer is triangular.

[1] de Saye Hutton 1990, p.228.

494

Daniel. Decorated with mauve prints and gilding

*c.*1830
PLATE 155
146mm (1982)
Painted pattern no. in red enamel: '4309'

Figure 100a

The strainer is deeply domed. Many factories made this shape of pot with a so-called 'Old English' handle: the most useful means of distinguishing them is the moulded foliage around the base of the spout. The version on this Daniel pot is shown in fig.100a, and a slightly different one on a Charles Bourne example (M1838) in fig.100b. The lines of these mouldings are often not followed by the gilt decoration with which they are picked out, and great care is needed in order to discriminate accurately between the different versions. Even then it seems that sometimes identical versions were used by more than one factory. The designs are usually slightly asymmetrical. The Bourne example mentioned has the factory's usual flat lozenge-shaped strainer.

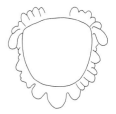

Figure 100b

495

Ridgway. Painted in green enamel with black outlining

*c.*1825–30
PLATE 155
137mm (1369)
Painted pattern no. in black enamel: '2/1325'

Figure 100c

The strainer is domed. Fig.100c shows the moulding at the spout base.

Other example: (1361) pattern 2/1851, black print of basket of flowers, painted over in green and brown; (1384) pattern 2/729, formal flowers in underglaze blue, pink, red and green enamels and gilding.

496

New Hall. Printed in red and painted over in other enamel colours

*c.*1825–30
PLATE 154
159mm (1736)
Painted pattern no. in red enamel: '3203'

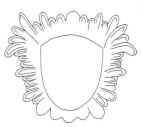

Figure 100d

The flat strainer is triangular. The shoulder of the pot does not have moulded foliage around the upper handle terminal as do the versions of other factories illustrated here. The moulding at the spout base (fig.100d) is similar to those used by Hicks, Meigh and Johnson (1984) and by other, unidentified factories (M1816, 1382). Fig.100e shows a slightly different version used by Rockingham (M1836).

Figure 100e

497

Machin. Painted with yellow borders and gilding

*c.*1825–30
PLATE 155
147mm (1375)

Figure 100f

Fig.100f shows the moulding at the spout base, with its two distinctive projections at the sides. The factory made a variant handle with a curved rather than angled lower section (M1833), which is found on a slightly taller shape (M1835). The strainer is flat.

pl.155

494 498
495 497

pl.156

500

502

498

Yates. Painted with enamel colours and gilding

*c.*1825–30
PLATE 155
129mm (M1842)

Fig.100g shows the moulding at the spout base.

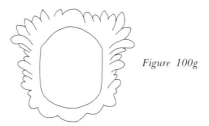

Figure 100g

499

Yates. Decorated with an underglaze blue ground, enamel colours and gilding

*c.*1830
COLOUR PLATE 22
129mm (M1862)
Painted pattern no. in enamel: '1560'

The handle is very distinctive, and similar to one found on Yates basalt stoneware (see no.333). A pot of matching shape bears the pattern number '1567' (M1863), and an Alcock pot (M1864) which was thought to come from the same '1567' service in fact does not.

500

Minton. Painted in enamel colours

*c.*1830
PLATE 156
139mm (1338)
Painted pattern no. in red enamel: 'N45'

The shape is illustrated as 'Shape E. Dresden Embossed' in the Minton shape book, some of whose pages are watermarked 1827.[1] The flat strainer is triangular.

[1] Godden 1968, pls.17–19; Miller and Berthoud 1985, pl.1854.

501

Alcock, Cobridge or Burslem, Staffs. Decorated with lavender-coloured applied reliefs and gilding

*c.*1830
COLOUR PLATE 22
165mm (M1888)
Painted pattern no. in brown enamel: '2331'

Samuel Alcock's partnership with Ralph Stevenson at Cobridge was dissolved in 1831. Alcock continued the Cobridge factory, but by 1833 was also working part of the Hill Pottery in Burslem, where he made further purchases and expanded his business during that decade.

502

Alcock. Decorated with underglaze borders, a pale yellow enamel ground and gilding

*c.*1830
PLATE 156
128mm (1364)
Painted pattern no. in puce enamel: '2004'

A low version of a standard Alcock shape (1365 and M1856) having the same handle and spout. The underside of the base on the low version is moulded in the form of a flower-head.[1] This low version is also found in lavender-coloured glazed stoneware (1258). The taller standard version has a knob with an undulating upper surface, which is sometimes found also on the low version. The neck of the present pot is moulded with the distinctive 'melting snow' border which has been used to attribute many pieces to Alcock.

[1] Miller and Berthoud 1985, pl.1860.

503

Hilditch. Printed in black and painted over in other enamel colours

*c.*1830
PLATE 157
166mm (1355)
Printed mark in brown enamel: crown over wreath enclosing 'H & S'

The flat strainer is triangular. A very similar shape was made by the two factories who marked their wares 'B & S' (M1899, and see no.467) and 'D' in an oval sunburst (M2262, and see no.466, p.274). The 'B & S' version has a taller cover than the other two.

504

Rathbone. Printed and washed-over in underglaze blue

*c.*1830
PLATE 157
154mm (1379)
Printed mark in underglaze blue: 'R' in sunburst. Painted pattern no.: '348'

The flat strainer is triangular. The factory made a lower shouldered shape with the same knob, handle and spout (M1827, 1378).

High Romantic Porcelain

505

Alcock. Painted in underglaze blue, red and green enamels and gilding

*c.*1830–5
PLATE 158
165mm (M1905)
Painted pattern no. in puce enamel: '2617'

The flat strainer is lozenge-shaped. This shape of pot was made both with four feet (as here) and without feet (M1911). The upper handle terminal is attached below the shoulder of the pot. John (M1904) and William (M1906) Ridgway made apparently identical versions which are similar to Alcock's, but the proportions of their handle are meaner and their pots can be distinguished from Alcock by their use of a domed strainer. The foliage moulding at the base of the Alcock spout is shown in fig.101a.

Figure 101a

506

Unknown factory. Painted in purple, red, green and brown enamels and gilding

*c.*1830–5
PLATE 158
181mm (1349)
Painted pattern no. in red enamel: '44'

Figure 101b

A very similar shape (as M1907, M1914) to the Alcock one (see previous entry). As with Alcock, the shape occurs with and without feet. The foliage moulding at the base of the spout is different, however, with fewer and larger leaves (fig.101b).

Other example: (1348) with feet.

507

Hilditch. Painted with blue enamel ground and gilding

*c.*1830–5
PLATE 159
165mm (1351)

The flat strainer is triangular. This shape was made both with four feet (as here) and without feet (1352, 1353). The upper handle terminal differs from Alcock's (see no.505 above) in being attached on top of the shoulder of the pot. Machin made a very

pl.159
507
508

similar shape (M1912) which, however, has a shorter cusp attaching the upper part of the handle to the pot, and moulded foliage around the spout base, which the Hilditch shape lacks.

Other Hilditch examples: (1352) pattern 162 painted in purple and green enamels; (1353) decorated with lavender sprigs.

508

Alcock. Painted in enamel colours

c.1835
PLATE 159
191mm (1397)

The flat strainer is lozenge-shaped. The more usual cover on this shape (M2009, 1396, 1398) has vertical ridges only on the upper part, and a much simpler open flower knob.

509

John Rose, Coalport. Painted with grey enamel borders and gilding

c.1835
COLOUR PLATE 23
207mm (1391)

Several other factories made versions of this popular shape, including Davenport (M1925), Hicks Meigh & Johnson[1] and at least two unidentified makers.

[1] Miller and Berthoud 1985, pl.1917.

510

Minton. Decorated with a green ground, enamel colours and gilding

c.1830
COLOUR PLATE 23
159mm (M1929)

The Minton shape book including paper dated 1827 in the watermark illustrates this shape as 'C. Bath Embossed'.[1] Grainger's Worcester made a similar shape known as 'Clarendon' (M1932).

[1] Godden 1968, pls.17–19.

511

Grainger's, Worcester. Painted with enamel colours and gilding

c.1830
PLATE 162
145mm (1263)

This is the factory's 'Dresden Embossed' shape of which wasters were found on the factory site.[1]

[1] Sandon 1989, pl.29.

291

512

Minton. Printed in underglaze blue and painted over with red and yellow enamels

*c.*1830
PLATE 160
144mm (1265)
Printed mark in underglaze blue 'Amherst Japan no.' with '824' painted in red enamel

This shape is 'G. Berlin Embossed' in the Minton shape book (see no.510 above).

513

Unknown factory. Painted with a grey border, other enamel colours and gilding

*c.*1830
PLATE 160
151mm (1310)

The flat strainer is lozenge-shaped.

514

Hicks, Meigh and Johnson. Decorated with blue bands, other enamel colours and gilding

*c.*1830
PLATE 162
165mm (M1879)

The shapes have been identified by linkage with marked 'stone china' dessert wares and teawares.[1] The strainer of the present pot is domed.

NB The reference in Miller and Berthoud 1985, xx, to their pl.1878 should be to the present pot.

[1] Godden 1988, p.412 pl.200.

515

Hicks, Meigh and Johnson. Decorated with lavender-coloured applied reliefs and gilding

PLATE 161
152mm (M1940)
Impressed mark: '28' on applied lavender-coloured pad in the form of a sunburst

For the accompanying cup shape see Berthoud 1982, pl.807, which connects this factory with a bird-spouted teapot similar to the Coalport shape (see no.509).[1]

[1] Miller and Berthoud 1985, pl.1917.

516

Coalport. Decorated with blue enamel bands and gilding

*c.*1835–40
PLATE 162
180mm (1416)
Painted pattern no. in gold: '3/337'

The same body and a very similar handle are found on another Coalport example (M1946) with a different spout, knob and foot.

pl.162

514   511
516   517

pl.163

518
519

517

Alcock. Painted with purplish-red enamel and gilding

*c.*1835–40
PLATE 162
167mm (1345)
Painted pattern no. in purplish-red: '5990'

A miniature example of matching shape is M1956. The shape is similar to the Coalport one (previous entry).

518

Rockingham, Swinton, Yorkshire. Decorated with a grey ground and gilding

*c.*1830–40
PLATE 163
184mm (M1922)
Painted pattern no. in gold: '1139'

The Bramelds' gallant venture into porcelain depended from the start on loans from Earl Fitzwilliam, and was doomed by their ambition to produce elaborate and costly wares at their small factory without making a large quantity of cheap and more profitable ware. The only surprise is that they were able to stave off disaster until 1842.

519

Chamberlain's, Worcester. Decorated with gilding

*c.*1835
PLATE 163
175mm (M1893)

520

Grainger's, Worcester. Decorated with an underglaze blue ground, enamel colours and gilding

*c.*1835
COLOUR PLATE 23
168mm (1347)
Painted pattern no. in brown enamel: '1847'

An example of matching shape is M1894. A related Grainger shape, taller and with different moulded details, is M1892.

521

Hilditch. Printed in red and painted over with enamel colours

*c.*1840
PLATE 164
183mm (1404)

The firm of William Hilditch and Sons became Hilditch and Hopwood in about 1835. Similar shapes were made by several unidentified factories (M2005, M2006).

pl.164

522

521

pl.165

523

524

522

Copeland and Garrett, Stoke-on-Trent. Decorated with gilding

*c.*1840
PLATE 164
178mm (1249)
Printed mark in cartouche in green on base and in brown inside cover: 'Copeland & Garrett
Felspar Porcelain Late Spode'
Painted pattern no. in gold on base and inside cover: '5349'

William Taylor Copeland and Thomas Garrett took over Spode's business in 1833.
They had previously been responsible for the retail side in London. In 1847 the
partnership was dissolved and the business continued under the name of Copeland
alone.

523

Alcock. Painted with enamel colours and gilding

*c.*1845
PLATE 165
197mm (M1963)

Other pieces of the service bore the pattern number 7705. The cover restraint at the
rear of the opening is shown in fig.102a.

Figure 102a   *Figure 102b*

524

Unknown factory. Painted with red enamel and gilding

*c.*1845
PLATE 165
212mm (1343)
Painted pattern no. in gold: '321'

A simplified imitation of the Alcock shape in the previous entry. The cover restraint at
the rear of the opening (fig.102b) differs from that of Alcock (see previous entry).

525

Grainger's, Worcester. Decorated with panels of blue enamel and gilding

*c.*1840
COLOUR PLATE 24
179mm (1254)

The rim of this shape (M1923 matches) has Grainger's 'leaf edge' moulding.[1]
[1] Sandon 1989, pl.33.

526

Daniel. Decorated with grey panels, other enamel colours and gilding

*c.*1830–5
COLOUR PLATE 24
163mm (1421)

A slight variation on a very similar shape (M1987) which has a bird's head spout.

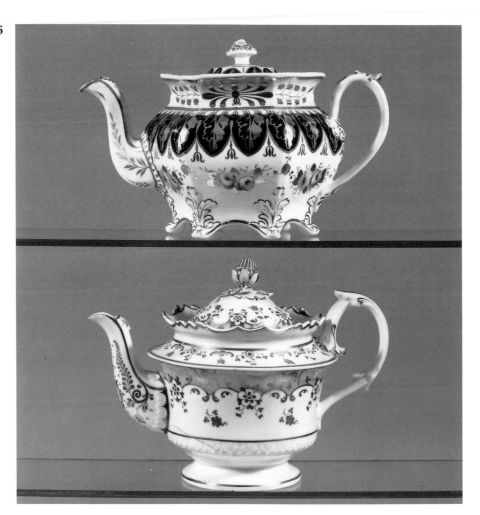

527

Daniel. Painted with an underglaze blue ground, enamel colours and gilding

*c.*1830–5
COLOUR PLATE 24
175mm (M1941)
Painted pattern no. in brown enamel: '4835'

The moulding has been classified as 'Shell Shape variant A'.[1]

[1] Berthoud 1980, p.80.

528

Daniel. Decorated with enamel colours and gilding

*c.*1830
COLOUR PLATE 24
146mm (M1972)

The tip of the spout is an incorrect modern replacement. The pattern is Daniel's 4307. For the accompanying cup shape see Berthoud 1980, pls.55 and 56.

529

Daniel. Decorated with a blue enamel ground and other enamel colours and gilding

*c.*1830–5
PLATE 167
150mm (1741)

A variant on the previous shape, moulded at the neck with Daniel's distinctive 'Shrewsbury' border.[1]

[1] Berthoud 1980, p.75 and pls.49 and 50.

530

Alcock. Painted with enamel colours and gilding

*c.*1835
COLOUR PLATE 24
157mm (1419)

A version of the Daniel shape seen in the previous two entries. The pattern is Alcock's 2368, also represented on a pot (M1913) whose shape matches no.505 but lacks the four feet.

531

Ridgway. Decorated with grey enamel borders and gilding

*c.*1840
PLATE 166
194mm (1357)
Painted pattern no. in red enamel: '2/3768'

An unusual shape which combines two features employed separately in the designs of most firms: the flared rim and the flange at the shoulder. Together they give it a tense and crowded appearance.

532

Ridgway. Painted with underglaze blue, pink enamel and gilding

*c.*1825
PLATE 166
168mm (M1957)
Painted pattern no. in red enamel: '2/1372'

An octagonal shape of large capacity.

533–5

*Mason. Painted with enamel colours and gilding over black prints, the
first two also over underglaze blue*

*c.*1830–5
COLOUR PLATE 23
159–165mm (M1935, M1939, M2041)

The late porcelains from the Mason firm, aimed at the lower end of the market, often
have a distinctive and vital barbarity, in strong contrast to the genteel aspirations of
many of their competitors.

536

Unknown factory. Painted with blue enamel and gilding

*c.*1840
PLATE 167
136mm (M1975)
Painted pattern no. in blue enamel: '36'

Figure 103

Versions of this assertively low, spreading shape were made by several as yet unidentified factories. On this pot the crude painted pattern detracts from the finely moulded detail of spout and feet (fig.103). For the accompanying cup shape see Berthoud 1982, pl.567. A rather different and less well-moulded version of this design was made by another unknown factory (M1979).

Other examples matching the present shape: (1309) pattern 52, trailing sprays with small flowers in blue enamel, gilt trim; (1422) cover missing, pattern 22, trailing sprays in brown, green and yellow enamel, gilt trim.

537

Alcock. Printed in puce and painted over in enamel colours

*c.*1845
PLATE 168
122mm (1515)

An unusual miniature version of a standard Alcock shape (M1988).

538

Alcock. Printed in brown and painted over in enamel colours and gilding

*c.*1845
PLATE 168
191mm (1428)
Printed mark in black on base and inside cover: Design Registry mark for 14 June 1843

The system of design registration was set up in 1839 in the aftermath of the Government's Design Commission of 1835, the first national inquiry into industrial design in Britain. It was not until 1842, however, that the diamond-shaped registration mark was introduced.

539

G.F. Bowers, Tunstall, Staffs. Decorated with black prints and gilding

*c.*1845
PLATE 168
190mm (M1998)

George Frederick Bowers began making porcelain about 1841 in partnership with Edward Challinor as G.F. Bowers & Co.[1] After the partnership was dissolved in 1849, Bowers continued alone and the '& Co.' was omitted. This form of pot has been found in a service including marked pieces.[2] For the cup shapes accompanying the present form of pot see Berthoud 1982 pls.775 and 791.

[1] Richardson and Brown 1987, pp.167–92.
[2] Brown and Richardson 1988, p.28.

540

G.F. Bowers. Decorated with a buff ground, other enamel colours and gilding

c.1845
COLOUR PLATE 24
197mm (M1993)
Painted mark in red enamel: '239 WORCESTER'
Printed in black with the Design Registry mark for 14 December 1843

The painted mark is thought to be that of Coningsby Norris, an independent decorator who bought porcelain in the white, enamelling and gilding it in his Worcester studio.[1] A similar mark 'WORCESTER 345' occurs on a Chamberlain's Worcester pot (M2234), whose shape matches no.519 above.

[1] Godden 1964, no.2894; Godden 1988, p.568.

Low Round and Later Pottery

541

Caneware. Wedgwood

c.1810
PLATE 169
82mm (1693)
Impressed mark: 'WEDGWOOD'

The strainer is domed. The knob is a spaniel. The upper and lower parts of the body are press-moulded and joined at the raised band. The shape was already in production in the 1770s for examples are known marked 'Wedgwood and Bentley'.[1] In September 1772 Wedgwood asked whether some fluted teapots were cracking 'in the middle in an horizontal line or across the bottom, those Teapots being made in two parts and pieced in the Middle below the band'.[2]

[1] Reilly I, p.428 pl.607.
[2] *Op.cit.* I, p.429.

542

Caneware, painted with blue enamel trim. Turner

c.1800
PLATE 169
114mm (1694)
Impressed mark: 'TURNER'

This Turner version of the same shape has a flat strainer and the standard Turner lion knob, with a very large head.

543

Redware with applied reliefs in black. Wedgwood

c.1810–20
PLATE 170
102mm (B188)
Impressed mark: 'WEDGWOOD'

The crocodile knob lacks the end of its tail. The strainer is domed. The use of black basalt reliefs on the redware body which Wedgwood had renamed 'rosso antico' does not seem to have been exploited until after 1800. A different, earlier version of this

'Ancient Egyptian' design, in black basalt with red reliefs, is in the Victoria and Albert Museum.[1] The motifs were derived from Montfaucon's *L'Antiquité Expliquée*, vol.II part 2. The increased popularity of the design in the early 19th century was probably due in part to increased interest in Egypt following the Napoleonic campaigns there.

[1] Reilly 1989, I, p.445 pl.632.

544

Redware with black applied reliefs. Spode

*c.*1810–20
PLATE 170
114mm (M1724)
Impressed mark: 'SPODE'

The end of the spout has a metal mount. The strainer is domed. There are various differences from the Wedgwood version in the previous entry: on the shoulder of the pot are four winged sun-discs, and the centre of each is a six-pointed star. The Wedgwood version has a six-petalled flower here. The fluted lunette under the spout forms only about a sixth of a circle, but on the Wedgwood version it forms a third of a circle. On top of the handles, in the central flower, the petals are grouped four over four, the lower four turned, as it were, 45 degrees. On the Wedgwood example it is the upper four leaves which are aligned in the cardinal directions of the pot, on the Spode it is the lower four. There is also a difference in the treatment of the crocodile's eye, both on the knob and in the relief on the pot: the Spode version is more of a slit, so that there is not room to show the pupil in the eyeball as on the Wedgwood version.

545

Basalt stoneware painted in enamel colours. Wedgwood

*c.*1820
PLATE 171
80mm (B133)
Impressed mark: 'WEDGWOOD'

This decoration known as 'Black Chinese Flowers', imitating Chinese 'famille rose' enamels, was popular at Wedgwood's between about 1810 and 1830. A larger pot of the same type is B132.

546

Pearlware, Wedgwood, with later painting in enamel colours

*c.*1810
PLATE 172
106mm (B605)
Impressed mark: 'WEDGWOOD'
Ref: Reilly 1989, I, p.297 pl.363B

The pot corresponds to shape 43 in the firm's 1817 shape book, and does not appear to be an 18th-century piece. The figures are, however, dressed in the costume of not later than about 1770, and suggest that a plain piece was 'improved' with enamel painting some time in the later 19th century, perhaps in France. A Wedgwood creamware dish with very similar painting has been noted.[1]

[1] *ECC* 6,1, 1965, pl.45.

547

Dark green stoneware with white applied reliefs, smear-glazed. Spode

*c.*1820
PLATE 171
101mm (M1721)
Impressed mark: 'SPODE'

548

Grey-green stoneware, smear-glazed, Minton

*c.*1840
PLATE 173
67mm (1708)
Mark in applied relief: cartouche including 'M', with 'No.64' impressed

549

Buff stoneware, smear-glazed. Cork and Edge, Burslem, Staffs.

*c.*1850
PLATE 173
97mm (1704)
Mark in applied relief: interlaced ribbon inscribed 'CORK & EDGE DELHI TEA SET'

Benjamin Cork and Joseph Edge were in partnership at the Newport Pottery, Burslem, from 1846, making Egyptian black, lustred wares and coloured stonewares. After 1860 the firm was styled Cork, Edge and Malkin.

550

Brown stoneware with iron-rich slip, salt-glazed. S & H Briddon, Brampton, Derbyshire

*c.*1840
PLATE 172
89mm (M1727)
Impressed mark: 'S. & H. BRIDDON'

The Walton Pottery at Brampton is said to have been founded by William Briddon in 1790 and remained in the family until *c.*1880. Samuel Briddon paid £51 duty on stone bottles in 1834.[1] Brown salt-glazed stoneware was now considered a rough and unsophisticated type of ware by those with social aspirations, but its makers sometimes produced reasonably up-to-date shapes like this, which closely copies one made in smear-glazed stoneware by William Ridgway (M1725), and shown also in the plates added about 1835 to the Wedgwood 1817 shape book as shape 70.[2]

[1] Oswald, Hildyard and Hughes 1982, p.164.
[2] Reilly 1989, II, p.549 pl.957.

551

Rockingham (Swinton), Yorkshire. Earthenware with manganese brown glaze and gilding

*c.*1830
PLATE 174
182mm (B342)
Impressed mark: 'ROCKINGHAM'

Very similar wares are known bearing the Rockingham 'C' mark in gilt.[1] The impressed mark is between 22 and 23mm long, the accepted length for the factory's

own version of this mark. Other factories also used the 'ROCKINGHAM' impressed mark, but in longer or shorter versions (see next entry).[2] The shape might be taken for a coffee-pot, but is found with gilt inscriptions indicating its use for tea.[3] At Wedgwood's factory a tall form of teapot made in redware was known as 'Rockingham' in 1828.[4]

[1] Cox and Cox 1983, p.109 pl.59.
[2] *Op.cit.* p.221, figs.36–8.
[3] *Op.cit.* p.108.
[4] Reilly 1989, II, p.493 pl.830.

552

Wedgwood. Earthenware with manganese brown glaze and gilding

*c.*1840–5
PLATE 174
140mm (M1715)
Impressed marks: 'ROCKINGHAM' and 'WEDGWOOD ETRURIA'
Ref: NCSN 72, 1989, p.18

The strainer is domed. The handle has been repaired with rivets. The pot can be closely dated by the 'WEDGWOOD ETRURIA' mark which was in use for only some five years. The impressed 'ROCKINGHAM' mark is some 25mm long (contrast the previous pot). Manganese-glazed wares were referred to in the trade as 'Rockingham', whoever made them, and the word was used as a mark by several manufacturers. When this mark is found alone, without the mark of the actual manufacturer, it can be very misleading, as on a Wedgwood pot in the Victoria and Albert Museum which matches the present one in shape.[1]

[1] Rice 1971, pl.9.

553

Chinese porcelain wine-pot, painted in enamel colours

early 19th century
PLATE 175
135mm (B513)

The opening is in the base instead of the top, and has a tube running up inside. This enables the pot to be filled upside down and not to empty itself when turned the right way up. For British imitations see the following entries.

554

Rockingham (Swinton), Yorkshire. Earthenware with manganese brown glaze, decorated with gilding

*c.*1830
PLATE 176
166mm (B551)
Painted mark in gold: 'C.1.2'

A direct imitation of the Chinese form (see previous entry). The British versions are known as 'Cadogans', but after which member of the family is uncertain. It seems unlikely that they were seriously intended for tea because of the virtual impossibility of clearing them of tea-leaves. A very similar example is known bearing the gilt inscription 'HOT WATER'.[1]

[1] Cox and Cox 1983, 111 pl.60.

555

Copeland and Garrett, Stoke-on-Trent. Earthenware with manganese brown glaze

1833–47
PLATE 176
160mm (B341)
Impressed mark: 'COPELAND & GARRETT'

The brown-glazed 'Cadogan' popularly associated with the Rockingham factory was also made by Spode and his successors Copeland and Garrett.

556

Unknown factory. Bone china painted in enamel colours

*c.*1830
PLATE 175
172mm (1295)

The 'Cadogan', as something of a novelty shape, was less often made in porcelain than in the cheaper earthenware.

557

Spode, earthenware with manganese brown glaze

*c.*1820–33
PLATE 177
140mm (B449)
Impressed mark: 'SPODE'

The factory also made this shape, imitating the bole of a tree, in dry-bodied stoneware,[1] and an unmarked basalt example (M543) may possibly be Spode.

[1] Miller and Berthoud 1985, pl.544.

558

Glazed grey stoneware, Wedgwood

*c.*1820
PLATE 177
143mm (B unnumbered)
Impressed mark: 'WEDGWOOD'

Another pot of this form (B126) is in a yellowish-buff stoneware body with a similar glaze. A silver teapot of 1831 in this shape is recorded.[1]

[1] Clayton 1985, p.417 pl.646.

559

J. and R. Godwin, Cobridge, Staffs. White earthenware printed in underglaze red

*c.*1834–50
PLATE 178
180mm (1715)

The shape matches a pot (1720) with a green sheet print and the back-stamp 'Moss J & RG'. John and Robert Godwin potted from about 1834 to 1866.

560

Rogers and Son, Longport, Staffs. White earthenware painted
in enamel colours

*c.*1820–40
PLATE 178
175mm (1544)
Impressed mark: 'ROGERS' and 'S'

A fanciful development from the London shape, complete with a bird knob. The
strainer is domed. After the death of George Rogers in 1815, his brother John took his
son Spencer into partnership. John died the following year, but the firm retained the
style 'and Son'.

561

Thomas Mayer, Stoke-on-Trent. White earthenware printed in
underglaze blue

*c.*1826–35
PLATE 178
176mm (1545)
Printed back-stamp: lion on heraldic wreath, 'Canova' in cartouche,
and 'T. MAYER STOKE UPON TRENT'

The inclusion of 'Stoke' in the mark indicates that the pot was made before 1836,
although Thomas Mayer continued to pot at a second factory at Longport until 1838.

562

William Adams and Sons, Tunstall or Stoke-on-Trent. White earthenware printed in underglaze blue

c.1830
PLATE 178
190mm (1548)
Printed back-stamp: 'ORIENTAL' in cartouche with 'W A & S Opaque China'

A large and very visible chip on the base occurred before the pot was glazed. When William Adams died in 1829 the firm continued under the same title since his eldest son was also called William.

563

Unknown pottery. White earthenware covered with a manganese-streaked slip. Cover missing

c.1900
PLATE 179
208mm (B436)

In the form of a woman seated in a chair, the back of which is incised in sgraffito through the unfired slip 'FYLL ME WYTH HOT WATER TO MAKE GOODE TEA'. There is a primitive form of bayonet socket for a cover. The 'ye olde' spelling of the inscription suggests that this pot is not early 19th-century as the costume would suggest, but was made to appeal to the taste of collectors like Bulwer for 'antiques'. A pot at Stoke-on-Trent Museum is apparently identical but for the inscription 'FIL ME WITH HOT WATER I'LL MAKE THE BEST OF TEA', and both pots have the curious feature of red slip painted into the incised letters to disguise the white body beneath.

Despite its late date the pot is included here because of the danger that collectors may be deceived by such a piece.

The reproduction of early English pottery was a flourishing industry around 1900. The versions of old Leeds Pottery made by the Seniors can be particularly misleading, as for example a pot of very white earthenware painted in underglaze blue (M380).

564

Minton, Stoke-on-Trent. Cream-glazed earthenware

c.1846–50
PLATE 180
160mm (1293)
Printed mark in brown: 'FS' in monogram and '1846 inv[eni]t', surrounded by garter inscribed
'SOCIETY OF ARTS PRIZE PATTERN Minton & Co. Staffordshire'

Henry Cole (1808–1882) was a dynamic civil servant interested in everything from railways to the postal system. He travelled the railway network with John Scott Russell, a civil engineer who was also Secretary to the Society of Arts. In September 1844 Cole noted in his diary that he had been experimenting at Minton's factory 'with turning tea cups, Patterns etc.' On 5 December 1845 after discussing railway business he and Scott 'passed the Evening preparing subjects for Prizes for the Society of Arts.' He apparently designed a competition for himself to win.

Prince Albert had become President of the Society of Arts in 1843 and was keenly interested in problems of industrial design. The society accordingly announced that it would award prizes 'for the production of a tea service and beer jugs for common use.'

pl.180
564

Cole's winning design for a tea service was entered in May 1846 under the pseudonym Felix Summerly and made by Minton. Cole followed up his success by commissioning leading artists to design household objects which were marketed as 'Felix Summerly's Art Manufactures'. He organised the Society of Arts annual exhibitions of British Manufactures, at which 'Felix Summerly' goods were prominent. From these grew the idea for the Great Exhibition of 1851, behind which he and Prince Albert were the prime movers.

Cole's teaset marks the beginning of institutional attempts to promote self-consciously 'good design' in Britain. As a dutiful civil servant he evidently took to heart the 1836 report of the Select Committee on Arts and Manufactures, which not only emphasised the importance of art in industrial design but also gave some support to the engineer James Nasmyth's theories about functional form. The severe body of Cole's teapot bears out the instructions he gave subsequently to his artist-designers, to create 'pure' forms' whose 'superior utility' was 'not to be sacrificed to ornament'. The subservient role of ornament in terms of the whole form is striking when one compares the pot with its contemporaries (eg pp.300 and 310).[1]

[1] Bury 1967.

Select Bibliography

Works referred to in abbreviated form

The place of publication is given for works published outside the U.K.

Adams 1975–6	E. Adams, 'James Tidmarsh of Cobridge: Discovering the History of an Unknown Potter', *NCSJ 2*, 1975–6
Adams 1987	E. Adams, *Chelsea Porcelain*, 1987
Adams and Redstone 1981	E. Adams and D. Redstone, *Bow Porcelain*, 1981
Albert Amor 1973	Albert Amor Ltd, *Exhibition of First Period Worcester Porcelain 1751–1784*, London, 1973
Al-Tajir 1989	*The Glory of the Goldsmith: Magnificent Gold and Silver from the Al-Tajir Collection*, catalogue of exhibition at Christie's, London, 1989
Austin 1977	J.C. Austin, *Chelsea Porcelain at Williamsburg*, 1977
Barker 1991	D. Barker, *William Greatbatch, a Staffordshire Potter*, 1991
Barker MS	D. Barker, manuscript notes on English red stoneware
Barker and Halfpenny 1990	D. Barker and P. Halfpenny, *Unearthing Staffordshire*, 1990
Barrett 1953	F.A. Barrett, *Worcester Porcelain*, 1953
Barrett and Thorpe 1971	F.A. Barrett and A.L. Thorpe, *Derby Porcelain*, 1971
Bell 1971	R.C. Bell, *Tyneside Pottery*, 1971
Bemrose 1906	W. Bemrose, *Longton Hall Porcelain*, 1906
Bemrose 1973	P. Bemrose, 'The Pomona Potworks, Newcastle, Staffs', *ECC 9, 1*, 1973
Bemrose 1975	P. Bemrose, 'The Pomona Potworks, Newcastle, Staffs', *ECC 9, 3*, 1975
Bennett 1978–9	C. Bennett, 'The Richard Patrick Teapot', *NCSJ 3*, 1978–9
Benson 1937	A.B. Benson (transl. and ed.), *The America of 1750. Peter Kalm's Travels in North America*, New York, 1937
Beresford 1924	J. Beresford (ed.), *The Diary of a Country Parson: the Reverend James Woodforde 1758–1802*, 1924
Berthoud 1980	M. Berthoud, *H. & R. Daniel*, 1980
Berthoud 1987	M. Berthoud, 'A Mystery Pattern Book', *Collectors' Guide* August 1987
Bidgood 1985	S. Bidgood, 'The Universally Respected Mr Potter', *Leeds Art Calendar 96*, 1985

Bidgood and Walton 1990	S. Bidgood and P. Walton, *Pots about People. Named and Dated Creamware and Pearlware 1760–1820*, Bar Convent Museum, York, 1990
Bimson, Ainslie and Watney 1966	M. Bimson, J. Ainslie and B. Watney, 'West Pans Story – The Scotland Manufactory', *ECC* 6, 2, 1966
Binns 1906	W. Binns, *First Century of English Porcelain*, 1906
Birmingham 1984	O. Fairclough, *The Grand Old Mansion: the Holtes and their Successors at Aston Hall*, Birmingham Museum and Art Gallery, 1984
Blakey 1984	H. Blakey, 'Thomas Lakin, Staffordshire Potter' 1769–1821, *NCSJ* 5, 1984
Boney 1957	K. Boney, *Liverpool Porcelain of the Eighteenth Century and its Makers*, 1957
Bradley 1978	H.G. Bradley, *Ceramics of Derbyshire 1750–1975*, 1978
Branyan, French and Sandon 1981	L. Branyan, N. French and J. Sandon, *Worcester Blue and White Porcelain 1751–1790*, 1981
Britton 1982	F. Britton, *English Delftware in the Bristol Collection*, 1982
Britton 1987	F. Britton, *London Delftware*, London, 1987
Brown 1978–9	R. Brown, 'The Furnace Farm Site at Melbourne', *NCSJ* 3, 1978–9
Brown and Cox 1984	R. Brown and A. Cox, 'Trial Excavations at Wirksworth', *NCSJ* 5, 1984
Brown and Richardson 1988	W. Brown and D. Richardson, 'An Update of Bowers Shapes and Patterns', *NCSN* 70, 1988
Burton 1906	W. Burton, *Porcelain, its Nature, Art and Manufacture*, 1906
Bury 1967	S. Bury, 'Felix Summerly's Art Manufactures', *Apollo* LXXXV 59, January 1967
Butler 1978	R. Butler, *The Arthur Negus Guide to English Furniture*, 1978
Capell 1953	G.W. Capell, 'Some Unrecorded or Rare Transfer-Printed Pieces', *Connoisseur* CXXXII 534, December 1953
Capell 1962	G.W. Capell, 'Rare Porcelain Decorated by Robert Hancock', *Connoisseur* CLI 609, November 1962
Castleford 1973	*The Castleford Pottery Pattern Book 1796*, reprinted 1973
Charleston 1963	R.J. Charleston, 'Jean Voyez – Fact and Fiction', *The Magazine Antiques*, October 1963
Charleston 1967	R.J. Charleston, 'A Decorator of Porcelain and Glass – James Giles in a New Light', *ECC* 6, 3, 1967
Charleston and Mallett 1971	R.J. Charleston and J.V.G. Mallet, 'A Problematical Group of Eighteenth Century Porcelains', *ECC* 8, 1, 1971
Charleston and Towner 1977	R.J. Charleston and D. Towner, *English Ceramics 1580–1830*, catalogue of English Ceramic Circle exhibition at Sotheby's, Belgravia, 1977
Chavagnac and de Grollier 1906	X. Chavagnac and A. de Grollier, *Histoire des manufactures françaises de porcelaine*, Paris, 1906
Chellis 1962	R.D. Chellis, *Wedgwood and Bentley Source Books*, Chicago, 1962
Clarke 1959	T.H. Clarke, 'French Influences at Chelsea', *ECC* 4, 5, 1959
Clayton 1985	M. Clayton, *The Collector's Dictionary of the Silver and Gold of Great Britain and North America*, 1985
Coke 1983	G. Coke, *In Search of James Giles*, 1983
Cook 1948	C. Cook, *The Life and Work of Robert Hancock*, 1948
Copeland 1980	R. Copeland, *Spode's Willow Pattern and other designs after the Chinese*, 1980

Cosnett 1823	T. Cosnett, *The Footman's Director and Butler's Remembrancer*, 1823
Cox and Cox 1980	A. and A. Cox, 'Chelsea, Bow and Worcester. Some Early Invoices', *ECC* 10, 4, 1980
Cox and Cox 1981	A. and A. Cox, 'Recent Excavations at the Swinton Pottery – the Leeds Connection 1785–1806', *ECC* 11, 1, 1981
Cox and Cox 1983	A. and A. Cox, *Rockingham Pottery and Porcelain*, 1983
Cox and Cox 1983 A	A. and A. Cox, 'Recent Excavations at the Swinton Pottery – White Saltglazed Stoneware and Creamware pre-1785', *ECC* 11, 3, 1983
Coysh 1974	A.W. Coysh, *Blue and White Transfer Ware 1780–1840*, 1974
Coysh and Henrywood 1982, 1989	A.W. Coysh and R.K. Henrywood, *The Dictionary of Blue and White Printed Pottery 1780–1880*, 1, 1982, II, 1989
Cumming 1988	N.R. Cumming, *Minton – Bone China in the Early Years (c.1800–16)*, 1988
Cumming 1990	N.R. Cumming, 'Lustre at Minton', *NCSN* 78, 1990
Cumming 1990A	N.R. Cumming, 'Minton Bone China and the 1817–26 Inventories', *NCSN* 78, 1990
Dawson 1984	A. Dawson, *Masterpieces of Wedgwood in the British Museum*, 1984
Dolmetsch 1979	E. Wolf, ' "The Prodigal Son" in England and America: A Century of Change'. *Eighteenth-Century Prints in Colonial America*, ed. J.D. Dolmetsch, Williamsburg, 1979
Don 1983	*Don Pottery Pattern Book 1807*, reprinted 1983
Doncaster 1983	*Don Pottery Exhibition Catalogue*, Doncaster Museum and Art Gallery, 1983
Drakard and Holdway 1983	D. Drakard and P. Holdway, *Spode Printed Ware*, 1983
Eaglestone and Lockett 1973	A.A. Eaglestone and T.A. Lockett, *The Rockingham Pottery*, 1973
Earle Collection Catalogue	C. Earle, *The Earle Collection Catalogue of Early Staffordshire Pottery*, 1915
Eatwell and Werner 1991	A. Eatwell and A. Werner, 'A London Staffordshire Warehouse', *NCSJ* 8, 1991
Edmundson 1989	R.S. Edmundson, 'Separating Caughley from Coalport', *NCSJ* 7, 1989
Edwards 1987	D. Edwards, *Neale Pottery and Porcelain*, 1987
Farrer 1906	K.E. Farrer, *Letters of Josiah Wedgwood*, 1906, 3 vols, reprinted 1973
Finer and Savage 1965	A. Finer and G. Savage, *The Selected Letters of Josiah Wedgwood*, 1965
des Fontaines 1969	J.K. des Fontaines, 'Underglaze Blue-Printed Earthenware with Particular Reference to Spode', *ECC* 7, 2, 1969
des Fontaines 1979	J.K. des Fontaines, 'Wedgwood Bone China of the First Period', *Proceedings of the Wedgwood Society* 10, 1979
des Fontaines 1983	U. des Fontaines, 'Wedgwood Blue-Printed Wares 1805–43', *ECC* 11, 3, 1983
des Fontaines 1983	J. des Fontaines, 'Ralph Wedgwood of Burslem, Ferrybridge and London (1766–1837)', *NCSN* 49, 1983
des Fontaines 1987	U. des Fontaines, 'Wedgwood or Wedg Wood? Filling a gap in Ceramic History', *NCSJ* 6, 1987
des Fontaines 1988	U. des Fontaines, 'Shedding Light on Lustre', *NCN* 70, 1988

Gabszewicz 1982	A. Gabszewicz, *Bow Porcelain. The Collection formed by Geoffrey Freeman*, 1982
Garner 1961	F.H. Garner, 'Liverpool Delftware', *ECC* 5, 2, 1961
Glanville 1987	P. Glanville, *Silver in England*, 1987
Godden 1964	G. Godden, *Encyclopaedia of British Pottery and Porcelain Marks*, 1964
Godden 1966	G. Godden, *Illustrated Encyclopaedia of British Pottery and Porcelain*, 1966
Godden 1968	G. Godden, *Minton Pottery and Porcelain of the First Period 1793–1850*, 1968
Godden 1969	G. Godden, *Caughley and Worcester Porcelains 1775–1800*, 1969
Godden 1970	G. Godden, *Coalport and Coalbrookdale Porcelains*, 1970
Godden 1974	G. Godden, *British Pottery*, 1974
Godden 1974A	G. Godden, *British Porcelain*, 1974
Godden 1979	G. Godden, *Oriental Export Market Porcelain*, 1979
Godden 1980	G. Godden, *Mason's China and the Ironstone Wares*, Antique Collectors Club, 1980
Godden 1982	G. Godden, *Chamberlain–Worcester Porcelain 1788–1852*, 1982
Godden 1983	G. Godden, *Staffordshire Porcelain*, 1983
Godden 1988	G. Godden, *The Encyclopaedia of British Porcelain Manufacturers*, 1988
Grigsby, 1990	L.B. Grigsby, *The Henry H. Weldon Collection: English Pottery 1650–1800*, 1990
Gunson and Robertshaw 1980	N. Gunson and I. Robertshaw, 'Dame Alice or the Widow of Zarephath', *NCSN* 40, 1980
Haggar 1952	R. Haggar, *The Masons of Lane Delph*, 1952
Haggar 1960	R. Haggar, *Concise Encyclopaedia of Continental Pottery and Porcelain*, 1960
Haggar 1980	R. Haggar, 'Three Frenchmen in Search of a Patron', *ECC* 10, 5, 1980
Halfpenny 1975	P. Halfpenny, 'Samuel Alcock and Co'., *NCSJ* 2, 1975–6
Halfpenny 1986	P. Halfpenny, 'The Wood Family', *Ceramics* 3, May/June 1986
Hampson 1986	R. Hampson, 'The Phillips Family of Longton, Potters', *NCSN* 64, 1986
Haskell and Penny 1981	F. Haskell and N. Penny, *Taste and the Antique*, 1981
Hildyard 1985	R. Hildyard, *Browne Muggs. English Brown Stoneware*, V&A exhibition catalogue, 1985
Hillier 1965	B. Hillier, *Master Potters of the Industrial Revolution. The Turners of Lane End*, 1965
Hillis 1984	L. and M. Hillis, 'Late Christian or Early Pennington?', *NCSJ* 5, 1984
Hillis 1987	M. Hillis, 'The Liverpool Porcelain of John and Jane Pennington *c.*1771–94', *NCSJ* 6, 1987
Hirsch 1986	R. Hirsch, 'Dutch Decorated English Creamware', *ECC* 12, 3, 1986
Holdaway 1986	M. Holdaway, 'The Wares of Ralph Wedgwood', *ECC* 12, 3, 1986
Hodgson 1920, 1921, 1923	Mrs Willoughby Hodgson, 'Old English Teapots in the Collection of Colonel and Mrs Bulwer', *Connoisseur*, LVIII

	no.232, December 1920; LX no.239, July 1921; LXVI no.261, May 1923
Holgate 1971	D. Holgate, *New Hall and its Imitators*, 1971
Holgate 1987	D. Holgate, *New Hall*, 1987
Hollens 1983	D. Hollens, 'Some Researches into Makers of Dry Bodies', *ECC* 11, 3, 1983
Honey 1934	W. Honey, 'Elers Ware', *ECC* 2, 1934
Horne VII 1987	J. Horne, *A Collection of Early English Pottery, Part VII*, 1987
Howell 1970	J. Howell, 'Transfer-Printed Lowestoft Porcelain', *ECC* 7, 3, 1970
Howell 1980	J. Howell, 'William Absolon of Great Yarmouth', *ECC* 10, 5, 1980
Irwin 1979	D. Irwin, *John Flaxman 1755–1826*, 1979
Jay 1978	R. Jay, 'Some Printed Sources of Decoration on Enamelled Salt-Glazed Stoneware of the mid 18th Century', *Leeds Art Calendar* 82, 1978
Jewitt 1878	L. Jewitt, *The Ceramic Art of Great Britain*, 1878
Jones and Joseph 1988	A.E. Jones and L. Joseph, *Swansea Porcelain: Shapes and Decoration*, 1988
Klaber and Klaber 1978	Klaber and Klaber, *Oriental Influences on European Porcelain*, exhibition catalogue, London, 1978
Ladies Amusement	*The Ladies Amusement* (Robert Sayer, 1762), reprinted 1966
Lawrence 1974	H. Lawrence, *Yorkshire Pots and Potteries*, 1974
Leary and Walton 1976	E. Leary and P. Walton, *Transfer-Printed Worcester Porcelain*, Manchester City Art Gallery exhibition catalogue, Manchester 1976
Leese 1984	M.E. Leese, 'The Turner Moulds', *NCSJ* 5, 1984
Legge 1984	M. Legge, *Flowers and Fables: A Survey of Chelsea Porcelain 1745–69*, catalogue of Exhibition at the National Gallery of Victoria, Melbourne, 1984
Lewis 1984	J. and G. Lewis, *Pratt Ware 1780–1840*, 1984
Lewis 1985	G. Lewis, *Collector's History of English Pottery*, 1985
Little 1969	W.L. Little, *Staffordshire Blue*, 1969
Lo 1986	K.S. Lo, *The Stonewares of Yixing*, 1986
Lockett 1972–3	T.A. Lockett, 'The Wirksworth China Factory', *NCSJ* 1, 1972–3
Lockett 1985	T. Lockett, 'The Mystery of Melbourne', *Ceramics* 1, 1985
Lockett 1985 A	T. Lockett, 'Early Davenport Wares – Recent Discoveries', *ECC* 12, 2, 1985
Lockett and Godden 1989	T. Lockett and G. Godden, *Davenport China, Earthenware and Glass 1794–1887*, 1989
Luxmoore 1924	C.F.C. Luxmoore, *Saltglaze with the Notes of a Collector*, 1924
Macfarlane 1990	M. Macfarlane, 'A Red Stoneware Teapot', *National Art-Collections Fund Review*, 1990
Mackenna 1948	F. Severne Mackenna, *Chelsea Porcelain. The Triangle and Raised Anchor Wares*, 1948
Mackenna 1951	F. Severne Mackenna, *Chelsea Porcelain. The Red Anchor Wares*, 1951
Mallet 1974	J. Mallet, 'Cookworthy's First Bristol Factory of 1765', *ECC* 9, 2, 1974

Mallet 1965	J. Mallet, 'A Chelsea Talk', *ECC* 6, 1, 1965
Mallet 1967	J. Mallet, 'John Baddeley of Shelton Part 2', *ECC* 6, 3, 1967
Markin 1989	T.L. Markin, 'Thomas Wolfe: Tea Wares at Liverpool and Stoke', *NCSJ* 7, 1989
Marshall 1954	H.R. Marshall, *Coloured Worcester Porcelain of the first period (1751–83)*, 1954
Marshall 1957	H.R. Marshall, 'Notes on the Origins of Worcester Decoration', *ECC* 4, 3, 1957
McNeile 1990	J. McNeile, 'The Stag Hunt Pattern 1745–1795', *ECC* 14, 1, 1990
Miller 1974	J.J. Miller II, *English Yellow-Glazed Earthenware*, 1974
Miller 1980	P. Miller, 'Factory Z, a Continuing Quest', *NCSJ* 4, 1980–1
Miller 1983	P. Miller, 'The Rathbones of Tunstall', *NCSN* 50, 1983
Miller and Berthoud 1985	P. Miller and M. Berthoud, *An Anthology of British Teapots*, 1985
Montfaucon	B. de Montfaucon, *L'Antiquité Expliquée et Représentée en Figures*, 1719–24
Mountford 1969	A. Mountford, 'Thomas Briand – A Stranger', *ECC* 7, 2, 1969
Mountford 1971	A. Mountford, *The Illustrated Guide to Staffordshire Salt-Glazed Stoneware*, 1971
Mountford 1972	A. Mountford, 'Thomas Whieldon's Manufactory at Fenton Vivien', *ECC* 8, 2, 1972
Mountford 1975	A. Mountford, 'Documents Relating to English Ceramics of the 18th and 19th Centuries', *Journal of Ceramic History*, 1975
Neild 1935	N. Neild, 'Early Polychrome Transfer on Porcelain', *ECC* I, 3, 1935
Niblett 1984	K. Niblett, 'A Useful Partner – Thomas Wedgwood 1734–1788', *NCSJ* 5, 1984
d'Oench	E. d'Oench, 'Prodigal Son and Fair Penitents: Transformations in Eighteenth Century Popular Prints', *Art History* 13, 3, 1990
Oman 1965	C. Oman, *English Silversmiths' Work, Civil and Domestic*, 1965
Oswald and Hughes 1974	A. Oswald and R.G. Hughes, 'Nottingham and Derbyshire Stoneware', *ECC* 9, 2, 1974
Oswald, Hildyard and Hughes 1982	A. Oswald with R.J.C. Hildyard and R.G. Hughes, *English Brown Stoneware 1670–1900*, 1982
Oxford 1912	A.W. Oxford (pref.), *Catalogue of Bristol and Plymouth Porcelain ... the collection made by Alfred Trapnell*, 1912
Parkinson 1969	M. Parkinson, *The Incomparable Art. English Pottery from the Thomas Greg Collection*, Manchester City Art Gallery, 1969
Parkinson 1971	M. Parkinson, 'The Thomas Greg Collection of English Pottery', *ECC* 8, 1, 1971
Paulson 1975	R. Paulson, *The Age of Hogarth*, 1975
de Plinval de Guillebon 1972	R. de Plinval de Guillebon, *Porcelaine de Paris*, Paris, 1972
Pomfret 1988	R. Pomfret, 'John and Richard Riley, China and Earthenware Manufacturers', *Journal of Ceramic History* 13, 1988
Priestley 1987	J. Priestley, 'British Election Ceramics', *The Magazine Antiques* CXXXI, 6 June 1987

Price 1959	R. Price, 'Some Groups of English Redware of the Mid-Eighteenth Century', *ECC* 4, 5, 1959
Price 1962	R. Price, 'Some Groups of English Redware of the Mid-Eighteenth Century Part II', *ECC* 5, 3, 1962
Rackham 1928, 1930	B. Rackham, *Catalogue of English Porcelain, Earthenware, Enamels and Glass Collected by Charles Schreiber Esq MP and the Lady Charlotte Elizabeth Schreiber*, Victoria and Albert Museum, I 1928, II 1930
Rackham 1935	B. Rackham, *Catalogue of the Glaisher Collection of Pottery and Porcelain in the Fitzwilliam Museum*, Cambridge, 2 vols 1935, reprinted 1987
Rackham 1951	B. Rackham, *Early Staffordshire Pottery*, 1951
Rackham and Read 1924	B. Rackham and H. Read, *English Pottery*, 1924, reprinted 1972
Rakow 1978	Dr and Mrs L. Rakow, 'B & W or W & B'. *The American Wedgwoodian*, 5, 1978
Rakow 1983	Dr and Mrs L. Rakow, 'The Sibyls and the Widows', *ECC* 11, 3
Ray 1968	A. Ray, *English Delftware Pottery in the Robert Hall Warren Collection*, 1968
Ray 1973	A. Ray, 'Liverpool Printed Tiles', *ECC* 9, 1, 1973
Reilly 1989	R. Reilly, *Wedgwood*, 2 vols, 1989
Ribeiro 1984	A. Ribeiro, *Dress in Eighteenth-Century Europe 1715–89*, 1984
Rice 1983	D.G. Rice, *Derby Porcelain: The Golden Years 1750–70*, 1983
Richardson and Brown 1987	D. and D. Richardson and W. Brown, 'The Start of a Dynasty: G.F. Bowers', *NCSJ* 6, 1987
Roberts 1947	K. and A.M. Roberts (transl. and ed.), *Moreau de St Mery's American Journey*, Garden City, 1947
Blake Roberts 1985	G. Blake Roberts, 'Mr Wedgwood and the Porcelain Trade', *ECC* 12, 2, 1985
Robertshaw 1984	I. Robertshaw, 'Samuel Hollins of Vale Pleasant', *NCSN* 54, 1984
Robin 1784	C.C. Robin, *New Travels through North America: in a series of letters . . . in the Year 1781*, 1784
Roth 1961	R. Roth, 'Tea Drinking in Eighteenth Century America: Its Equipage and Etiquette', *Bulletin of the Smithsonian Institution* 225; Contributions from the Museum of History and Technology, 1961
Edwards Roussel 1982	D. Edwards Roussel, *The Castleford Pottery 1790–1821*, 1982
Sandon 1969	H. Sandon, *The Illustrated Guide to Worcester Porcelain 1751–1793*, 1969
Sandon 1973	H. Sandon, *Coffee Pots and Teapots for the Collector*, 1973
Sandon 1981	J. Sandon, 'Recent Excavations at Worcester 1977–79', *ECC* 11, 1, 1981
Sandon 1989	H. and J. Sandon, *Grainger's Worcester Porcelain*, 1989
Savage 1952	G. Savage, *18th Century-English Porcelain*, 1952
de Saye Hutton 1990	A. de Saye Hutton, *A Guide to New Hall Porcelain Patterns*, 1990
Scarfe 1988	N. Scarfe (transl. and ed.), 'A Frenchman's Year in Suffolk', *Suffolk Records Society* xxx, 1988
Schroder 1988	T. Schroder, *The National Trust Book of English Domestic Silver*, 1988
Scott 1964	J.M. Scott, *The Tea Story*, 1964

Seligmann 1975   D. Seligmann, *Two Ceramic Artists: William Greatbatch and David Rhodes*, Antique Dealer and Collector's Guide, May 1975

Sitwell 1940   O. Sitwell (ed.), *Two Generations*, 1940

Shaw 1929   S. Shaw, *History of the Staffordshire Potteries*, 1929

Smith 1970   A. Smith, *Liverpool Herculaneum Pottery 1796–1840*, 1970

Smith 1972   A. Smith, 'Thomas Wolfe, Miles Mason and John Lucock at the Islington China Manufactory, Upper Islington, Liverpool', *ECC* 8, 2, 1972

Smith 1974   S. Smith, 'Norwich China Dealers of the Mid-Eighteenth Century', *ECC* 9, 2, 1974

Smith 1975   S. Smith, *Lowestoft Porcelain in Norwich Castle Museum*, Volume 1, 1975

Smith 1977   S. Smith, 'Lazowski and Lowestoft Porcelain', *Connoisseur* 194, 780, February 1977

Smith 1978   A. Smith, 'An Enamelled, Tin-glazed Mug at Temple Newsam House', *Leeds Art Calendar* 82, 1978

Smith 1985   S. Smith, *Lowestoft Porcelain in Norwich Castle Museum*, Volume 2, 1985

Spero 1984   S. Spero, *Worcester Porcelain: The Klepser Collection*, 1984

Spode 1966   *Spode Copeland 1765–1965*, temporary exhibition catalogue, Stoke-on-Trent, 1966

Stoke 1981   *New Hall Porcelain Bicentenary Exhibition 1781–1981*, City Museum and Art Gallery, Stoke-on-Trent, 1981

Stoke 1982   *Stonewares and Stone Chinas of Northern England to 1851*, catalogue of Northern Ceramic Society exhibition at the City Museum and Art Gallery, Stoke-on-Trent, 1982

Stoke 1986   *Creamware and Pearlware*, catalogue of Northern Ceramic Society exhibition at the City Museum and Art Gallery, Stoke-on-Trent, 1986

Street-Porter 1981   J. and T. Street-Porter, *The British Teapot*, 1981

Stretton 1967   N. Stretton, 'Thomas Rothwell, Engraver and Copper-Plate Printer 1740–1807', *ECC* 6, 3, 1967

Stretton 1970   N. Stretton, 'Early Sadler Prints on Wedgwood Creamware', *Proceedings of The Wedgwood Society* 8, 1970

Stretton 1976   N. Stretton, 'Liverpool Engravers and their Sources', *Connoisseur* 192, 774, August 1976

Stretton 1983   N. Stretton, 'Two Liverpool Engravers, Jeremiah Evans and Thomas Billinge', *Antique Collecting*, October 1983

Taggart 1967   R.E. Taggart, *The Frank P. and Harriet C. Burnap Collection of English Pottery in the William Rockhill Nelson Gallery, Atkins Museum, Kansas City*, Missouri, 1967

Tait 1963   H. Tait, 'The Bow Factory under Alderman Arnold and Thomas Frye (1747–1759)', *ECC* 5, 4, 1963

Tait 1964   H. Tait, 'Some Consequences of the Bow Porcelain Special Exhibition', part 4, *Apollo* LXXII, October 1960

Tait and Cherry 1980   H. Tait and J. Cherry, 'Excavations at the Longton Hall Porcelain Factory', Part 2, *Post-Medieval Archaeology* 14, 1980

Thornton and Tomlin 1980   P. Thornton and M. Tomlin, *The Furnishing and Decoration of Ham House*, Furniture History Society, 1980

Thorpe 1962   A. Thorpe and F. Barrett, 'Furnace Farm Pottery, Melbourne Derbyshire', *ECC* 5, 3, 1962

Tilley 1957   F. Tilley, *Teapots and Tea*, 1957

Toppin 1948	A. Toppin, 'The Origin of Some Ceramic Designs', *ECC* 2, 10, 1948
Towner 1957	D. Towner, *English Cream-Coloured Earthenware*, 1957
Towner 1959	D. Towner, 'David Rhodes – Enameller', *ECC* 4, 4, 1959
Towner 1963	D. Towner, 'William Greatbatch and the early Wedgwood Wares', *ECC* 5, 4, 1963
Towner 1963 A	D. Towner, *The Leeds Pottery*, 1963
Towner 1964	D. Towner, 'Leeds Pottery Records', *ECC* 5, 5, 1964
Towner 1967	D. Towner, 'The Cockpit Hill Pottery, Derby', *ECC* 6, 3, 1967
Towner 1971	D. Towner, 'The Melbourne Pottery', *ECC* 8, 1, 1971
Towner 1974	D. Towner, 'Robinson and Rhodes – Enamellers at Leeds', *ECC* 9, 2, 1974
Towner 1978	D. Towner, *Creamware*, 1978
Turner 1904	W. Turner, *William Adams – An Old English Potter*, 1904
Twining 1956	S.H. Twining, *The House of Twining*, 1956
Twitchett 1980	J. Twitchett, *Derby Porcelain*, 1980
Ukers 1935	W.H. Ukers, *All About Tea*, New York, 1935
V&A 1948	*English Pottery and Porcelain*, catalogue of *ECC* exhibition at the V&A, 1948
V&A 1984	*Rococo: Art and Design in Hogarth's England*, catalogue of exhibition at the V&A, 1984
Valpy 1982	N. Valpy, 'Extracts from Eighteenth Century London Newspapers', *ECC* 11, 2, 1982
Valpy 1983	N. Valpy, 'Extracts from Eighteenth Century London Newspapers and Petworth House Archives', *ECC* 11, 3, 1983
Valpy 1985	N. Valpy, 'Extracts from Eighteenth Century London Newspapers', *ECC* 12, 2, 1985
Valpy 1987	N. Valpy, 'A-Marked Porcelain: A for Argyll?', *ECC* 13, 1, 1987
Valpy 1991	N. Valpy, 'Extracts from the Daily Advertiser 1792–1795', *ECC* 14, 2, 1991
Walton 1976	P. Walton, *Creamware and other English Pottery at Temple Newsam House, Leeds*, 1976
Walton 1980	P. Walton, 'An Investigation of the Site of the Leeds Pottery', *ECC* 10, 4, 1980
Walton and Lawrence 1973	P. Walton and H. Lawrence, 'The Rothwell Pottery and its Wares', *Leeds Art Calendar* 73, 1973
Warner 1947	O. Warner, 'The Bulwer Teapots', *Apollo* XLVI no.273, November 1947
Warrington 1983	*Herculaneum – The Last Liverpool Pottery*, Warrington Museum exhibition catalogue, 1983
Watney 1955	B. Watney, 'Longton Hall', *Antique Collector*, 26 nos 1, 2 and 4, 1955
Watney 1957	B. Watney, *Longton Hall Porcelain*, 1957
Watney 1959	B. Watney, 'Four Groups of Porcelain, possibly Liverpool Parts 1 and 2', *ECC* 4, 5, 1959
Watney 1960	B. Watney, 'Four Groups of Porcelain, possibly Liverpool Parts 3 and 4', *ECC* 5, 1, 1960
Watney 1964	B. Watney, 'The Porcelain of Chaffers, Christian and Pennington', *ECC* 5, 5, 1964

Watney 1966	B. Watney, 'Engravings as the Origin of Designs and Decorations for English 18th Century Ceramics', *Burlington Magazine* cvii 761, August 1966
Watney 1972	B. Watney, 'Origins of Designs for English Ceramics of the 18th Century', *Burlington Magazine* cxiv 837, December 1972
Watney 1972 A	B. Watney, 'Notes on Bow Transfer-Printing', *ECC* 8, 2, 1972
Watney 1973	B. Watney, *English Blue and White Porcelain of the 18th Century*, 1973
Watney 1981	B. Watney, 'Two Bishops and a China Factory that failed', *ECC* 11, 1, 1981
Watney 1989	B. Watney, 'The Vauxhall China Works 1751–64', *ECC* 13, 3, 1989
Watney 1990	B. Watney, 'Recent Excavations on London Porcelain Sites: Vauxhall and Limehouse', *ECC* 14, 1, 1990
Watney and Charleston 1966	B. Watney and R. Charleston, 'Petitions for Patents concerning Porcelain, Glass and Enamels with special reference to Birmingham, "The Great Toyshop of Europe" ', *ECC* 6, 2, 1966
Webster 1979	M. Webster, *Hogarth*, 1979
Whitehead	*The Whitehead Catalogue 1798*, (James and Charles Whitehead), reprint 1978
Whiter 1970	L. Whiter, *Spode*, 1970
Williams-Wood 1981	C. Williams-Wood, *English Transfer-Printed Pottery and Porcelain*, 1981
Williams-Wood 1986	C. Williams-Wood, 'Yellow Transfer Printed Brown-ware', *Antique Collecting* 20, 8, January 1986
Wills 1969	G. Wills, *English Pottery and Porcelain*, 1969
Wills 1980	G. Wills, 'The Plymouth Porcelain Factory I. Letters to Thomas Pitt 1766–69', *Apollo* cxii 226, December 1980
Wills 1981	G. Wills, 'The Plymouth Porcelain Factory II. Letters to Thomas Pitt 1766–69', *Apollo* cxiii 227, January 1981
Zoffany 1977	*John Zoffany, RA* Catalogue of National Portrait Gallery exhibition 1977

Appendix

Pots listed by Miller and Berthoud (1985) and the Norwich collection

The Norwich collection includes all those ceramic pots listed as 'Miller' in the captions to the plates in Miller and Berthoud (1985) except the following plate numbers:

61	245	290	471	960	1059	1255	1574	1840	2077
69	246	291	524	980	1069	1305	1590	1861	2135
157	273	293	661	993	1093	1351	1699	1867	2137
176	276	294	667	1024	1172	1386	1720	1881	2138
177	281	298	697	1041	1209	1445	1757	1969	2267
229	283	398	719	1051	1230	1522	1777	2017	
243	289	427	793	1055	1240	1547	1820	2052	

Index

The main entries for factories listed in the contents are not repeated here